A HISTORY OF BUILDING MATERIALS

'The Frieze of the Archers' from the Royal Palace at Susa, Persia, about 500 B.C.; now in the Louvre, Paris (see pages 69, 162).

A HISTORY OF BUILDING MATERIALS

NORMAN DAVEY
O.B.E., D.Sc., Ph.D., F.S.A.

With frontispiece, 48 pages of plates and 134 illustrations in text

DRAKE PUBLISHERS LTD.
New York 1971

ISBN 87749-082-1

Published 1971
Drake Publishers Ltd.
440 Park Avenue South
New York, N.Y. 10016

Contents

Illustrations

PLATES

Illustrations

TEXT FIGURES

Acknowledgments

The author and publishers are grateful to:

le Directeur de la Caisse Nationale des Monuments Historiques, Paris, for the frontispiece;
the Director of Building Research, for Plate I, 1 to 9;
Rowland Mainstone, Esq., for Plates V, 1 to 6, and LI, LIII;
the late Professor V. Gordon Childe, for Plate VII;
R. M. Wynne-Edwards, Esq., for Plate IX;
the Director of the Department of Antiquities, Iraq Government, for Plates XX, XXIX, XXXV, XLIX;
J. Wacher, Esq., for Plate XIII;
Dr K. Kenyon, Director of the British School at Jerusalem, and to the Jericho Excavation Fund, for Plates XIV, XV, XVI, XVII;
the Director of Forest Products Research Laboratory, for Plate XVIII, 1 to 4;
the late Werner Bischof, and Magnum Photos, Zürich, for Plate XIX;
H. St G. Gray Esq., for Plate XX;
W. Kinniburgh, Esq., for Plate XXI;
the Director of the Art Institute of Chicago, for Plate XXII;
the Trustees of the British Museum for Plates XXIII, XXXI, XXXII, XXXIII, XXXIX, LV;
H. E. G. Salkild, Esq., Director of the Norfolk Reed Thatchers, for Plate XXVIII, 1 to 4;
the Director of the Central Building Research Institute, India, for Plate XXX;
the Society for Antiquaries of London for Plate XXXIV, 1;
the Director of the Guildhall Museum, London, for Plates XXXIV, 2 to 4, and LXIII a, b, d;
the Director of the Colonial National Historical Park, United States Department of the Interior, for Plate XXXVIII;
the Ministry of Works, London, for Plate XLIII;
J. G. Brinson, Esq., for Plate XLVI;
Mrs H. E. O'Neil, for Plate XLVII;
Direccion General del Turismo, Madrid, for Plate LII;
the Cement and Concrete Association, for Plates LIV, LXIX, LXX;
J. B. Cookson, Esq., for Plate LVI;
M. Jean Simonin, for Plate LVII;
The Times Publishing Company for Plate LVIII;
the Director of the Victoria and Albert Museum, London, for Plate LX;
the Director of the Guildford Museum, for Plate LXIII, c, and LXIV, a, b;
the Director of the Leicester Museum for Plate LXIV, c;
the Copper Development Association, for Plate LXV;
the London Museum, Plate LXVI;
the Director of the Timber Development Association, for Plate LXVII;
Messrs Pilkington Brothers, for Plates LXXI and LXXII.

Preface

MAN'S BASIC NEED, after food and clothing, has always been protection from the weather, from the heat of the sun, from driving rain and cold. His first attempts to provide this shelter were very simple—screens and windbreaks of interwoven branches and walls of turves or slabs piled one upon the other. He slowly acquired, by practical experience, a knowledge of the elementary principles of building: how best, for example, to stabilize a screen or wall by strutting or buttressing; how to build, in beehive fashion, with complete ring walls, a self-supporting and stable structure. Not until later did he acquire sufficient understanding of more advanced structural principles to enable him to build a true arch or a trussed roof.

Through the ages man searched continuously for new and better materials with which to build and decorate his structures; and these new materials have often demanded new techniques of application. The book describes, in part at least, some of this development; for a better understanding of the early development and use of building materials can be of immense help to all who have an interest in and affection for buildings, whether ancient or modern—the architect, the builder, the owner or occupier, the antiquarian, and not least the archaeologist. The field is so vast and the information so scattered that the book cannot claim to be exhaustive.

The archaeologist is better able to establish the probable form of the early buildings he excavates if he can identify the few remaining material fragments, for each material has its own message, and upon the character of each depended the type of building that could have been erected, and its method of construction. Some readers may be responsible for old buildings and be concerned with their conservation and repair. There are also those among the inquiring public, the intelligent amateurs of archaeology, art, the crafts, history, and topography, as well as students, for whom the subject may have a more general appeal. To all these the book is addressed in the hope that some of the information in it will help them in their work, or at least stimulate and encourage them to study other sources for more detailed information. References to some of the more important sources are given throughout the text.

Late Prehistoric and Historic Chronology from *c* 3000 B.C. to the Birth of Christ

TIME-SCALE	VARIOUS EASTERN COUNTRIES	MESOPOTAMIA Periods	MESOPOTAMIA	PALESTINE Periods	PALESTINE	EGYPT King-doms	EGYPT Dyna-sties	EGYPT Kings	GREECE AND THE AEGEAN	TIME-SCALE
0								ROMAN PROVINCE CLEOPATRA		0
100					SELEUCIDS IN SYRIA			PTOLEMIES IN EGYPT	CORINTH DESTROYED BY ROMANS	100
200										200
300			Destruction of Persian Empire by Alexander				31–28	ALEXANDER the GREAT	ARISTOTLE	300
400			XERXES I				27		PERSIAN WARS	400
500			CYRUS conquers BABYLON		TEMPLE rebuilt; The RETURN					500
600			NEBUCHADREZZAR; NINEVEH destroyed; ASHUR-BANI-PAL	IRON AGE	Fall of JERUSALEM		26; 25		CORINTHIAN WARE	600
700			SENNACHERIB; SARGON II; TIGLATHPILESER III		Fall of SAMARIA	LATE PERIOD	24		(ROME FOUNDED)	700
800			ASHUR-NASIR-PAL II; SHALMANESER III		JEHU; Battle of KARKAR; AHAB		23; 22		GEOMETRIC	800
900					OMRI					900
1000					SOLOMON; DAVID		21		PROTO-GEOMETRIC	1000
100			TIGLATH-PILESER I		GIDEON		20		SUBMYCENAEAN	100
200									LATE MIN. III or	200
300		CASSITE PERIOD		LATE BRONZE AGE		NEW KINGDOM	19	RAMESES II; RAMESES I	LATE H. III	300
400					JOSHUA takes JERICHO; The EXODUS			TUTANKHAMEN; EL-AMARNA TABLETS; AMENHETEP III	LATE MIN.	400
500							18	THOTHMES III	I+II or; MYCENAEAN	500

Date	Iran / India		Mesopotamia		Palestine		Egypt			Aegean	Date
700	INDUS VALLEY CIVILIZA[TION]		FIRST BABYLONIAN DYN.		MIDDLE BRONZE A[GE]		2ND INTERMEDIATE PERIOD	15 14 13	HYKSOS	MIDDLE MINOAN or MIDDLE HELLADIC	700
800				HAMMURABI		ABRAHAM?			AMENEMHET IV		800
900				SUMULAILUM			MIDDLE KINGDOM	12			900
2000			UR THIRD DYN.	NAPLANUM of LARSA SUMERIAN REVIVAL at UR				11	AMENEMHET I	E. MINOAN III or LATE E. H. II+III	2000
100				GUDEA of LAGASH		ABRAHAM?	1ST INTERMEDIATE PERIOD	10–7			100
200		S.T. II A	AGADE	SARGON I	EARLY BRONZE AGE					EARLY MINOAN II	200
300	ANAU III	SHAH TEPE II B	EARLY DYNASTIC	Kings with Semitic Names			OLD KINGDOM	6			300
400				FIRST DYNASTY: ROYAL TOMBS of UR				5	PEPI I	or	400
500									SAHURE	EARLY HELLADIC II	500
600								4	CHEOPS SENEFERU	EARLY MINOAN I or	600
700							PROTODYNASTIC OR ARCHAIC PERIOD	3	ZOSER	EARLY HELLADIC I	700
800								2			800
900											900
3000				JEMDET NASR | URUK III		CHALCOLITHIC ↓		1			3000
100	ANAU II	SHAH TEPE III							NARMER KING SCORPION		100
200							PRE-DYNASTIC				200
300											300

By permission of The Clarendon Press

I

Stone

Types of Building Stone

ROCKS OF MANY different kinds have been used for building, but they fall broadly into two main groups: the primary, or igneous, rocks, such as granite, syenite, diorite, dolerite, and basalt, formed by the cooling and solidification of a molten magma; and the secondary, or sedimentary, rocks such as sandstones and limestones, formed by the disintegration and decomposition of the primary rocks and the subsequent deposition and consolidation of the products in a stratified form.

There is a further group of rocks termed metamorphic. They are derived from pre-existing solid rock masses, either igneous or sedimentary, by the action of heat, pressure, or chemical fluids acting separately or together to form a distinctive new type of stone. For example, gneiss, which generally has the same composition as granite, is derived by crystallization from igneous rocks; quartzite is similarly produced by crystallization from sandstone; marble by metamorphism from limestone; and slate is derived from argillaceous sediments or fine-grained volcanic ashes by metamorphism.

Igneous Rocks

The igneous rocks are divided into three groups: Plutonic, Hypabyssal, and Volcanic. Those in the *Plutonic* group include granite, syenite, diorite, and gabbro, and they occur in nature as major intrusions of material which solidified well below the earth's surface under conditions of slow cooling. They are completely crystalline and coarse grained. The *Hypabyssal* group, including quartz porphyry, syenite porphyry, diorite porphyry, and dolerite, occur naturally as minor intrusions of material which solidified below the earth's surface in small wall-like or sheet-like bodies known respectively as dykes or sills. They are either completely or almost completely crystalline and fine grained. Rocks of the *Volcanic* group include ryolite, obsidian, trachyte, andesite, and basalt. They exist as surface extrusions of materials discharged at the surface of the earth or on the sea bed and are incompletely crystalline and very finely grained or are non-crystalline (glassy).

Obsidian is a natural volcanic glass which when blown into froth by the sudden escape of gases during eruption produces pumice. Basalt is also sometimes scoriaceous and porous in structure.

Associated with volcanic igneous rocks are a number of *fragmental* rocks which may almost be classed as sedimentary rocks. They include volcanic agglomerates or coarse tuffs, tuffs and ashes, trass and pozzolana (pozzuolana). In addition to quartz they contain various other materials such as felspar and mica.

Igneous rocks are generally more intractable than the secondary or sedimentary rocks, but they can be worked to a fine degree and highly polished. In consequence their use has been mainly confined to structures of a monumental character, or for slabs for floors, paving, and wall lining. In Egypt, for example, where there are some of the oldest and largest stone buildings in the world, roughly dressed granite slabs were used for pavement[1] and wall linings as far back as the 1st Dynasty (*c.* 3100–2900 B.C.).

Sedimentary Rocks

Of the sedimentary rocks, *sandstones* consist essentially of the more durable fragments of igneous rocks, such as quartz, felspar, and mica cemented together by siliceous matter, calcium and magnesium carbonates, iron compounds, or clay. They are formed by the degradation of the igneous rocks by weathering processes, followed by the transportation of the weathered fragments by wind and water, and their deposition on land or in water where their partial or complete consolidation may occur by the introduction of cementing material in solution, and by subsequent pressure. Depending on the type of cementing material sandstones are classed as siliceous (like Darley Dale stone of Carboniferous Age), calcareous, or dolomitic (like Red Mansfield stone of Permian Age in Nottinghamshire), ferruginous (like Coarsehill stone from the Trias beds of Dumfriesshire, in Scotland) or argillaceous (clay cemented). Their texture varies from coarse to very fine, particularly in those samples which were formed from wind-blown deposits. Siliceous sandstones, like those from Craigleith, Darley Dale, and Stancliffe (Plate I, 6) are very durable. Calcareous and dolomitic sandstones which, as their name implies, are cemented with calcium carbonate and magnesium carbonate, are generally rather less durable than the siliceous type.

Sometimes sandstones are classified according to their geological age rather than on a lithological basis; for example, Jurassic sandstones, Cretaceous sandstone, Rhaetic and Triassic sandstone, Permian sandstone, or Carboniferous sandstone, but the classification based on type of cementing material is perhaps more useful.

Limestones consist essentially of calcium carbonate formed either by precipitation from sea water as small spheroidal (oolitic) calcareous grains, or by the accumulation of the shells and skeletons of marine organisms. The deposits are further cemented together by calcium carbonate in solution. Limestones can be grouped lithologically according to their composition and physical characteristics as follows. Shelly limestone (like Hopton Wood stone from Middleton, near Wirksworth, Derbyshire, of Carboniferous Age) containing shells of marine organisms; crinoidal limestone containing fragments of stems and 'arms' of crinoids, the so called 'sea-lilies'; foraminiferal limestone (like Beer stone from Devon) containing microscopic marine animals in shells, known as foraminifera; coral limestone, containing skeletons of coral and calcareous algae, stromatoporoids, and mollusca (of Devonian and Carboniferous Age); bryozoa limestone (like the magnesian limestones of Yorkshire) containing bryozoa or mosslike animals; dolomitic and magnesian limestone (like the carboniferous limestones of Derbyshire and South Wales), formed either by the alteration of normal limestone or chemically deposited rock (like Mansfield and Bolsover Moor stone of Permian Age); oolitic limestone like Ketton stone, often called oolite or roestone, composed mainly of small spherical bodies (oolites) consisting of concentric rings of calcium carbonate deposited around sand grains or fragments of shell or coral, and cemented together with crystalline calcite (calcium carbonate); tufa, known to the Greeks as *poros*; and travertine limestone, often porous, formed by the re-deposition of calcium carbonate taken up in solution by water flowing through older calcareous rocks. Geologically, tufa and travertine are the more recent of the limestones; and they occur in localized deposits, around springs.

As in the case of sandstones, limestones may also be classified according to their geological age, e.g. Permian limestone, Rhaetic and Triassic limestones, Carboniferous limestone, and Devonian limestone.

As the sedimentary rocks have been deposited in water in successive layers they can be split fairly readily along more or less well-defined planes of stratification, or 'natural beds'. Blocks with parallel top and bottom surfaces can be produced and this makes them very useful for building purposes.

Some limestones were laid down in fairly still conditions and have a very even texture. They can be easily worked and carved and were some of the earliest so-called 'freestones' to be used. A microphotograph of a sample of oolitic limestone from Ketton is shown in Plate I, 2. Similar stone is also obtainable from Oxfordshire. Other limestones laid down under a somewhat different condition may contain much more shell and are coarse grained—Clipsham (Plate I, 3) and Barnack stones being typical examples. Taynton stone from Oxfordshire is an intermediate type, a shelly oolitic limestone. For more detailed and authoritative information on building stones the reader should consult Howe[2] and Watson.[3]

In Britain the systematic quarrying of building stone does not appear to have been practised to any extent until the Roman occupation, although there is evidence that stone had been roughly worked many centuries earlier. At Stonehenge lintels had been roughly dressed and mortised to the upright stones.

In the west of England, as at Bath, the Romans used limestone from several local sources, Bath stone itself and Ham Hill stone, a coarse-textured limestone varying in colour from yellow grey to yellow brown and composed mainly of comminuted shell fragments. Another limestone used by the Romans for more decorative and monumental work and sometimes for paving was Purbeck marble, from the Purbeck Beds near the top of the Upper Jurassic rock in the Isle of Purbeck near Swanage. It was a favourite material with English medieval architects, particularly for slender clustered columns and sepulchral monuments. It consists of myriads of shells of the fresh water snail *Paludina carinifera*, embedded in a greenish or bluish-grey limestone, and can easily be confused with some varieties of Sussex marble which occur in thin beds in the Wealden Clay, of Lower Cretaceous Age, and which contain shells of *Paludina*, principally *P. sussexienis* and *P. fluviorum*. Examples of its use are the altar stones and episcopal chair in Canterbury Cathedral. Examples of the use of Purbeck marble can be seen in the columns in the nave of Westminster Abbey, in part of the Shrine of Edward the Confessor, in the Temple Church, London, and in the Cathedrals of Lincoln, Winchester, Worcester, and Salisbury. A microphotograph of this stone is shown in Plate I, 9.

One of the earliest stones used by the Romans in London was Kentish ragstone (Plate I, 8) from the Hythe Beds of the Lower Greensand of the Weald, probably near Maidstone. It is mainly a sandy limestone, with round grains of sand and shelly fossils. It is very hard and intractable but could be hewn into rough blocks suitable for rubble walling. The Roman city wall was built with it but also had a plinth of ferruginous sandstone consisting, as seen in the microphotograph (Plate I, 5), of quartz grains cemented with ferruginous material which shows as a dark film round the grains.

The Normans imported a great deal of limestone in the eleventh century from Caen in Normandy and used it very widely; a good example is the interior of the Church of St Bartholomew the Great, Smithfield, but it can also be seen at the Tower of London. Reigate stone (Plate I, 7), a soft calcareous sandstone from Surrey, sometimes known as Gatton, Merstham, and Malmstone, was used by the Normans as a substitute for Caen stone although it was greyer in appearance. This stone can also be seen at the Tower of London, for example in the crypt of Wakefield Tower, in parts of Westminster Abbey, in the Crypt of the Guildhall, and in many of the old city churches. Large quantities were used for the Palace of Nonsuch built by Henry VIII. Portland stone (Plate I, 1), a limestone from the Isle of Portland, Dorset, consists of shells and oolites of much finer grain than in Ketton stone, firmly cemented together and consequently much harder. Although the Romans are known to have quarried the stone, as they used it for coffins found in the Isle of Portland, they do not appear to have brought it to London, and it was not until the middle of the fourteenth century that it seems to have been first used in London. Fragments can be seen in the piece of wall of that date, which once enclosed the precincts of Westminster Abbey. It was used later by Inigo Jones for refacing Old St Paul's in 1633, and for building a new portico. It was also used for repairs to the Banqueting House, Whitehall, in 1623, and the York Water Gate, Embankment Gardens, in 1626. Sir Christopher Wren did much to popularize its use. He also used other limestones such as Beer stone from Devon, Burford stone, and Taynton stone from Oxfordshire, in the rebuilding of St Paul's Cathedral.

In East Anglia flint walling has been used since the Roman occupation. The walls were built of layers of flint nodules bedded in lime mortar, sometimes split to give a fair face. The finest flint work is to be seen in Suffolk and Norfolk, the home of flint-knapping. The sample in Plate II, 3, at the Parish Church of SS. Peter and Paul, Cromer, is of the

Early Perpendicular Period and shows how skilfully the flint blocks were squared so that they could be laid with the thinnest of joints. Two other types of flint walling, also at Cromer, show in Plate II, 1 knapped flint nodules set in courses with smaller flints occasionally set in between, and in Plate II, 2 similar knapped flints with galleted joints consisting of flint flakes closely embedded in the mortar. In Perpendicular work in East Anglia great use was also made of flint for decorative infillings in association with stonework on walls and buttresses.

Marble

It is most important that archaeologists should keep samples of building stone recovered from excavations, for subsequent examination. Many types of stones for decorative purposes, particularly marbles, were transported long distances by the Romans, and it is of great interest to identify the source of these, but it must always be borne in mind that the same types of marble may in fact be found in different quarries; also that several different kinds of marble may be found in the same quarry. Miss Margaret Morris, of the Geological Survey, identified a number of different types of marble which had been used by the Romans at Colchester. They included Cipollino, a white and green banded marble from the Greek quarries on the Island of Euboea; Africano, with white, purple, and pink fragments in a black or very dark green ground, probably from Asia Minor; Carrara (Plate I, 4), the well-known white crystalline marble from Italy; Giallo Antico, yellow stone with red veins, from Algeria and Tunisia; Pavonazzetto, white or pale cream with purple and red veins, from Phrygia in Asia Minor; and Rosso Antico, an unpatterned marble of deep red colour from the Cape Matapan peninsular of Greece. Some of these marbles were also used in Rome, and elsewhere throughout the Empire. Miss Morris also identified from Colchester some Green Greek Prophyry from quarries between Sparta and Marathonisi. Pieces of alabaster, a soft, white, and fine-grained gypsum with red veining, may have been either of British or foreign origin.

Giallo Antico and Pavonazzetto marbles were used extensively in Rome. In the pavement of the Basilica Julia in Rome both these marbles are found together with Africano marble, and it is interesting that these three—with others—should also have been found in close association at Colchester in Britain, so far from Rome and from their sources of origin a thousand miles or more away. Brindley[4] records the use of Giallo Antico and Pavonazzetto marbles for columns in the Pantheon; also that Cipollino marble was used for monoliths 40 feet high in the temple of Antoninus and Faustina; and that Africano marble was used for immense columns in the Garden of the Vatican—the largest known, and measuring 31 feet long and 4 feet 8½ inches in diameter. Other marbles were quarried by the Romans in practically all the countries bordering the Mediterranean Sea, not only in Italy itself, but in Greece and Asia Minor, Egypt, Sicily, Corsica, Sardinia, North Africa, Spain, and France.

Where marble was used in the finest architecture of classical Greece, it was nearly always either the close-grained Pentelic marble from Mt Pentelicus in Attica or the coarser-grained translucent Parian and Naxian varieties from the Aegean islands of Paros and Naxos respectively; and to a lesser extent the soft, white marble from Sunium at the southern extremity of Attica, and the blue, clouded marbles from Hymettus, near Athens, and from Doliana, near Tegea, in Arcadia. The Elgin marbles from the Parthenon at Athens, now in the British Museum, are of Pentelic marble. Parian marble was used for the statue of Venus de Medici. The White Carrara marble quarried at Carrara, Massa, and Serravezza was used by Michelangelo for his finest works.

Generally the Greeks preferred white marble, often using it as a white ground for the application of colour, traces of which are sometimes seen on freshly excavated material. The Romans, on the other hand, made great use of coloured marbles, porphyries, and granites, more so after their conquest of Egypt. Not only did they transport obelisks from Egypt but they themselves seem to have adopted from the Egyptians the idea of using monolithic columns. Many excellent examples could be mentioned of the use and re-use of marble for decorative work, but the photograph of the interior of the Cathedral at Torcello in Plate III serves very well to illustrate the extent to which marble could be used. The church, which is typical Venetian Byzantine work, was founded in A.D. 639, but extensively altered in 864 and again in 1008. The basilican interior has ten bays separated by marble columns with fine capitals. In the foreground of the photograph is part of the marble pavement of *opus Alexandrinum*, in which pieces of coloured marble are inlaid in meandering bands. The pulpit and ambo from the earliest church are also of marble, and the four elaborately carved transennae (ninth century) of the iconostasis, two of which can be seen in Plate III, are themselves classic examples of late Byzantine design. Even the shutters to some of the windows of this beautiful church are hinged slabs of stone.

REFERENCES

(1) PETRIE, W. M. FLINDERS, 1901, *The Royal Tombs of the Earliest Dynasties*, Kegan Paul, II, 9–10.

(2) HOWE, J. ALLEN, 1910, *The Geology of Building Stone*, Arnold.

(3) WATSON, J., 1911, *British and Foreign Building Stones*, Cambridge University Press.

(4) BRINDLEY, W., 1887, 'Marble—its uses as suggested by the past', *Journal* of the Royal Institute of British Architects, III (new series).

2

Building in Stone

WHERE THE STONE was suitable and man had the necessary tools to split it and work it into blocks of convenient shape and size, walls could be built with close jointing without the necessity of filling intervening gaps with smaller stones. Greater stability was thus assured.

It is to Egypt that we have to look for the earliest stone buildings of this type, for here there was an abundance of good stone, and as early as the fourth millennium B.C. there were copper and bronze tools, hardened by hammering, available in addition to those of stone. But stonework in Egypt was reserved almost entirely for palaces, temples, tombs, and monuments, the dwellings of the people being of reeds and mud, or sun-dried bricks, as many are to this day. A very early example of dressed stonework is that of 1st Dynasty date, when cut slabs of limestone were used for lining and roofing a small chamber in a tomb at Saqqara,[1] but possibly the earliest complete building of stone that can be dated is the pit chamber of the tomb of King Khasekhemui excavated by Petrie at Abydos,[2] of 2nd Dynasty date. Although different courses vary somewhat in thickness, they average about 1 foot, and each individual course is surprisingly uniform. Some of the faces of the limestone blocks follow the natural bedding planes, but many appear to have been hammer-dressed and then adzed to level them. The joints with gypsum plaster in them are flush-pointed.

Sandstone was also used in ancient Egypt but in no great quantity until the 18th Dynasty; and granite, alabaster, basalt, and quartzite were reserved mainly for monumental and decorative purposes. The most remarkable and perhaps the finest of all Egyptian structures in worked stone were the pyramids, and the earliest was the Step pyramid at Saqqara, the tomb or cenotaph of Pharaoh Zozer of the 3rd Dynasty. It was built with relatively small blocks of roughly-dressed brownish limestone, and cased with more finely finished white limestone from the Mokattam Hills.[3] The pyramids erected at Gizeh in the 4th Dynasty (*c.* 2600–2500 B.C.) were of much larger blocks—Cyclopean in character as shown in Plate IV. The Great Pyramid, 482 feet in height, was built as his tomb by the greatest king of the dynasty, named Khufu, or called Cheops by the Greeks. The next pyramid was that of Khafra or Chephren (Greek) seen in the background of the photograph. A third and smaller pyramid was that of Menkaura or Mykerinos (Greek). These three pyramids were built with a core of local fossiliferous limestone blocks bedded in gypsum mortar. Those of Khufu and Khafra, and the upper portion of that of Menkaura, were faced with closely-jointed blocks of finer grained limestone transported from across the Nile,[4] and all laid carefully in horizontal courses, worked flat, and squared with extreme accuracy.

There was a break in pyramid construction for a long time, until the 12th Dynasty, when a revival in building, lasting about two hundred years, took place, but the new pyramids were built of sun-dried mud bricks, and were only faced with stone, instead of being of stone throughout.

In general the quality of masonry work declined in Egypt after the 4th Dynasty, and did not attain the high degree of perfection and grandeur again until the New Kingdom of the second millennium B.C., when there was a short-lived revival of large-scale building. The finest and most impressive of all Egyptian temples built in sandstone is that of Amen-Re at Karnak (14th–12th centuries B.C.). Its masonry is of high quality and carefully bedded, but a point of interest is the large number of oblique rising joints. After this short-lived revival, Egyptian architecture declined in quality and the art of fine building was absorbed by the Minoan-Mycenaean culture which was spreading throughout the Eastern Mediterranean. To the early phase of the Minoan culture belongs the magnificent palace of King Minos at Knossos (*c.* 2500 B.C.) and to later phases the fine buildings at Mycenae, its palace, the 'beehive' tomb of Agamemnon, also known as the Treasury of Atreus, and that of Clytemnestra, and the Lion Gate (Gate of Lions), which has a stone lintel 16 feet 6 inches in length. The post and lintel construction of this gateway, the clear opening of which is 10 feet, is shown in Figure 1. The corbelled stones above the lintel form a triangular opening which relieves it of load and is a feature which also occurs over the doorway to the nearby tomb of Agamemnon (*c.* 1450 B.C.). The triangular space above this latter doorway is empty but that above the Lion Gate is filled with a triangular slab about 10 feet high and 12 feet wide, of brownish limestone, on which is a relief of two lions rampant on either side of a central half column, tapering downwards with moulded capital and square abacus carved with four discs. The corbelled dome in the interior of the tomb of Agamemnon is 48 feet 6 inches in diameter, and in construction follows earlier Cretan patterns; and the later corbelled roof of the sanctuaries in the Temple of Seti I at

Fig. 1. The Lion Gate, Mycenae.

Abydos, in Egypt, commenced in 1350 B.C. and completed by Rameses II about twenty years later is very similar. Here each horizontal course also projected beyond the one immediately below, the soffit being then worked by chisel into the form of a vault.

In the middle of the second millennium B.C. there was very close intercommunication between Crete and Egypt and it is not surprising to find recurrent architectural features common to both.

The stonework of the Hellenistic Period (700–146 B.C.) still tended to be megalithic in character. It was carefully worked and close jointed and generally more refined than the earlier Mycenaean, and it was during the relatively short period between about 500 and 300 B.C. that the masterpieces of Greek architecture were built. The Acropolis at Athens is perhaps the crowning glory, but there are a bewildering number of beautiful buildings in Greece in such places as Corinth, Delphi, Epidauros, Olympia, Eleusis, and the Island of Delos to mention but a few, and outside Greece in Southern Italy, Sicily, and Asia Minor. The Greeks showed much greater versatility in masonry construction than their predecessors had done, and they fitted blocks together with extraordinary precision and artistry. The different types of stone walling were many and varied. An early type used by the Greeks and other Aegean people was built with very large and irregular pieces of rock, some weighing several tons, only roughly trimmed, piled up very skilfully and wedged together by filling the interstices with smaller pieces of stone and sometimes bedded in clay. A good example, and an early one, is the enormous wall over 20 feet in thickness at Tiryns, built shortly before 1400 B.C. This type of work is sometimes known as Cyclopean, so called because it was thought by simple folk to have been the work of a gigantic Thracian race called Cyclopes. Pausanias[5] (second century A.D.) speaking of the walls of Tiryns says: 'the wall, all that is left of the ruins of the city, is the work of Cyclopes and built of unhewn stones, each of which is so large that a yoke of mules would be incapable of moving even the smallest of them in the least. In bygone times small stones had been placed in the gaps between them in order to connect them as far as possible'. Lawrence[6] records that this type of masonry gave way to that constructed with polygonal blocks cut with straight or nearly straight facets, a good example of which is the mixed polygonal and curvilinear walling on the face of the terrace of the great temple of Apollo at Delphi, shown in Plate V, 1. The stones are covered with inscriptions. In the middle of the fifth century, there was a tendency towards horizontal coursing in the polygonal masonry, as represented by the example in Plate V, 2 of the retaining wall of the tomb of Lysimachides in the Ceramicus cemetery at Athens. There was a renewal of polygonal masonry later in the Hellenistic period, largely for decorative purposes, and the facets of the blocks, as in the terrace wall at Cnidus of the third to second centuries B.C., were very accurately cut so that the joints were very fine (Figure 3).

There were many forms of rectangular block walling. A good example of random coursed masonry of the Mycenaean period (*c.* fifteenth century B.C.) is the walling at the entrance to the tomb of Agamemnon, at Mycenae (Plate V, 3). Greek work was more refined and regular, like that of mid-fifth century B.C. date from the platform of the

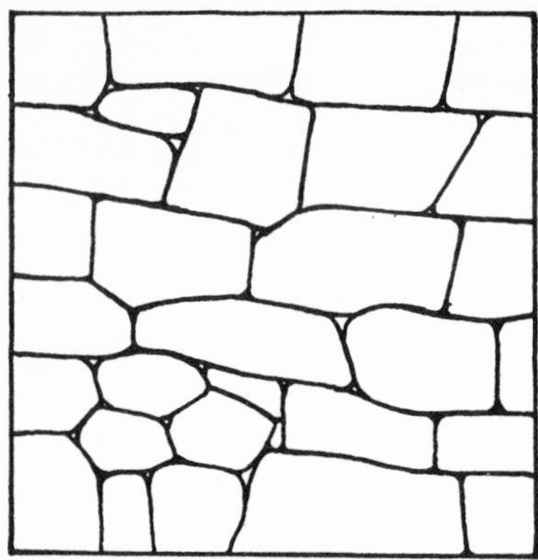

Fig. 2. Curvilinear masonry; temple platform, Old Smyrna, seventh century B.C.

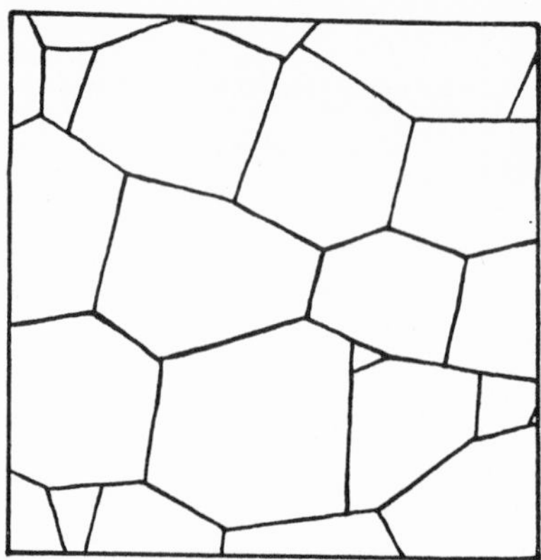

Fig. 3. Polygonal masonry; terrace wall, Cnidus, third to second centuries B.C.

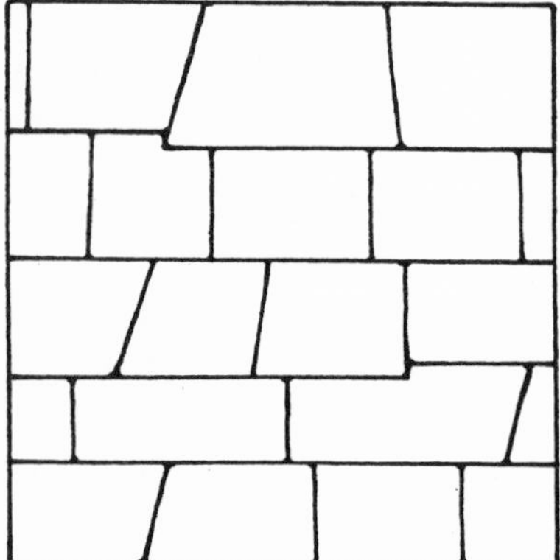

Fig. 4. Rectangular and trapezoidal masonry; city wall, Messene, mid-fourth century B.C.

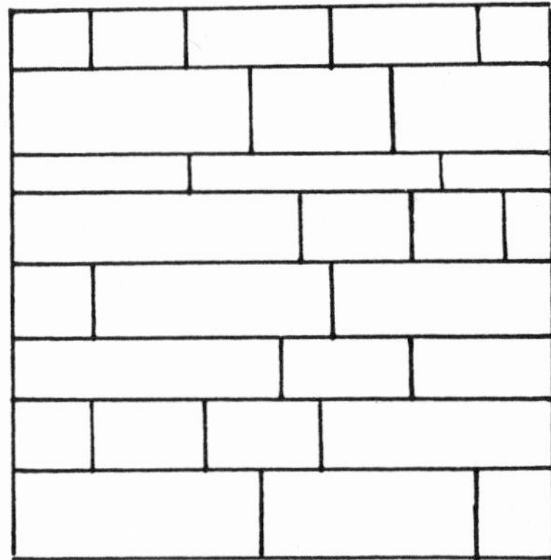

Fig. 5. Rectangular masonry; platform of the Temple of Poseidon, mid-fifth century B.C.

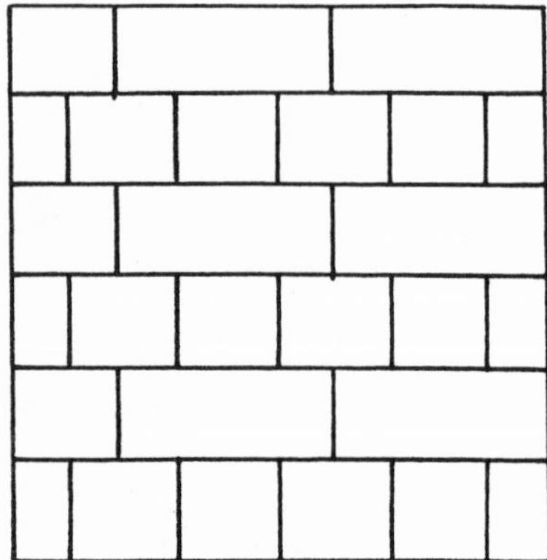

Fig. 6. Alternate rows of long and short blocks; Attic frontier fort, Aegosthena, *c.* third century B.C.

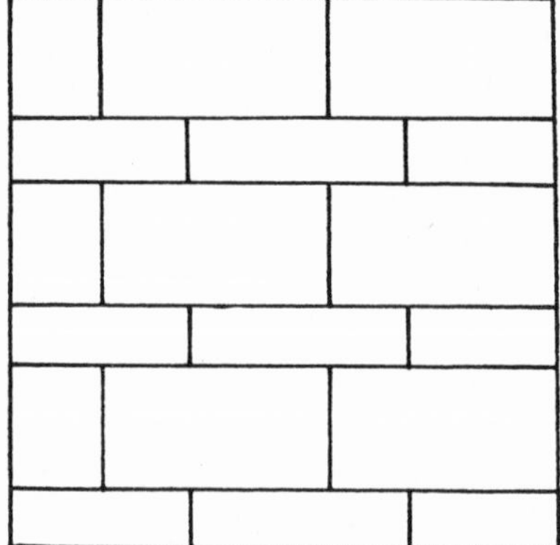

Fig. 7. Pseudisodomic masonry, alternate rows of different thickness; Acropolis of Smyrna, third century B.C., and pedestal of the monument of Agrippa outside the Propylaea, *c.* 175 B.C.

Temple of Poseidon at Paestum (Figure 5). The courses in this case are of varying height; but about this time isodomic masonry was developed in which the courses of blocks were of uniform height and length, with the joints in alternate courses placed vertically above each other. The example of this type shown in Plate V, 4 is the south wall of the Propylaea on the Acropolis at Athens (of the fifth century B.C.) and is particularly interesting as it shows that the marble blocks still retain the bosses for lifting them into place. They would normally have been trimmed off flush with the face of the wall, but it is thought the work of building was interrupted at the outbreak of the Peloponnesian war in 431 B.C., and never finished. Two of the bosses at the bottom of the photograph have been partially trimmed back. Such walls with all the blocks of uniform size and shape were rather uninteresting in appearance, and to relieve the monotony other types of bonding were introduced, the first being to lay the same sized blocks in alternate rows of headers and stretchers (Figure 6). Another type was called pseudisodomic, in which alternate courses were of two very different heights. An example of this is shown in Plate V, 5 of the retaining wall of the theatre stage at Delphi, *c.* 159 B.C., and another example given by Lawrence is the pedestal of the monument of Agrippa outside the Propylaea at Athens, dating from *c.* 175 B.C. (Figure 7). In some cases the thin blocks pass through the whole thickness of the wall, to reinforce it considerably.

There is another feature which may have had its origin in Egypt, and was copied by the Mycenaean and later the Greeks. It was the sporadic use of slanting rising joints, of the type illustrated in Figure 4, of the mid-fourth century B.C. city wall at Messene, on the retaining walls of the gymnasium at Delphi, and on the towers of the Attic frontier fort of Eleutherae, also of fourth century B.C. date. Similar jointing can be seen in the much earlier Temple of Amen-Re at Karnak in Egypt (14th–12th centuries B.C.). The Greeks, however, deliberately accentuated the effect for decorative purposes in late work, as seen in the retaining wall of the theatre at Delos, of early second century B.C. date (Plate V, 6).

Examples of construction in Cyclopean masonry are to be found in Asia Minor and in the Middle East. It seems that the Persians must have adopted methods of building in stone from their neighbours in Urarta (modern Armenia) in Asia Minor, when the former were living to the west of Lake Urmia in north-west Iran. In about the eighth century B.C. the Persians left this part, travelled south-eastwards, and settled in the Bakhtiari mountains. Here they built some imposing structures in Cyclopean masonry, in some respects very like those in the Eastern Mediterranean. The photograph in Plate VI shows part of the imposing terrace built against the mountainside at Masjid-i-Sulaiman, which Ghirshman[7] considers may be the first of the royal cities of the Persians, built perhaps by Achaemenes or Teispes; and that this and possibly a neighbouring site at Bard-i-Nishandah may have been the prototypes of the famous terrace at Persepolis with its palaces built by Darius I (521–485 B.C.) and Xerxes (485–465 B.C.). The whole enclosure wall at Masjid-i-Sulaiman was built with buttresses and recesses, and seems to have been designed for defence. Five staircases, one over 75 feet wide (shown in the photograph) led up to the terrace. Excavations revealed that princely dwellings once stood upon it. Ghirshman states that neither the Elamites, Babylonians, or Assyrians (the other neighbours of the Persians), nor the original inhabitants of the area, were ever associated with this type of construction. It seems probable therefore that the influence came from the Eastern Mediterranean.

Miss Blake[8] has dealt in great detail with the development of stone masonry in Italy from prehistoric times up to the time of Augustus. In addition to giving a description of the various types of stone available, and a brief survey of their sources, she has described the various ways of building in stone adopted by the Romans. The earliest Cyclopean walls, like those of Greece and elsewhere, were crude. However, it was not long before the smoothing of the exposed surface of the stones was resorted to, followed by the gradual smoothing of the adjacent faces of abutting blocks and the shaping of the angles until there were no gaps to be filled with small stones. Thus developed the polygonal form of walling of the type already described, perhaps not so much in Rome itself as in the limestone regions of Central Italy where the limestone was more readily worked. Good examples of Cyclopean and polygonal masonry occur at Ameria, Norba, and Praeneste. Stone which tended to split with a horizontal cleavage was preferred and very soon an irregular quadrangular masonry developed as a consequence of its use. The blocks varied considerably in size but were carefully fitted in with close joints. Later the closely-fitting squared blocks were laid in regular horizontal courses, a type of masonry called by the Romans *opus quadratum*. The blocks were fairly large, often as much as 2 feet by 4 feet or more in elevation, and sometimes held together with iron cramps set in lead.

The Romans in Rome itself had abundant local materials for general construction but they went farther afield to obtain rare marbles and other stones with which to cover their walls and floors. The local tufaceous stone of volcanic origin provided the chief supply, and the sequence in which these were used often provides a means of dating certain structures. For example, Monte Verde stone was generally used earlier than the Anio variety; also the succession of colours of the various types of pozzolana used, ranging from grey, dark reddish grey, to reddish brown and even black, has a useful chronological value, for in the course of time the Romans dug deeper and deeper, and went farther and farther afield opening up new beds of material in their search for fresh supplies.

All these walls depended for stability on the weight and massiveness of the stone blocks, but during the second century B.C., the principle of wall construction underwent a complete revolution. By developing mortar which attained considerable strength on hardening, it was found possible to erect walls with a core of concrete capable of taking most of the load, but faced, largely for appearance and convenience, with stones smaller than those used previously (pieces roughly 3 to 4 inches across). The form of wall known as *opus incertum* was thus developed and became the most common facing for ordinary concrete walls in the second and first centuries B.C. At first the pieces of stone used for the facing were rather shapeless, but in the first century B.C. the form of wall-facing developed into the *opus reticulatum* work in which small carefully cut wedge-shaped blocks of stone, usually of volcanic tuff, presented square faces accurately set at 45° so that the joints made a reticulate of oblique lines. This type of walling, often with stone quoins, flourished up to about the middle of the first century A.D., when brick quoins became the rule.

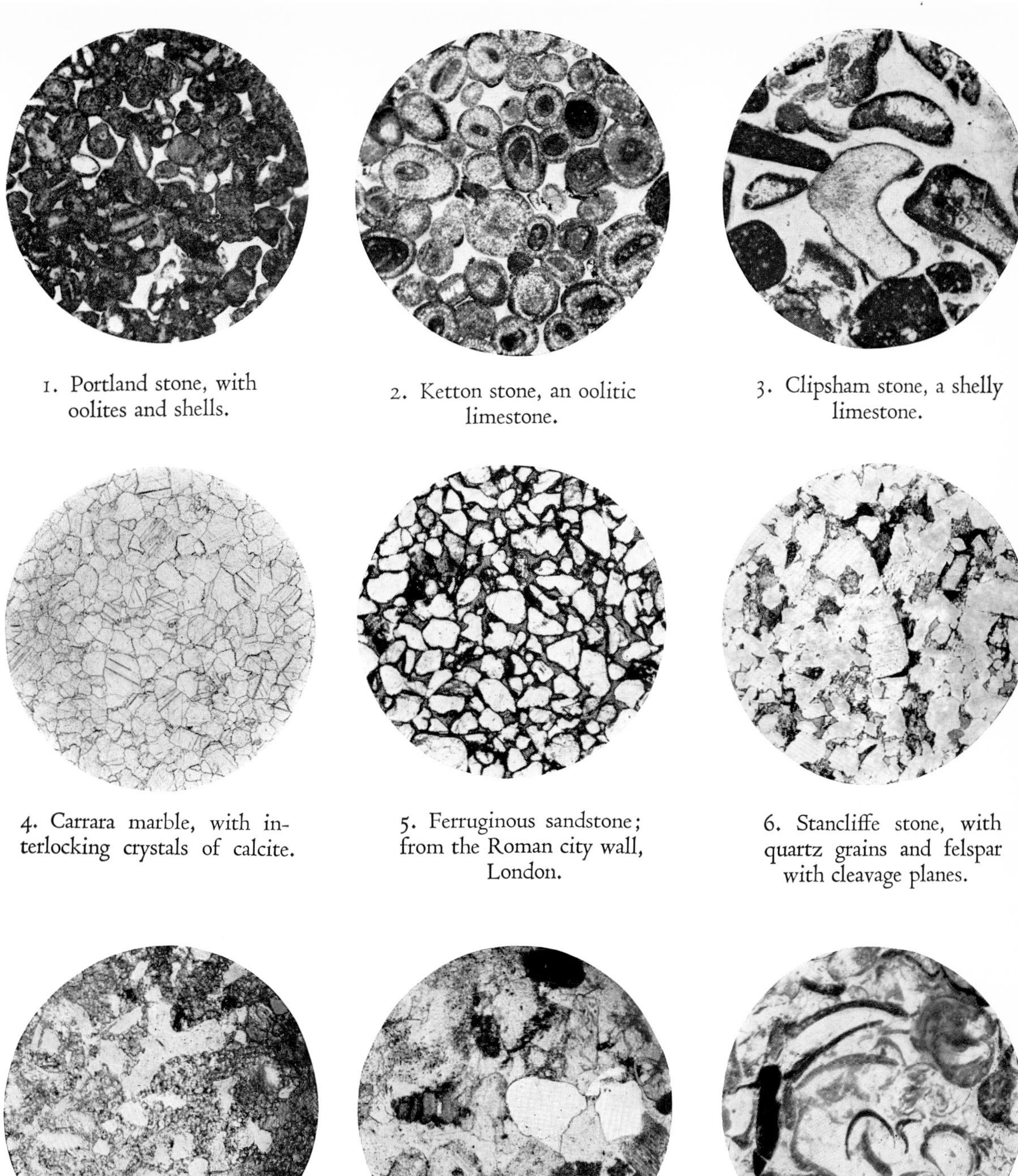

1. Portland stone, with oolites and shells.

2. Ketton stone, an oolitic limestone.

3. Clipsham stone, a shelly limestone.

4. Carrara marble, with interlocking crystals of calcite.

5. Ferruginous sandstone; from the Roman city wall, London.

6. Stancliffe stone, with quartz grains and felspar with cleavage planes.

7. Reigate stone, a soft calcareous sandstone; sponge fragments in a calcareous base, quartz grains, and greenish grains of glauconite and a small amount of iron.

8. Kentish ragstone, a sandy limestone; from the Roman city wall, London.

9. Purbeck marble, a shelly limestone.

Plate I. Types of building stone (microphotographs) (see Chapter I).

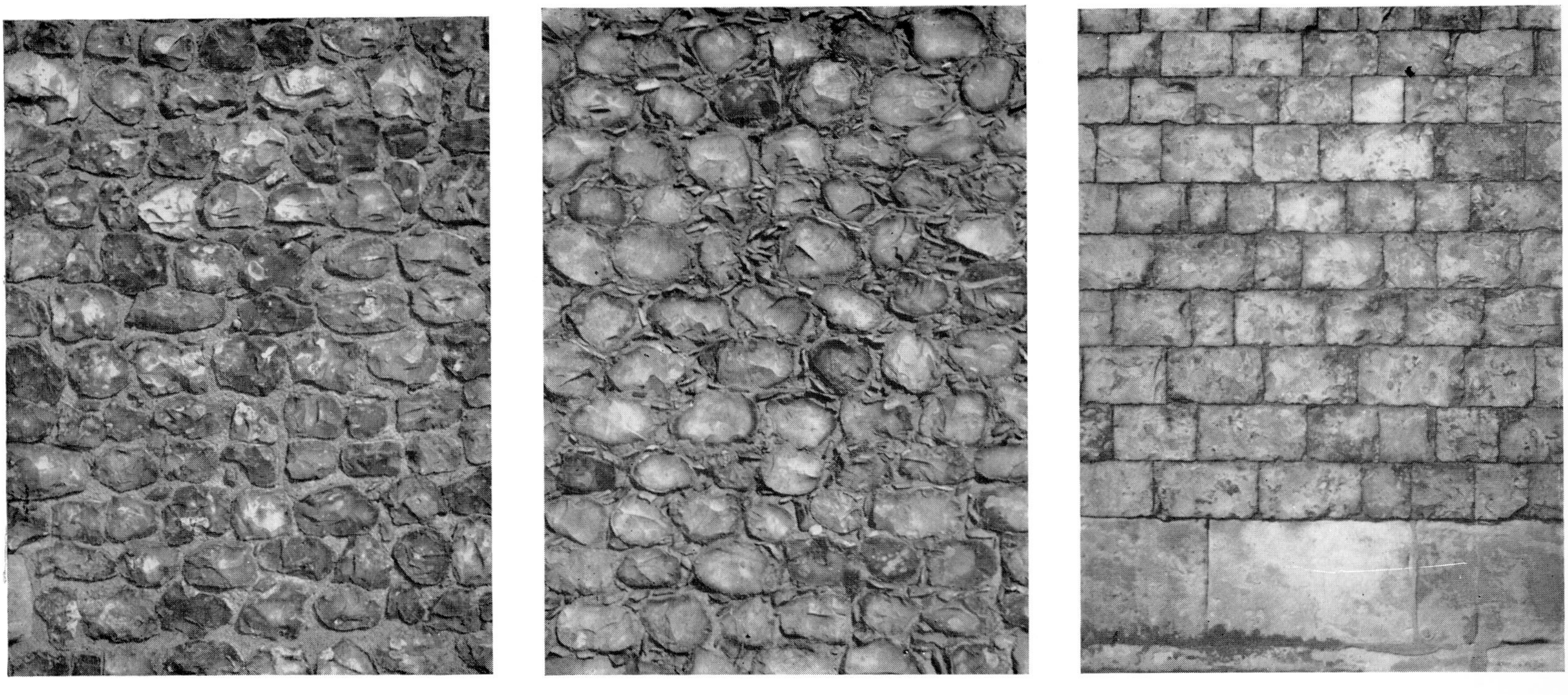

1. Knapped flint walling.

2. Knapped flints with galleted joints.

3. Squared flint walling.

Plate II. Types of flint walling (see pages 4–5).

The transition from stone to concrete walls came when instead of small stones used as a facing to the concrete core, the stones were laid in layers in formwork, each layer having poured over it a grout of mortar, string courses of stone or tile being inserted every 3 or 4 feet to increase the stability of the work. The final step came in the second century B.C. when the concrete as we know it today was made by incorporating the stone in the mortar mix before placing. The podium of the second Temple of Concord, in Rome, erected by Opimus in 121 B.C., is the earliest known example of this type of mass concrete.

In Britain as in many other parts of the world the earliest stone structures were of a religious character, places of worship and tombs. As Wheeler[9] has pointed out: 'the great chambered tombs of the so-called megalithic period must have been associated intimately with a certain range of religious ideas and practices which doubtless differed in detail locally, but normally bore the impress of a common type. In a small degree these chamber tombs, like the Pyramids of Egypt which are themselves over-grown chamber tombs, testify to the co-ordinated effort of large communities, disciplined and directed by rulers whose authority doubtless owed much to a powerful religion.' These chamber tombs fall roughly into two groups, the simple dolmen type and the passage type derived from or associated with them. The dolmen type consisted essentially of a quadrangular enclosure, made by setting up vertically four stone slabs and placing over them a covering slab. The chamber so formed, after it had received its contents, was usually heaped over with stones and earth. From the simple dolmen was derived the passage-grave type which was in fact a 'covered alley', also lined with vertical slabs, and sometimes having side chambers. Alternatively the dolmen itself might have a *dromos*, or approaching corridor, similarly constructed. The distribution of dolmen-type tombs extends over Britain, Scandinavia, Denmark, Germany, Yugoslavia, France, Spain, Portugal, Corsica, Sardinia, Italy, North Africa, Syria, the Caucasus, the Black Sea area, and various parts of India. Passage tombs occur in the same areas with the addition of Greece, Egypt, parts of Asia Minor, and Japan.

In Europe the dolmens appear to be characteristic of districts bordering upon or easily reached from the sea, and this does suggest that there may have been communication probably by sea between these various countries. Wheeler has also commented that the transportation, for example, of the so called 'blue stones' of Stonehenge, from the Prescelly mountains of South Wales to Wiltshire in the second millennium B.C., implies the same social and political discipline that enabled the erection of large capstones on the dolmens, sometimes weighing as much as forty tons. The recent discovery of carvings of daggers of Mycenaean pattern on the stones at Stonehenge lends substance to the suggestion of there having been communication with other megalithic builders. If in fact the Mycenaean or Aegean influence was present at Stonehenge it is not surprising that we should also find there some of the earliest examples in Britain of masons' work, including the practice of tenoning and mortising the stonework.

In this same megalithic period there were dwellings with dry-built stone walls, formed with odd-shaped pieces of weathered stone found lying on or close to the surface of the ground. To stabilize the walls the joints were often wedged with small pieces of rock and stone, and the interstices filled with clay. Sometimes such walls were given extra stability by backing with earth, as in the buildings at Skara Brae on the Bay of Skail, Orkney. These were excavated by the late Professor Gordon Childe[10] and others, and were roughly rectangular in plan with rounded internal corners as shown in Plate VII, and were partly roofed by corbelling with stone. Each dwelling was entered through a narrow opening about 4 feet high. In the centre of each dwelling was a square hearth on which a peat fire was burned, while on either side were beds enclosed by stone slabs. There were storage recesses and stone furniture including a two-tiered dresser of stone slabs, for the construction of which it may be presumed no local timber was available. Somewhat similar houses, discovered by James Yorston, were excavated by Grant at Rinyo, Rousay.[11] The so-called 'wheelhouses' of the Bronze—Iron Age at Jarlshof, Shetland, represent an interesting development which arose from the difficulty experienced in roofing over large buildings with stone. To overcome this a series of internal radial walls was introduced, thus dividing the area into smaller elements which could each be more readily covered by corbelled stone slabs. The effect was to produce a central court from which a series of rooms with domed roofs opened. Comparatively modern buildings with corbelled stone roofing are still in use today in various places, for example at Haran (Charan), in Northern Syria, and in Southern Italy, where particularly good examples can be seen at Alberobello. The remains of stone houses with corbelled dome-shaped roofs are to be found in the Outer Hebrides where some of the buildings are reputed to have been inhabited up to the middle of the nineteenth century.

Stone houses, probably occupied during the period 200 B.C. to A.D. 300, can be seen at Chysauster, Cornwall. The plans are generally more irregular than those of the 'wheelhouses', but none the less the internal planning arrangements seem very purposeful. Traces of eight houses formed a village community. The entrances, generally facing in roughly an easterly direction, lead to a large open space, or court, probably too large to be roofed over. The area of the court on the left-hand side on entering was somewhat larger than that on the right-hand side, and may have had a lean-to roof to form a cattle stall. Opposite the entrance was a large round or oval room with areas of rough paving. At or near the centre of the floor was a large flat stone with a small hollow. The purpose of this may have been to provide a means of locating the lower end of a pole to support the roof of these larger rooms. It does seem that these houses may have incorporated timber in the roofs and not stone as at Skara Brae.

The method of building a wall with flat retaining slabs set vertically in the ground and backed by rubble is well illustrated in the Stone Circles at Clava near Inverness, which are perhaps among the best remains of this type. As far south in Britain as Devon the same principle of construction was followed in building huts of Bronze Age date. In the examples at Grims Pound the average height of the slabs was 3 feet, and the spaces between were filled with smaller pieces of stone and the whole backed by turves. Across the entrance, which was about 2 feet wide, was a stone lintel. The floor was beaten clay or occasionally paved with rough stone blocks. In some cases there was a sort of dais up to a foot in height which may have served as a sleeping place. Near the centre of the floor, as at Chysauster, was a flat slab of stone which probably carried a post supporting the roof, which appears to have been of boughs and probably turf.

Lucas[12] has pointed out that 'the quarrying of stone could not, and did not, begin until it was rendered possible by the advent of metal (copper) tools'. Before this, stone was obtained from weathered rocks found lying at the foot of cliffs, or from boulders, and sarcens, deposited in river valleys. As soon as metal tools were available the systematic quarrying of the sedimentary rocks—limestone and sandstone—presented no great difficulty. The methods used by the Egyptians have been described by Somers Clarke and Engelbach,[13] Reisner,[14] and Flinders Petrie,[15] and the generally accepted view is that to detach a block of stone, narrow trenches, or grooves, were cut along four sides, wooden wedges were driven in dry and then saturated with water to cause them to swell, and the block was then prised from its natural bed below with wooden levers.

Quarrying of hard igneous rocks which had no natural even beds along which they could be easily split like the sedimentary rocks, was a much more laborious process. Engelbach[16] has studied ancient Egyptian methods, and reached the conclusion that the surfaces were prepared to the desired profile by pounding with balls of diorite, and that slots into which wooden wedges could be driven were cut with a metal hoe. The subsequent treatment can be deduced from the drawing in the 18th Dynasty Tomb of Rekhmara at Thebes (Figure 122). It shows the curved surfaces of the granite statuary being pounded and rubbed with stones, and, below, large blocks of limestones are being squared up by chiselling, and tested by means of boning rods. There is evidence from the markings left on granite statuary that cutting and drilling were possible. Cutting may have been achieved by using an abrasive such as emery, fed to a soft metal blade, and drilling by feeding the abrasive down a soft copper tube, a technique that has survived to this day for boring holes in glass. The hard grains of abrasive bedded themselves in the soft copper, in very much the same way that diamonds are embedded in cutting discs used by lapidaries. Softer stones like limestones could be cut with a toothed saw.

In Roman times sand was fed as an abrasive to saw blades without teeth to cut hard stones, and with teeth for soft stones.[17] At first the Roman saws were hand operated but later they were also driven by water power. The Gallic-Roman poet Decimus Magnus Ausonius[18] (A.D. 310-396) mentioned saw-mills in the Ruiver valley in which the stone slabs for the buildings of the Imperial City of Trèves were cut.

> 'The swift Celbis [R. Kyll] the Erubris [R. Ruiver], famed for marble, hasten full eagerly to approach with their attendant waters; renowned is Celbis for glorious fish, and that other, as he turns his millstones in furious revolutions and drives the shrieking saws through smooth blocks of marble, hears from either bank a ceaseless din.'

The Romans also quarried stones of enormous size. Neuburger[19] describes the great quantity of large blocks in various stages of extraction and working, lying in the quarries at Odenwald, from which the Romans procured material for their towns at Oppenheim, Mannheim, Mainz, Trèves, Wiesbaden, and Aix-la-Chapelle. One large block, now called the 'Altar Stone', is particularly interesting as it clearly shows the technique of cutting and extraction. Its length varies at different sections from 10 to 15 feet, and it is 6 feet high. At least two long blocks had already been removed for making pillars, but there are still to be seen the deep saw cuts about one-sixth of an inch wide, running the full length of the block, and supplemented by holes into which wedges were to have been inserted with the intention of detaching more blocks 20 to 24 inches in thickness. Close by, towards the village of Reichenbach, lies a column 30 feet long, just over 5 feet diameter at the bottom and just over 4 feet diameter at the top, weighing about 140 tons. Other enormous stones occur at places in other countries, at Palmyra and at Baalbek for instance. At the former site pillars 36 feet in height, each cut from one block, form an avenue. At Baalbek part of the wall of the famous temple enclosure on the north-western side is formed of enormous blocks of stone. Three of these, probably of second century date, built into the wall 20 feet from the ground and most accurately masoned, are each roughly 62 feet by 14 feet by 11 feet, and weigh about 600 tons, while a companion stone somewhat larger, shaped but not entirely detached from its bed, can still be seen in the quarry on the outskirts of Baalbek.

How such great stones as these and the enormous single stone forming the cupola roof about 36 feet in diameter over the tomb of Theodoric at Ravenna (*c.* A.D. 530), were placed in position is a matter for conjecture. The Egyptians and Assyrians dragged massive blocks of stone along on sledge-runners, and there seems no reason why they could not be pulled up temporary inclined ramps to the required height.

Methods of stone quarrying and stone working have changed but little in course of time. Picks, bars, and wedges are still used for quarrying the sedimentary stone, as they were many centuries ago, advantage always being taken of the natural bedding planes as the best positions for splitting it. Once the upper surface and one side of an unhewn block has been exposed, it then remains for it to be split off from the back and the other side with wedges, and finally prized off its natural bed. It is then sawn into blocks of convenient sizes and sent to the mason's yard. The igneous rocks have no natural uniform beds and can only be hewn or blasted out in irregular blocks. These are either split with wedges and feathers or cut by mechanically operated toothless iron bandsaws fed with chilled iron shot. The dressing of the stones is carried out with tools of various types, including the axe, the gab, the scabber, the puncheon, and plain and serrated chisels of different sizes. Notes on some of the quarryman's and mason's tools are given in the Appendix (Figs. 121, 123). To utilize the stone to the best advantage from the point of view of strength and resistance to weathering it is customary to lay it on its natural bed, if it has one, or in such a way that the natural bed is set at right angles to the direction of the thrust. The stone voussoirs of an arch for example are cut and placed so that their natural bedding planes lie radially.

In Figures 8 to 13 are shown the main types of bond used today in stone walls. The common, rough uncoursed, or random rubble wall shown in Figure 8, is made of odd-shaped pieces of rock, very often pieces of naturally weathered rock, and it is probably only at the quoins that they need to be dressed. Random rubble, built to course, as shown in Figure 9, makes a stronger wall. Intractable rocks, ragstone and granite for example,

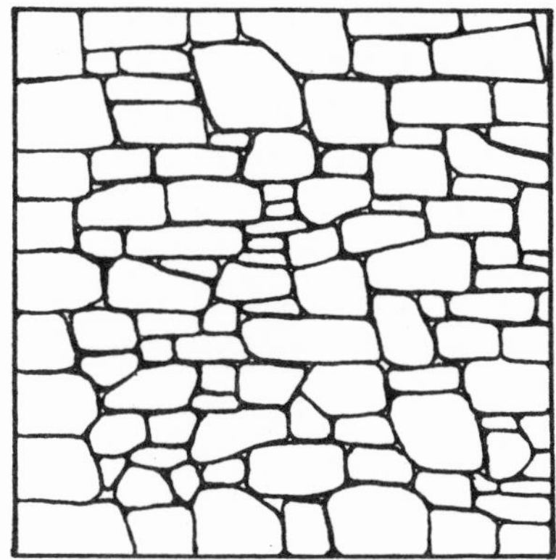

Fig. 8. Common rough uncoursed, or random, rubble.

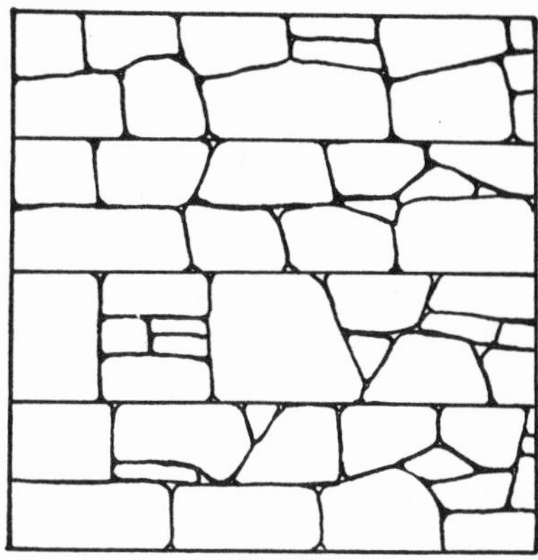

Fig. 9. Random rubble built to course.

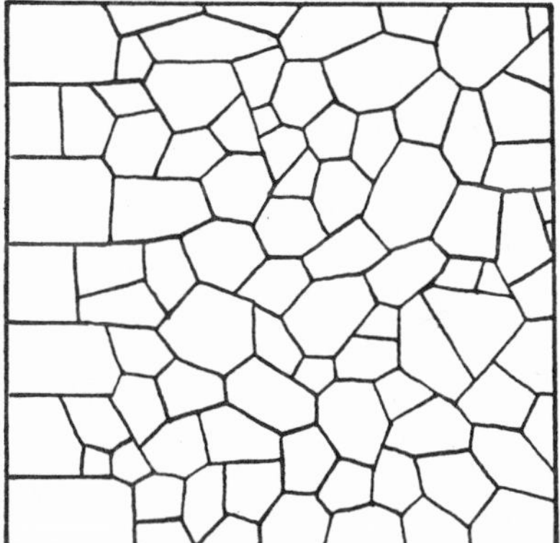

Fig. 10. Polygonal random rubble with hammer-dressed joints.

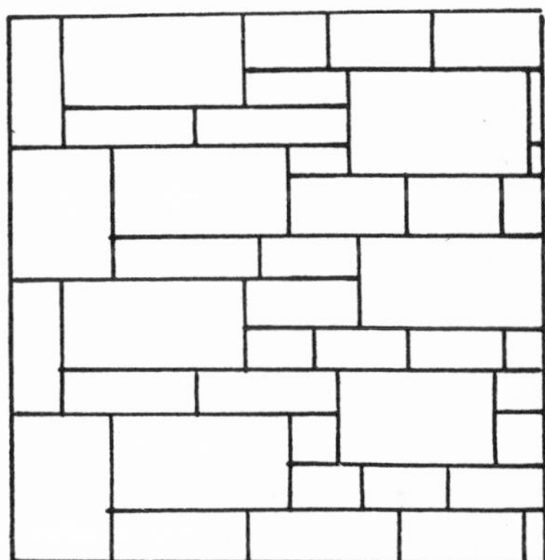

Fig. 11. Irregular coursed, snecked, or square random, rubble.

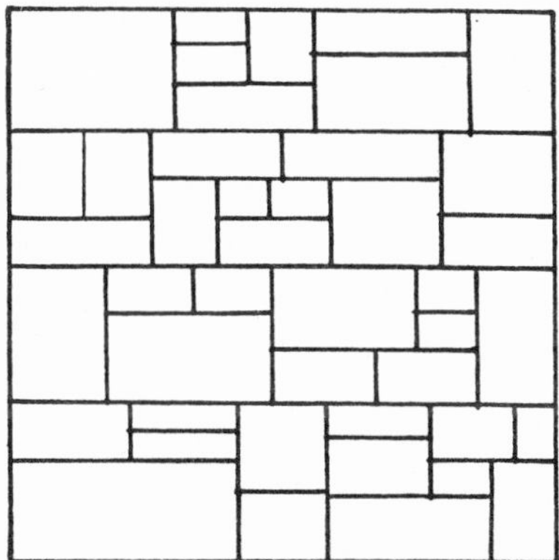

Fig. 12. Random rubble built to courses with beds horizontal and joints vertical.

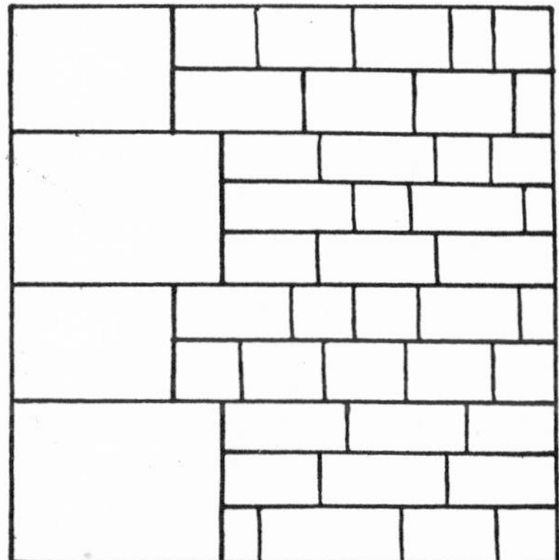

Fig. 13. Coursed rubble.

which fracture into odd shapes can be utilized in polygonal random rubble. In the best work the surfaces are hammer-dressed to give close joints as shown in Figure 10. Random rubble walls in which the stones are squared but of irregular size, with small stones or snecks introduced to break the course, as shown in Figure 11, are common in Scotland, and this type of work is called snecked rubble. Squared random rubble brought to courses is shown in Figure 12 and the last example in Figure 13 shows coursed rubble of squared stone laid in courses to suit the heights of the cornerstones, or rybats.

REFERENCES

(1) QUIBELL, J. E., 1912–14, *Excavations at Saqqara*, Quaritch, 3–5.

(2) PETRIE, W. M. FLINDERS, 1901, *The Royal Tombs of the Earliest Dynasties*, Kegan Paul, II, 13.

(3) *Antiquity*, Vol. II, No. 8, December 1928, 461.

(4) LUCAS, A., 1948, *Ancient Egyptian Materials and Industries*, Arnold (3rd revised edition).

(5) PAUSANIAS, Book II, 25, 7.

(6) LAWRENCE, A. W., 1957, *Greek Architecture*, Penguin Books.

(7) GHIRSHMAN, R., 1954, *Iran*, Penguin Books.

(8) BLAKE, MARION E., 1947, *Ancient Roman Construction in Italy from the Prehistoric Period to Augustus*, Carnegie Institution of Washington, Publication 570.

(9) WHEELER, R. E. M., 1925, *Prehistoric and Roman Wales*, Oxford University Press.

(10) CHILDE, V. GORDON, 1947, *Prehistoric Communities of the British Isles*, Chambers (revised edition).

(11) CHILDE, V. G., and GRANT, W. G., 1938–9, 'A Stone Age Settlement at the Braes of Rinyo, Rousay, Orkney', First Report, *Proceedings of the Society of Antiquaries of Scotland*, LXXIII (7th Series), Vol. 1.

(12) LUCAS, A., 1948, *Ancient Egyptian Materials and Industries*, Arnold (3rd revised edition).

(13) CLARKE, SOMERS and ENGELBACH, R., 1930, *Ancient Egyptian Masonry*, Oxford University Press, 12–22.

(14) REISNER, G. A., 1931, *Mycerinus*, Oxford University Press, 69–70.

(15) PETRIE, W. M. FLINDERS, 1933, *The Arts and Crafts of Ancient Egypt*, Davies, 70.

(16) ENGELBACH, R., 1923, *The Problem of the Obelisks*, 23, 26, 34, 36, 42, Fisher Unwin.

(17) VITRUVIUS, *De Architectura*, Book II, VII, 1.

(18) AUSONIUS, *The Moselle*, Book X, translated by Hugh G. Evelyn White, Loeb Classical Library, Heinemann.

(19) NEUBERGER, A., 1930, *The Technical Arts and Sciences of the Ancients*, translated by Henry L. Brose, Methuen.

3

Earth Walling

IN MANY PARTS of the world there is little to build walls with but mud. The earliest attempts to build solid walls of mud and clay must have been very disappointing in consequence of the slow drying of the mass and subsequent shrinkage and cracking. It was soon realized that it was better to work the mud or clay into small lumps roughly shaped in suitable sizes, and allow them partially to dry and shrink in the sun for some days before ramming them into position in the wall. The inclusion of chopped straw, grass or other vegetable matter not only helped to give the material more coherence, but assisted evaporation of moisture from the interior and tended to distribute cracking more evenly and thus reduce the risk of distortion of the finished work.

The principal methods of building earth walling are:

(*a*) without shuttering or formwork, as in 'cob' or 'chalk mud' construction;
(*b*) with shuttering or formwork, as in *pisé de terre*;
(*c*) with earth blocks of varying types such as hand-moulded clay lumps, as in 'adobe' work;
(*d*) with mud bricks formed in a mould, and air-dried or sun-dried before use.

(a) Building without formwork

Possibly the most primitive method of building an earth wall was to use turves laid with the grass downwards. It was suitable for walls of dwellings of a primitive or temporary character, or for the revetting of minor earthworks. Another method was to compact a mixture of mud and chopped straw, reed, or grass in layers while still damp, without the use of formwork or timber shuttering.

For thousands of years this method has continued in use all over the world. It survives in England particularly in Devonshire, where it is called cob construction, and the men who carry out the work are known as 'cob-masons', but in other parts cob is known by other names, such as 'cleam', 'clob', and 'clom'. The clay and straw are mixed with just sufficient water to give a suitable consistence for easy compaction. In times past this mixing operation was often carried out near a pond and a horse sometimes used to tread the clay and straw together, although men usually did this. In the best work, and in order to protect the lower part of the wall from rising damp and disintegration by rain splashing, it has been customary to lay a base wall or plinth of stone, flint, or brick, at least 9 inches high and 2 feet thick. Lawrence[1] records that similar protection to mud-brick walls was provided in Greece as far back as the Neolithic and early Bronze Age period (*c.* 3000 B.C.), the protective plinth being either a single course of stone, or a dwarf wall of stone several feet high.

The cob-waller nowadays stands on the wall and receives the cob which is pitched up to him with a special fork rather like a trident. He places it, and treads it down in layers about a foot in height without the use of shuttering, beginning at one corner of the building and following right round the perimeter, by which time the layer has stiffened enough to receive the next layer. When trodden down the layer of cob projects an inch or so beyond the face of the plinth wall but this excess is pared off with a 'paring iron' or 'cob parer' (Fig. 131). The walls are then often left several months before they are plastered and limewashed. Left unprotected, cob and chalk mud walls are liable to be disintegrated by rain and frost. Sometimes a rough-cast rendering known in Devonshire as 'slap-dash' is applied; but often the surface is tarred and finally whitewashed. Such walls may last for many years, several hundred in fact, if the roof, which is often of thatch, is well maintained and provided with good overhanging eaves, to protect the upper part of the wall at least from the rain.

Alternatively a well-trodden mixture of crushed chalk and straw, called 'chalk mud' in Wiltshire, or a mixture of up to three parts of crushed chalk to one of clay and straw, as used in Hampshire, makes equally good walls.

(b) Building with formwork

The second method of construction also extremely old was to compact the mixture into wooden formwork or basketwork. In some ancient round dwellings in Ireland, for example, the walls were made by compacting the mixture into the annular space, about a foot or so in width, between two concentric rings of basketwork. Pliny[2] refers to earth walls in Africa and Spain, known as *formoceau* walls, which he says were moulded by 'enclosing earth within a frame of boards'. Many examples of this type of work have been revealed in the excavation of buildings of Roman date. A particularly interesting example was excavated by Sheppard Frere[3] in 1956 at Verulamium, in one of the town houses. The lower 2 feet or so of the walls were of normal masonry construction consisting of coursed flint in lime mortar. The tops of these walls were flat and smooth, and were crossed by transverse slots at intervals of about 8 feet. These slots had apparently held timber batons and the smoothed mortar of the wall top had occasionally bridged them. It is thought that they were used for fixing the timber shuttering which was employed for retaining the clean yellow clay of which the upper wall was built. This was finally impressed in chevron fashion while still moist, to provide a key for the wall plaster. The technique was very similar to the present day German *Lehmstampfwände*, in which timber stud walls are infilled with mud clay or with mud bricks.

In more recent times the use of robust wooden formwork has allowed relatively dry earth mixtures to be successfully rammed into place to produce what is known in France as *pisé de terre*. The technique is practised in other parts of Europe, and in Africa, America, and the Far East. The best earth mixture for *pisé de terre* is one containing not more than 30 per cent. of clay and the remainder sand, with only sufficient water to render the mixture moist and never wet. If crushed chalk is used instead of earth, as is sometimes done in France and England, the product is called *pisé de craie* or 'chalk pisé', and there are many old examples of this type of work. Quite often, as in Wiltshire, a mixture of chalk and clay roughly in the proportions of three parts of chalk to one of clay is used. Tools for pisé work are illustrated in Fig. 132.

(c) Building with Earth Blocks

The third method of wall construction has been to shape the material by hand into loaf-shaped pieces of convenient size which, perhaps after some preliminary air drying, are laid in mud mortar in horizontal courses. The mixture is the same as that used for cob construction. This type of construction is practised in many parts of the world and is often known as 'adobe', the Spanish name for mud. The method is also of great antiquity. Lloyd and Safar[4] record that the earliest clay huts of the fifth millennium B.C. at Hassuna, twenty-two miles south of Nineveh, which themselves were built of clay lumps in which fine straw or pounded scrub was incorporated, overlay emplacements of tents or shelters of nomads which had walls of coarse rammed or kneaded clay.

In warm climates it was possible to bake the clay lumps in the sun before laying them in the wall, thus reducing the amount of subsequent shrinkage and avoiding cracking of the wall. This method is shown in Plate VIII, being carried out in Kuwait in the traditional manner for the construction of a house. The mud and chopped straw is kneaded to a plastic condition and formed into lumps of elongated 'plano-convex' shape, which are left in the sun for several days, then turned on their sides for a further few days, before being laid in the wall. Then they are trodden and beaten into position to form a dense, stabilized mass, which is afterwards rendered with mud.

This ancient method is used in other parts of the world, but the shape and size of the clay 'bricks' may vary. For example, in West Africa today, pear-shaped 'bricks', or *tubali*, are made by hand from a mixture consisting of clay soil, water, and short pieces of fresh or dried grass. These *tubalis* are laid in the wall, in a bed of mud mortar, with their wide base downwards, three, four, or even more abreast. Successive courses of *tubalis* are placed with their bases interlocking between the pointed tops of those already in position in the course below, and the whole is well compacted.

The air view of Kuwait in Plate XI shows what a town built of mud looks like, the only other material used being the date stems and leaves incorporated in the flat mud roofs to strengthen them. No doubt the older towns in this part of the world looked very much the same.

Clay-lump walling was used very considerably in England up to the eighteenth century. In East Anglia and the Midland Black Country particularly it was a well developed technique, and the houses of some towns were almost entirely of this form of construction. The town of Lye, in Worcestershire, for example, was known in the seventeenth and eighteenth centuries as the Mud City, as practically all the dwellings in it were of clay-lump walling built and lived in by the local mining community. The clay lumps, after being laid in the wall, were dubbed out—that is, smoothed by smearing mud over the joints—and then whitewashed. The walls were protected by the overhang of the thatched roof.

Whatever method of construction is used for earth walling the success of the work depends on the good compaction of the mixture to obtain as dense and as durable a material as possible. In recent years so-called stabilizers such as lime, Portland cement, and bitumen have been added to the mixture to increase the density and hence the durability of the resulting product. Bitumen stabilizers have been much used in America in recent years, and the product resulting from their use has been called Bitudobe—a typical mixture being pulverized earth with about 20 per cent. of water and between 5 and 6 per cent. of bituminous emulsion. The mixture is well kneaded and pressed into shallow moulds measuring about 15 inches by 12 inches by about 5 inches in thickness.

(d) Mud Bricks

The most convenient and most extensively used method of constructing earth walls has been to form the mud or clay into conveniently sized bricks, and, after some preliminary air drying or sun drying, to lay them in the wall in mud mortar.

Dr Kenyon's recent excavations at Jericho have revealed mud-brick buildings of this type of the pre-pottery Neolithic phases 'A' and 'B' of the sixth millennium B.C. or possibly earlier. She has found two types of building. The earliest buildings tended to be rounded in plan (Plate XIV) with mud floors and walls built of sun-dried lumps of varied size and shape, about 6 to 12 inches long (Plate XV), which she describes[5] as being 'hog-back' in shape. The later buildings of period 'B' tended to be more rectangular in plan (Plate XVI) with walls built with 'cigar-shaped' bricks, about 8 or 10 inches long, about 3 inches wide and about the same depth, with a double row of thumb impressions on the upper surface. These bricks were laid more or less in courses (Plate XVII). The walls and floors of these later buildings were rendered with plaster.

Much evidence of the early use of mud bricks comes from many other parts of the Middle East, Egypt, and India. The extraordinary excavations at Eridu, seen in Plate X, the holy city of the Sumerians near Ur in South Iraq, revealed no fewer than eighteen successive levels of buildings in mud brick, dating from the fourth millennium onwards.

Professor Mallowan[6] excavated at Arpachiyah, four miles east of Nineveh, some very early mud buildings which were circular in plan and had domical roofs of mud. The buildings, ten in number, were identified as *tholoi*, or shrines, and he attributed them to the Halaf culture of the late fifth millennium B.C. They are by far the earliest domed structures yet found in Asia and consisted of circular rooms, 12 feet or more in diameter, with walls sometimes up to 8 feet in thickness and built with irregular pudding-shaped lumps of clay. Seven of the buildings were built on stone foundations. Professor Mallowan found part of the springing of the mud vault in position and he records that buildings of this type have very rarely been discovered in Mesopotamian pre-dynastic sites, the most notable being a large round house at Tepe Gawrah, probably of the Uruk period of the middle of the fourth millennium B.C. This form of building was practised in Crete in 2700 B.C. and has survived in North Iraq, North Syria, and in South-east Asia Minor to this day.

In the fourth millennium B.C. many of the bricks in Mesopotamia were rectangular, about 16 inches by 8 inches by 2 inches thick formed in moulds, but the local variations in size were quite considerable. About 3000 B.C. bricks of smaller size not moulded but formed by hand, about 8 or 9 inches by 4 inches by 3 inches in thickness, were also made. The period from 2800 to 2300 B.C. produced its own very characteristic type of moulded brick, described as 'plano-convex', but of different shape from those found at Jericho. The mud was heaped into a rectangular mould and rounded off with the hands, the effect being to produce a brick flat or plane on the bottom surface and rounded or convex on the upper surface, 8 to 10 inches long by 6 to 7 inches wide, 1½ inches thick at the edges and 2½ inches thick at the centre. It often had finger or thumb impressions or finger drawn striations along its surface. A peculiar technique of laying was developed which is also characteristic of this period. The bricks were often laid in herringbone fashion, as shown in Figure 14, the bricks leaning in one direction for two or three courses, then followed by two or three courses laid flat with the convex face uppermost, then more courses laid with the bricks sloping diagonally in the opposite direction. The horizontal courses no doubt helped to even up and stabilize the work, but bonding as we understand it today seems to have been virtually unknown. Walls of great thickness, sometimes up to 20 feet, were built with these bricks. From 2000 B.C. till the fall of Babylon in the seventh century B.C. the crude mud bricks were about 12 inches by 6 inches by 6 inches, and others 14 to 15 inches square and up to 4 inches thick. Some enormous structures of mud brick were erected, but they were usually cased with burnt brick set in bitumen to protect them. Each large city usually had its

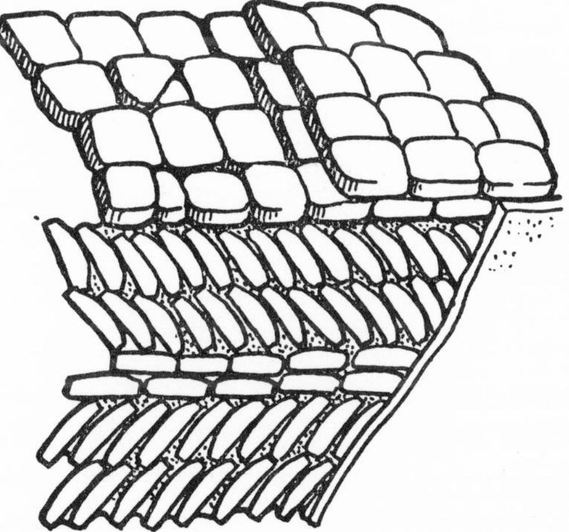

Fig. 14. Plano-convex brick construction; third millennium B.C.

tower, or ziggurat, on which a shrine was erected, and these also were of sun-baked brick cased in burnt brick, but one at the town of Erech had its outer surface protected by thousands of pieces of pottery hammered into the brickwork while it was still slightly plastic. A close-up view in Plate IX, of part of the interior brickwork of the Kassite ziggurat of about 1400 B.C. at Aqar Quf near Baghdad, shows how the work was interrupted at intervals of six courses by a layer of reed matting running horizontally through the mass. These layers facilitated the drying of the mass, and tended to even out the shrinkage, thus reducing the risk of uneven settlement.

The ziggurat at Ur built in 2300 B.C. by Ur-Nammu—'The mighty man, King of Ur, King of the Four Quarters of the World', was 210 feet by 140 feet and about 55 feet to the top stage. The solid core was of mud brick laid in mud mortar, and faced to a thickness of 8 feet with burnt bricks 14 inches square set in bitumen, with reed matting laid in some of the horizontal joints.

In Egypt kiln-burnt bricks were not used until the Roman occupation of the country.[7] Before then, and back to pre-dynastic times (fourth and fifth millennia B.C.) the chief building material for houses in particular was sun-baked brick; it still is today. The oldest bricks so far recovered in Egypt are probably those excavated by Petrie at Naqada[8] and Abydos in Upper Egypt.[9] The manner of making bricks at Thebes, the capital of Upper Egypt, is illustrated in the wall painting of the 18th Dynasty (*c.* 1500 B.C.) discovered in the tomb of Rekhmara there. It depicts (Figure 15) foreign captives preparing the clay or mud, moulding it into bricks on the ground, stacking them when they have dried and finally transporting them. There is striking resemblance between this procedure and that being followed by a Persian bricklayer in modern time (Plate XII).

To the left of Figure 15 are seen two men filling water jars from a well or small pool surrounded by trees. To the right of the well are several men digging earth with hoes, mixing it with water and pressing out bricks by means of a wooden mould. An overseer watches the operations. The inscription states that the men are making bricks for a new storehouse at Karnak. The horizontal line of hieroglyphs over the group to the right records that the workers are captives brought by his Majesty (Thothmes III) for the works of the temple of Amen-Re. These men are carrying the sun-dried bricks to the bricklayers and an officer says to them, 'The stick is in my hand, be not idle!'

The Romans used mud bricks to a great extent in Rome and other parts of Italy, but only to a small extent in the moister climate of Britain and the other Western Provinces. An interesting example, however, was brought to light by Wacher[10] in 1958 during the

Fig. 15. Brickmaking in Egypt, as depicted in a wall painting in the tomb of Rekhmara at Thebes; *c.* 1500 B.C.

excavation of a Roman building in Leicester. A wall, shown in Plate XIII, was exposed in which mud bricks approximately 17 inches by 11 inches by 3 inches thick had been used. They were bedded in a loamy sand and the vertical joints between the bricks were also filled with this material. The required width of the wall was made up by extra pieces of mud brick cut to size. The surfaces of the wall were rendered with a rough coat of lime mortar with grass or straw incorporated in the mixture, about half an inch in thickness. There was a second coat of lime mortar, which was finished with a skimming coat of lime and this was decorated by colour work.

The dimensions of the full-sized bricks found at Leicester are of particular interest as they are practically the same as for one of the mud bricks (*lateres*) known to the Greeks and Romans as a *lydium* (Vitruvius). A *lydium* measured one by one and a half feet, by one palm in thickness, and as the Roman foot was equivalent to 11·6 inches its dimensions were therefore 17½ inches by 11½ inches by 3 inches.

REFERENCES

(1) Lawrence, A. W., 1957, *Greek Architecture*, Penguin Books.

(2) Pliny, *Natural History*, Book XXV, XI, viii.

(3) Sheppard Frere, S., Jan.–Apr. 1957, 'Excavations at Verulamium 1956', Second Interim Report, *The Antiquaries' Journal*, XXXVII, Nos. 1, 2.

(4) Lloyd, S. and Safar, F., 1945, 'Excavations at Hassuna', *Journal of Near Eastern Studies*, 4 (iv), 255.

(5) Kenyon, K. M., July–Dec. 1956, 'Excavations at Jericho', *Palestine Exploration Quarterly*.

(6) Mallowan, M. E. L., *Twenty-five years of Mesopotamian Discovery (1932–1956)*, British School of Archaeology in Iraq; and *Iraq*, II, Part 1.

(7) Lucas, A., 1948, *Ancient Egyptian Materials and Industries*, Arnold (3rd revised edition).

(8) Petrie, W. M. Flinders, and Quibell, J. E., 1896, *Naqada and Ballas*, Quaritch, 54.

(9) Newberry, P. E., 1900, *The Life of Rekhmara*, Constable.

(10) Wacher, J., unpublished information.

4

Physical Characteristics of Wood

BEFORE CONSIDERING SOME of the ways in which wood has been used in building construction, a brief description of its chief physical characteristics will be given, and for this purpose one can hardly do better than to quote from the Forest Products Research Record No. 21.

It records that wood, like all plant tissues, has a cellular structure. The cells vary in size and shape and in the thickness of their walls, but for the most part they are long, narrow, tubular elements commonly called 'fibres'. As so many of the characteristics which distinguish wood from other raw materials are closely connected with its structure and composition it will be appropriate to consider in the first place how wood is formed in the growing tree.

The trunk and branches of a tree increase in thickness by the division of a very thin layer of cells known as the cambium, immediately underneath the bark (see Figure 16). When a cambium cell divides into two, the new cell formed on the inner side increases its size and the thickness of its walls until it is a fully developed wood (xylem) element, and this process is continued throughout the growing season by the repeated division of the cambium cells. In the same way the cells which are cut off on the outer side of the cambium develop into new phloem, or inner bark. In temperate climates growth begins in the spring and under normal conditions continues until a month or two before the fall of the leaves in autumn. So in the course of a growing season a complete sheath of new wood is laid down all over the tree between the bark and the old wood. Viewed in cross-section this zone of new wood appears as a complete annual ring encircling the trunk.

In many common British timber trees the structure of the wood formed in the early part of the season, that is, the early wood or spring wood, is of a more open and porous nature than the late wood or summer wood, and it is the contrast in the density of these two layers which marks the growth of successive years on the cross-section of a log.

In tropical climates seasonal growth does not always correspond exactly with annual periods. In such cases the zones of periodic growth which may be visible on the end-grain are better termed growth rings than annual rings.

Four of the predominant native timbers of Britain and north-western Europe used for constructional work are birch, pine, oak, and beech, and end-grain microphotographs of these prepared by the Forest Products Research Laboratory are shown in Plate XVIII, 1 to 4, to reveal their characteristic structure.

Building timbers are divided into two groups, softwoods and hardwoods. The classification rests on a botanical distinction. The softwoods are derived from the comparatively

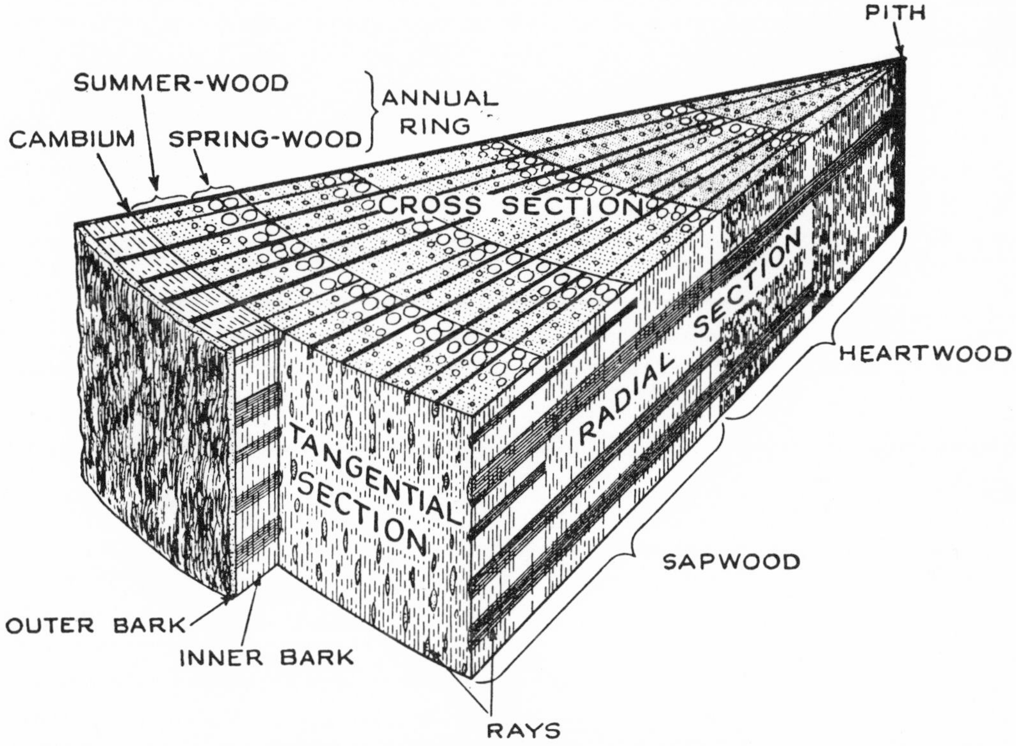

Fig. 16. Structure of wood in a growing tree.

small class of cone-bearing trees, mostly with evergreen needles or scale-like leaves, known as conifers, or Coniferae. The conifers form extensive forests in cool temperate regions and in mountainous districts, and supply the bulk of the world's commercial timber. The structure of their wood is of a simple, primitive type, distinctly different from that of the hardwoods. Softwood timbers are generally well suited for constructional use as they are comparatively soft and easy to work, light in weight but strong enough for most practical purposes.

The hardwoods are furnished by the great group of broad-leaved trees, which have seeds in a seed case, and include the vast majority of species in the forests of the world today. The small number of hardwood trees native to the British Isles gives no idea of the enormous variety to be found in the great hardwood regions of the world, especially in the tropics, where the number of different species of timber trees runs to many thousands. The structure of the hardwoods is more complex and their technical properties show a much wider range of variation than is the case with the softwoods. It should be clearly understood that softwood and hardwood are now universally recognized as conventional technical terms for the two main classes of timber defined above. The fact that some coniferous timbers are indeed hard and some broad-leaved trees furnish a comparatively soft grade of wood does not affect the use of the terms in their special technical sense. Pitch pine, for example, although classed as a softwood, is actually physically harder than some timbers classed as hardwoods such as balsa, lime, and willow.

The botanical system of classifying timbers is illustrated in the accompanying table, reproduced by permission of Her Majesty's Stationery Office, from Forest Products Research Record No. 21, which shows the sub-division of softwoods and hardwoods into families, genera, and species. The list is in no sense complete; it simply includes a few well-known commercial timbers selected to show their botanical relationship. Many of the timbers were used in antiquity.

SOFTWOODS

FAMILIES	GENERA	SPECIES
Pinaceae, Pine family	*Pinus*	*P. sylvestris*, Scots pine or redwood; *P. strobus*, Canadian yellow pine; *P. palustris*, American pitch pine, etc.
	Picea	*P. abies*, common European spruce or whitewood; *P. glauca*, Canadian spruce; *P. sitchensis*, Sitka spruce, etc.
	Abies	*A. alba*, silver fir; *A. balsamea*, balsam fir, etc.
	Larix	*L. decidua*, European larch; *L. sibirica*, Siberian larch, etc.
	Tsuga	*T. canadensis*, eastern hemlock; *T. heterophylla*, western hemlock, etc.
	Pseudotsuga	*P. taxifolia*, Douglas fir or British Columbian pine
	Cedrus, etc.	*C. libani*, cedar of Lebanon; *C. deodara*, deodar, etc.
Cupressaceae, Cypress family	*Chamaecyparis*	*C. lawsoniana*, Lawson's cypress or Port Orford cedar; *C. nootkatensis*, yellow cypress or yellow cedar, etc.
	Thuja	*T. plicata*, western red cedar; *T. occidentalis*, white cedar, etc.
	Libocedrus	*L. decurrens*, incense cedar
	Juniperus, etc.	*J. procera*, African pencil cedar; *J. virginiana*, Virginian pencil cedar
Taxaceae, Yew family	*Taxus*, etc.	*T. baccata*, common yew
Araucariaceae, Monkey puzzle family	*Araucaria*	*A. cunninghamii*, hoop pine; *A. angustifolia*, Parana pine, etc.
	Agathis	*A. australis* and other species, kauri

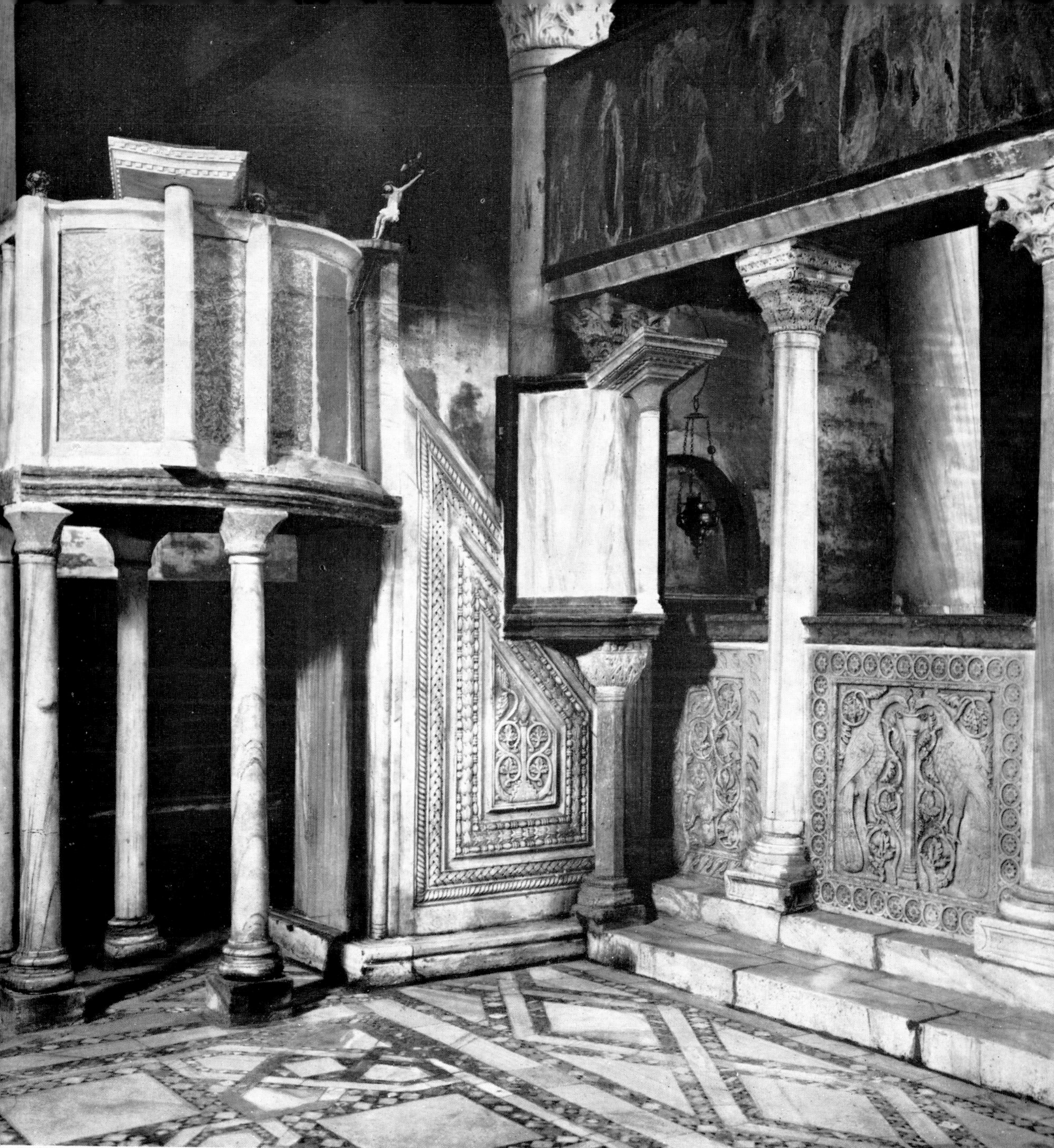

Plate III. Venetian Byzantine marble work in the Cathedral (L'Assunta) at Torcello (see page 6).

Plate IV. The Great Pyramids at Gizeh, Egypt, *c.* 2600–2500 B.C. (see page 7).

SOFTWOODS—*cont.*

FAMILIES	GENERA	SPECIES
Podocarpaceae, Podo family	*Podocarpus*	*P. dacrydioides*, New Zealand white pine; *P. spicatus*, matai; *P. gracilior* and other species, podo or yellow-wood, etc.
	Dacrydium, etc.	*D. cupressinum*, rimu or New Zelaand red pine, etc.

HARDWOODS

FAMILIES	GENERA	SPECIES
Fagaceae, Beech family	*Fagus*	*F. sylvatica*, common European beech, etc.
	Nothofagus	*N. menziesii*, New Zealand beech; *N. cunninghamii*, Tasmanian myrtle, etc.
	Quercus	*Q. robur*, common European oak; *Q. alba*, American white oak; *Q. cerris*, Turkey oak, and many other species
	Castanea, etc.	*C. sativa*, European chestnut; *C. dentata*, American chestnut, etc.
Betulaceae, Birch family	*Betula*	*B. alba*, common European birch; *B. lutea*, Canadian yellow birch, etc.
	Alnus	*A. glutinosa*, common alder, etc.
Salicaceae, Willow family	*Salix*	*S. alba*, white willow, etc.
	Populus	*P. alba*, white poplar; *P. nigra*, black poplar; *P. tremula*, aspen, etc.
Meliaceae, Mahogany family	*Swietenia*	*S. mahogoni*, Cuban mahogany; *S. macrophylla*, Honduras and Central American mahogany, etc.
	Khaya	*K. ivorensis*, African mahogany, etc.
	Entandrophragma	*E. cylindricum*, sapele; *E. utile*, etc.
	Cedrela, etc.	*C. mexicana*, cigar-box cedar, etc.
Myrtaceae, Eucalyptus family	*Eucalyptus*, etc.	*E. marginata*, jarrah; *E. diversicolor*, karri; *E. obliqua*, Tasmanian oak, and many other species
Dipterocarpaceae, Gurjun family	*Dipterocarpus*	*D. alatus*, *D. turbinatus*, and many other species, known as gurjun (Burma and India), keruing (Borneo and Malaya), yang (Thailand), etc., according to the country of origin
	Shorea	*S. acuminata*, *S. leprosula*, and many other species, known as seraya (North Borneo), meranti (Malaya and Sarawak), lauan (Philippine Islands), etc., according to the country of origin
	Dryobalanops, etc.	*D. aromatica* and other species, kapur or Borneo camphorwood
Leguminosae, Pea family	*Pterocarpus*	*P. dalbergioides*, Andaman padauk; *P. macrocarpus*, Burma padauk, etc.
	Dalbergia	*D. nigra*, Brazilian rosewood; *D. latifolia*, Indian rosewood; *D. melanoxylon*, African blackwood, etc.
	Acacia	*A. melanoxylon*, Australian blackwood, and many other species
	Robinia, etc.	*R. pseudoacacia*, false acacia

Deterioration of Timber

Since some readers may be responsible for old buildings, remarks on the causes and treatment of decay of wood will not be out of place. It should be realized, however, that treatment is a job for the specialist. A valuable series of articles dealing with the repair and preservation of old buildings was published in the *Architects' Journal*.[1]

Wood is liable to decay in a very damp still atmosphere. Under these conditions it may be attacked by dry-rot, the most serious form being caused by the fungus *merulius lacrymans*. This fungus often forms roots called 'hyphae', at first hair-like and fine, but later as strands called 'rhizomorphs' which may reach pencil thickness. The 'hyphae' may also unite to form a snowy-white growth like cottonwool, covered with a rusty-red powder which is the spores. When well established the fungus will produce a flower and fruit body, or 'sporophore', producing millions of spores, or seeds. At first the sporophore is silvery grey in colour and gradually becomes a thick, flat, pancake-like structure, leathery and clammy. Decay may then proceed rapidly.

The dry-rot fungus may creep through neighbouring brickwork and masonry if that too is damp and porous. Wood consists of about two-thirds of cellulose and one-third of lignin. The fungus feeds on the cellulose and leaves the lignin in a dry and desiccated form entirely devoid of structural strength. It is necessary therefore to prevent the spread of any attack by removing all infected timbers, and thoroughly treating all adjacent timber with a wood preservative. Any brickwork or stonework that has been in contact with the decayed wood should also be treated. This can often be done by heating it with a powerful blowlamp until the surface becomes too hot to touch, and then applying a liberal application of a fungicide, which could be either (i) sodium pentachlorphenate in the strength of 8 ounces to a gallon of water; (ii) mercuric chloride, or corrosive sublimate, in the strength of 1 part to 1,000 parts of water or methylated spirits, very effective, but highly poisonous, and needing great care in handling; or (iii) magnesium silico-fluoride in the strength of 16 ounces to a gallon of water, or sodium fluoride in a saturated solution in water, i.e. about 6 ounces to a gallon.

But above all, the cause of the outbreak of dry-rot must be identified and measures taken to avoid a further outbreak. Dampness must be eliminated from the building or greatly reduced, and ventilation improved.

There are other types of fungal growths often referred to as 'wet-rot' which are generally not so serious as dry-rot. Cellar fungus, or *coniophora cerebella*, is the most common, but it cannot live in timber with a moisture content of less than 25 per cent. It appears as fine dark brown or blackish strands, and has a green and leathery fruiting body. Another type is pore fungus, or *poria vaillantii*, which has spreading string-like strands. It is usually a fairly easy matter to overcome the trouble by cutting out the defective timber and treating the area with fungicide.

Wood can also be attacked by beetles of varying types, and although not so serious as dry-rot, this may none the less cause anxiety. In some old structures, medieval roofs for example, timbers may have lost up to 50 per cent. or more of their effective cross section by this form of attack. The two main types of insect involved are the death watch beetle, *xestobium rufovillosum*, and the furniture beetle, *anobium punctatum*. Another type is the house longhorn beetle, *hylotrupes bajulus*, which at present in Britain at least has confined its attacks to areas in Surrey. The treatment is usually to inject powerful insecticides such as benzene hexachloride, DDT, or dieldrin in a solvent base, which may be volatile like petroleum or coal tar distillates, or in a less volatile type like diesel oil. Fumigant insecticides are only really effective if the whole object can be treated in a fumigation chamber.

In favourable conditions wood may last many hundreds of years. For example the Horiuji Temple in Japan, built of cypress wood in the year A.D. 607 by Prince Shotoku, is still standing, and is reputed to be the oldest wooden building in the world.[2] In 1937 Professor Liang Ssŭ-Ch'êng discovered that the wooden Buddhist Temple building in the village of Tou-Shên Ts'un, in Shansi Province, China, was dated by an inscription to the year A.D. 857.[3] Even in the inferior British climate oak has survived exposure for over nine hundred years in the walls of the church at Greenstead in Essex.

REFERENCES

(1) INSAL, D., 28 Aug., 4, 11, 18, 25 Sept. 1958, 'The Repair and Preservation of Old Buildings', *The Architects' Journal.*

(2) LATHAM, T., 1957, *Timber—its development and distribution*, Harrap.

(3) SICKMAN, L., and SOPER, A. C., 1956, *The Art and Architecture of China*, Part 2, *Architecture*, Penguin Books, 215.

5

Building in Wood

WOOD IN ITS MANY and various forms has been man's most useful building material, and until the comparatively recent innovation of metallic forms, it remained the only material with which he could make complete structural frameworks, or component parts such as beams, rafters, and purlins all capable of withstanding bending and tension.

The type and quality of timber available to man has naturally depended on the prevailing climatic conditions and on the condition of the soil, and this has been reflected in the types of structure he has erected, and in their durability. Jean Brunhes[1] refers to the good example of this presented as one traverses from north to south the vast plains of European Russia. In the northern tundra zone, where the subsoil is frozen and no flora exists other than a scanty one of cryptogams, the only human dwellings are simple huts. Next comes the great northern forest with its much more substantial wooden houses, followed further south by the grassy steppes with their rich black earth, but practically devoid of trees, so that here the houses are built of earth and mud, and roofed with thatch or turf. Then come the stony steppes of the Crimean and Caucasus mountains where stone dwellings predominate, and where, on the southern slope of the Western and Central Caucasus, the warm damp climate produces trees and shrubs with flexible stems, the use of which produces its own characteristic types of building. Countless other examples of this type of succession occur all over the world. The fact that some ancient or modern dwellings in different parts of the world may be of very similar design and construction is more likely to be due primarily to the availability and use of similar types of building materials, than to any racial or cultural affinity of the builders.

Man seems always to have understood the elementary principles of building, and to have been endowed with a sense of structure, and given similar raw materials—timber, mud, and stone—he did very much the same sort of things with them; and wherever he lived, by applying the same initiative and manipulative skill, he often built the same basic type of structure. An instance of this is the simple primitive shelter used by nomadic peoples throughout the world today. Basically it is the same today as it seems to have been in far-off Palaeolithic times. Plate XIX shows such a hut in course of erection by a nomadic family in Greece. It is a simple self-supporting framework, made by planting a ring of branches firmly in the ground and bending them over towards the centre where they are interlaced and bound together, forming a continuous wall and roof to be filled in later by interwoven branches and other vegetable material.

In hot dry countries like Egypt good timber has always been scarce. Here the indigenous trees throughout Dynastic times, such as the acacia, sycamore, fig, tamarisk, date palm, sidder, persea, and willow,[2] provided only relatively light timbers for building purposes, and many of the finer and exotic woods used in the construction and decoration of temples, palaces, and tombs had to be imported from Lebanon, famous for its cedars, and other places in Asia Minor. Theophrastus[3] (370–285 B.C.) records that the Greeks and Romans had oak, box, alder, and silver fir, in addition to those mentioned above.

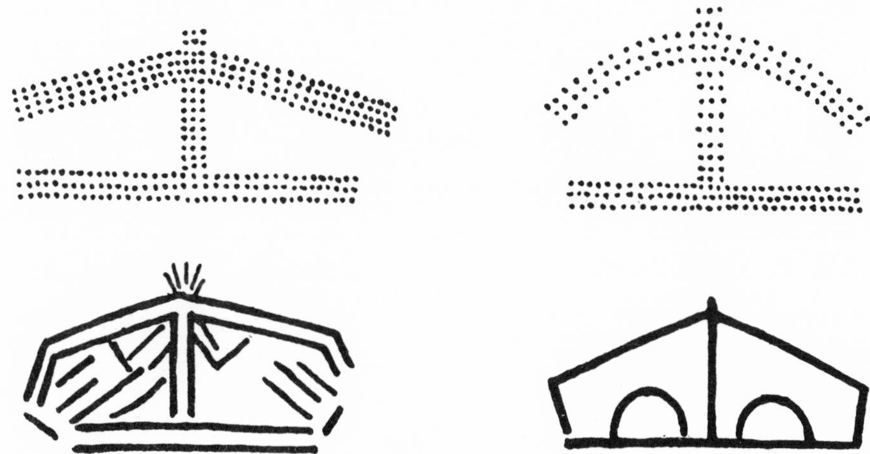

Fig. 17. Drawings on the wall of the cave at Font de Gaume, Dordogne, France, probably depicting Magdalenian huts (based on the drawings of L'Abbé Breuil).

The types of timber in any one territorial zone have also varied greatly during the passage of time due to intense climatic changes, and this has led to successive changes in building forms. Immediately after the close of the Ice Age the climate and vegetation of much of north-western Europe, for example, including Britain, were very similar to those existing today in arctic and tundra regions. There were no trees of any appreciable size, but mainly dwarf vegetation, mosses, and lichens; and there was little to tempt man away from his warmer surroundings in the south. He did leave some drawings on the walls of caves at Font de Gaume, in Dordogne, Southern France, where the climate was more tolerable, which would seem to represent shelters or hides or even animal traps he may have used in his hunting expeditions. If in fact they are any of these, they reveal, as indicated in the sketches in Figure 17, based on those made by L'Abbé Breuil, structural features worthy of note. In each case, for example, there is what appears to be a central post supporting rafters which slope downwards, but not down to floor level. It is as though either the floor was sunk below ground level with the sides of the pit revetted, or the turves and soil were scooped out from the shallow pit and piled around the perimeter to form a dwarf wall in the manner suggested in Figure 18. This shows a conjectural reconstruction based on a rectangular plan, but it could quite well have been circular, or some other less regular shape.

As the temperature rose, during the pre-Boreal, or Early Forest, Period, between 10,000 and 7500 B.C., trees began to appear, first the willow and the birch, then the aspen poplar, followed in the dry and warm Boreal, or Continental, Period, between 7500 and 5500 B.C., by the pine, the hazel, and the alder, the hazel spreading very rapidly to form the undergrowth to the oak trees which now appeared in the area the first time.

Fig. 18 Reconstruction of a Magdalenian hut.

The afforestation of the area naturally brought with it much animal and bird life, and with its improved climate now provided a rewarding hunting ground, at least during the summer months, for the nomadic Mesolithic tribes from the south. Some of their camping sites have been discovered and excavated. What their shelters really looked like must remain largely a matter for conjecture, for often only a few rather vague impressions of post-holes remain to show at least that they used some type of timber framework.

In the Ukraine at Gagarino and Kostienki, and in Siberia at Mal'ta[4] the remains of houses of various shapes and sizes built by the Palaeolithic mammoth hunters have been exposed. They were sunk in the soil with earth banked up around the perimeter, and roofed over with skins and birch bark. Whereas at Gagarino, a house-pit was round and less than 20 feet across, another at Kostienki was 113 feet long and up to 18 feet wide with eight hearths down the centre, and presumably could accommodate a number of families united in one great household.

A land submergence occurred during the Atlantic period between 5500 and 2500 B.C., and the climate in north-west Europe became very humid. It remained warm, however, and there was a vast increase in the number of broadleaved trees, the oak, lime, and elm. The beech and the hornbeam made their first appearance, but the pine trees decreased in number. Neolithic man penetrating the area was able to follow a more settled existence than any of his predecessors, living in large communities in the elevated and drier parts, in Britain, for example, in places like Salisbury Plain, the Cotswolds, and the wolds of Lincolnshire and Yorkshire. He practised the art of agriculture and his timber buildings were generally robust, as timber was plentiful.

Dwellings of rectangular plan with single or multiple rows of posts to support the roof became well established,[5] and their interior was often subdivided into compartments or rooms by partitions framed with mortised timbers. Floors were also often covered with rough-hewn timber planking and occasionally with birch bark. In warmer, drier areas where timber was of poor quality the buildings were still somewhat flimsy. Lawrence[6] has described, for example, structures in Greece dating from the fourth millennium B.C. Their remains indicated that both walls and roofs were sometimes made of intertwined reeds fastened to a wooden framework, and plastered with clay, or were covered with brushwood, rushes, or straw with or without the impervious coating of clay, presumably very like the modern example referred to above. The buildings, which varied in shape, some rectangular, others circular or oval, were short-lived.

The primitive houses of Egypt of this Neolithic period also were of very simple, light construction, and a contemporary sketch reproduced in Figure 19, of one of them engraved on ivory and dating from the early 1st Dynasty (*c.* 3000 B.C.), was described by the late Flinders Petrie,[7] and gives some idea of what they were like. It shows a reed hut with upright sides and hemispherical roof, and provided with a doorway. Professor Petrie likened the hut to the Bisharin tents of Aswan, where palm-ribs form the curved framework which is covered with palm-leaf mats. That such mats were used in early construction, he concluded, is shown by the impressions in mud plaster on the roofs of the Royal Tombs.

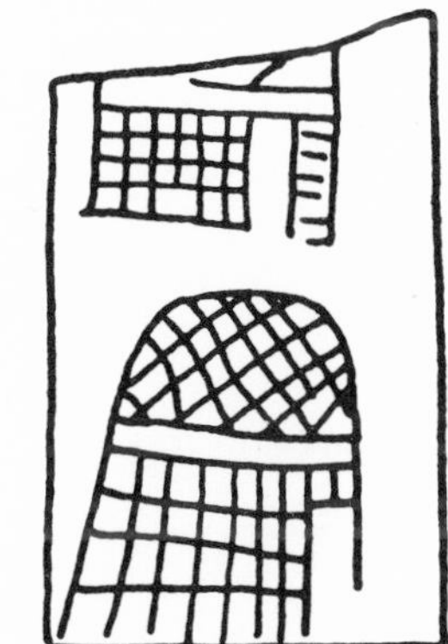

Fig. 19. Reed hut with domed roof; engraving on ivory, early 1st Dynasty, *c.* 3000 B.C.

In the following sub-Atlantic period from 2500 to 1500 B.C. the climate became drier in what is now Western Europe and Great Britain. Oak forests predominated, although beechwoods increased rapidly. By about 500 B.C. the climate had deteriorated, becoming cold and damp, but there followed a slow improvement and by Roman times the climate was much as it is now.

Figure 20 shows the possible reconstruction of a late Iron Age hut based on the evidence revealed by the excavations by Bulleid and St G. Gray[8] at the Iron Age marsh settlement just north of Glastonbury, in Somerset. The village consisted of about seventy dwellings clustered in an area of $3\frac{1}{2}$ acres on an artificial island, or crannog. Their floors, mostly circular in plan and varying from 18 to 35 feet in diameter, were of clay superimposed on layers of timber and brushwood and the walls were formed of posts driven through the clay, the spaces between being filled with wattle, daubed with clay; the roofs were thatched. The foundations of a rectangular hut of the same period were exposed by St G. Gray at Meare Lake village, near Glastonbury. The technique of laying cross-timbering for the floor is similar to that

Fig. 20. Reconstruction of an Iron Age dwelling.

used in the round huts referred to above, and the mortising of the timbers seen in Plate XX was very like that in the Neolithic hut at Aichbühl (Figure 21).

Rectangular houses, much larger than that at Meare, also of the Iron Age, were excavated by Dr A. E. Van Giffen[9] at Ezinge in Holland. Long walls of posts with wattle and daub were inclined to be unstable, particularly in high winds, and it is not surprising to find that additional strutting of the wall posts was necessary.

In most of the buildings already referred to the walls were filled in with interwoven branches or wattle. In the forest zones, however, where timber was plentiful more solid walls of trunks or substantial planks were built.

Timber in the form of split tree trunks set up vertically side by side to form a wall was used in Neolithic Europe, examples having been excavated in the moor settlements at Köln-Lindenthal[10] and Aichbühl.[11] At the former site the split timbers were embedded in

1. Mixed polygonal and curvilinear walling on the face of the terrace of the Great Temple of Apollo, Delphi; sixth century B.C. (see page 9).

2. Polygonal masonry with horizontal coursing: retaining wall of the tomb of Lysimachides of Acharnes, Ceramicus cemetery, Athens; middle of the fifth century B.C. (see page 9).

3. Random coursed masonry: walling at the entrance to the tomb of Agamemnon, Mycenae; *c.* fifteenth century B.C. (see page 9).

4. Isodomic masonry: south wall of the Propylaea, Athens; fifth century B.C. (see page 11).

5. Pseudisodomic masonry: retaining wall of the theatre stage, Delphi; *c.* 159 B.C. (original buildings fourth century B.C.) (see page 11).

6. Slanting rising joints used for decorative effect: retaining wall of the theatre, north side, Delos; first half of the second century B.C. (see page 11).

Plate V. Types of masonry walling.

Plate VI. The terrace at Masjid-i-Sulaiman, Persia, built in Cyclopean masonry; *c.* eighth century B.C. (see page 11).

Plate VII. Dry-built stone walling at Skara Brae, Orkney (see page 14).

Plate VIII. Building with mud blocks in Kuwait, 1946, a survival of an ancient technique.

Plate IX. The Kassite Ziggurat at Aqar Quf, showing layers of reeds inserted every sixth course of brickwork; second millennium B.C. (see page 24).

Plate X. During excavations at Eridu no fewer than eighteen successive building layers were uncovered; all the buildings were of mud (see page 22).

Plate XI. Kuwait, a town built of mud, seen from the air (1946).

a wall trench but sometimes only part of a wall was made with them, the rest being composed of wattle and daub. A plan of a house at Aichbühl (Figure 21) shows the remains of the walls, after excavation, and reveals also a beam with mortise holes lying in front of the open hearth, presumably intended to support a frame for drying. This method of wall construction continued through the Iron Age to Norman times. In a Viking fortress at Trelleborg, in Denmark, built by the Viking King Sven Forkbeard, father of Canute the Great, and dating about A.D. 1000, all the buildings were of timber with walls of

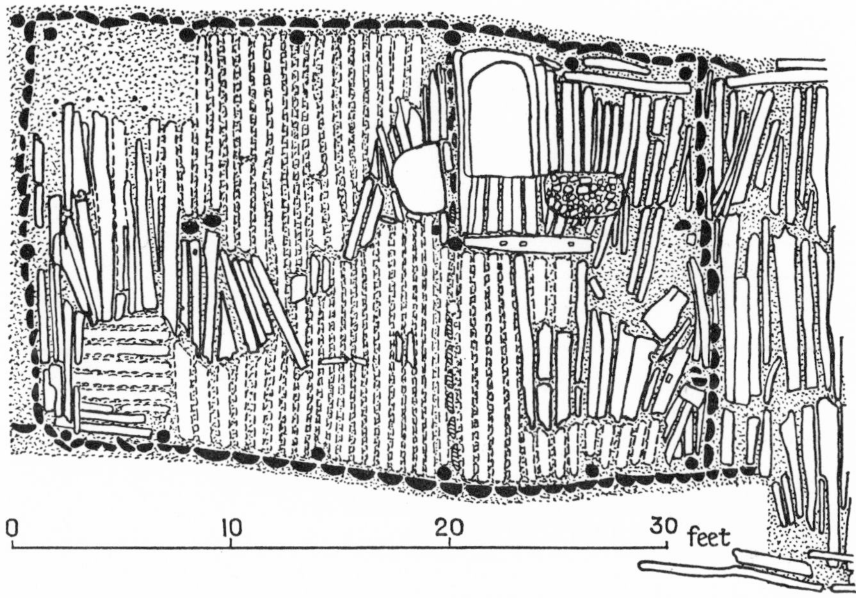

Fig. 21. Neolithic hut at Aichbühl (after Schmidt).

upright planks or staves; and the eleventh-century churches in Denmark, such as that of S. Maria Minor at Stavkyrkans, and others in Gotland, were of similar stave construction with the timbers grooved along their sides and tongues of wood let in. Unfortunately none of these Danish buildings has survived, and only fragmentary remains have been revealed by excavation by Dr Olaf Olsen and others. England is more fortunate in having a surviving stave church of this period (*c.* A.D. 1013) at Greenstead, near Ongar, Essex. Its walls are formed of half trunks of oak set upright with the split face inwards. Originally the upper end of each half trunk was chamfered and roughly tenoned into a plate, and the lower end into a sill, and fixed with two pegs in each tenon. The sill was originally at ground level but unfortunately this rotted and in 1848 was replaced by a low brick wall and a new sill. Godwin[12] records that before its restoration in 1848 the walls of the nave of Greenstead church were formed of split trunks of oak trees placed upright, their sides being grooved, and tongues of oak let into them, and the construction, therefore, in its original form must have been very similar to that of the Danish stave churches. As seen today the staves are about 2 feet shorter than they were originally, and the joints are covered, on the inside of the building, with strips of wood.

The staves at Greenstead and in the earlier of the Danish churches were half-trunks, but in later buildings they were trimmed to form planks with flat faces back and front.

Another method of wall construction, already mentioned, was that in which timbers, often roughly squared or sawn into planks, were laid horizontally and interlocked at each corner of the building. It is a type that has persisted in the great forests of straight-trunked trees—pine, fir, and beech—which extend from Scandinavia across Central Europe, the

Fig. 22. Log cabin at Skansen, Stockholm, with low-pitched roof and eaves boards to retain the snow.

French and Swiss Alps, Northern Italy, Czechoslovakia, Finland, Russia, Siberia, the Himalayas, and Canada in the forest belt circling the Northern Hemisphere. Some early evidence for this form of building comes from the site at Wasserburg-Buchau on the Federsee in Central Europe. Here nine large farmhouses, dating from about 900 B.C., were constructed on the log-cabin principle with interlocking logs.

Vitruvius,[13] a Roman architect writing at the time of Augustus, referred to the houses with these horizontal timbers built by the people of Colchis in the Pontus district of north-eastern Asia Minor, bordering the Black Sea. He states that the gaps between the timbers were blocked with splinters of wood and clay. This 'log-cabin' type of construction is still very common, but its roof construction varies with climatic conditions. In upper mountainous regions and regions with prolonged periods of snow, for example, strong low-pitched roofs have been customary, the purpose being to retain the snow in midwinter, thus providing an additional insulating layer to keep the occupants warm. A log-cabin of this type re-erected at Skansen, Stockholm, is shown in Figure 22. Its roof is insulated with birch bark, and is provided with special boards at eaves level to assist in the retention of the snow. The galleried store-house of the Alvros farmstead at Härjedalen,

Plate XXI, which has also been re-erected at Skansen, is dated A.D. 1666, and is an ancient type characteristic of North Swedish architecture. It has two floors and is built of heavy logs, and covered with a fivefold layer of birch bark kept in position by a wooden roof of half-round split logs, laid with the flat surface uppermost.

The problem of making these log cabins weathertight is an important one, and it is of interest to consider how, for example, the Ukrainians do this.[14] In the forest region of the Ukraine, the hut walls are composed of roughly squared full logs, and the walls are coated inside and outside with clay; in the north of the region the logs are left in their natural

Fig. 23. Barn at Bilchengrund, near Gleiwitz, Germany, with steeply-pitched roofs to shed the snow.

state on the outside of the wall, and the chinks between the logs are filled with clay. The surface of the logs on the inside of the walls is roughly trimmed and rendered with clay. For the sake of warmth, the lower part of the wall is often increased in thickness by a projecting plinth, which is made of earth rammed between the wall of the hut and a low fence of planks or brushwood, erected parallel to, and a foot or so away from, the wall. This plinth as well as the wall of the hut is coated with clay. An almost identical method of insulating their log cabins is followed by Canadian lumberjacks today who instead of filling the plinth with earth, fill it with sawdust and pieces of bark.

In the Carpathian area the logs, which are of oak, alder, or lime, are very neatly squared and close fitting and there is no necessity for the clay rendering. Another method used in parts of Russia has been to hollow the underside of the logs throughout their whole

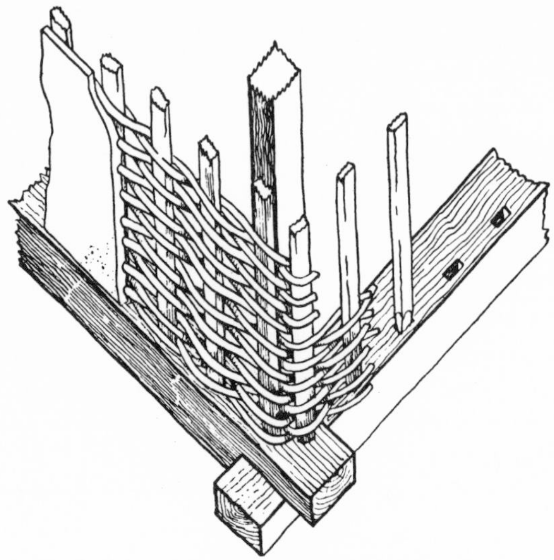

Fig. 24. Wattle and daub construction of Iron Age date.

length so that they rest saddlewise on the ones beneath, and to fill the interstices with moss.

In the lowland regions and in areas not subjected to such long periods of snow, the roofs are much more steeply pitched, enabling them to shed the snow easily to be rid of it. A typical building of this type is shown in Figure 95, of a church at Larchenhag, in the forest area near Gleiwitz, in Upper Silesia. The whole building is of timber construction and the roof, covered with wood shingles, forms a protective cloak, extending almost to ground level, and in this case provides a dry covered way round the outside of the building. A smaller barn at Bilchengrund in the same area shows a similar apron roof designed to shed the snow (Figure 23).

Solid walls of the types described are extravagant with timber, and in areas where timber supplies were diminishing it was found to be much more economical to construct wooden frameworks and to fill in the interspaces with other materials, such as plastered panels.

As already noted, the mortising of timber framework for walls and partitions was practised in the Neolithic period, and the construction of house frames was well established by the Iron Age, as seen at Meare near Glastonbury, where it was used in conjunction with wattle and daub infilling, as shown in Figure 24. There were many variations in the construction of these walls during the next fifteen hundred years. In Romano-British work, for example, the wall plate was bedded on a dwarf masonry wall, or even buried in a trench below floor level. Both these methods of construction have been found at Verulamium, as shown in Figure 25. At this site some of these timber-framed buildings were destroyed by fire. This baked the clay daub which had

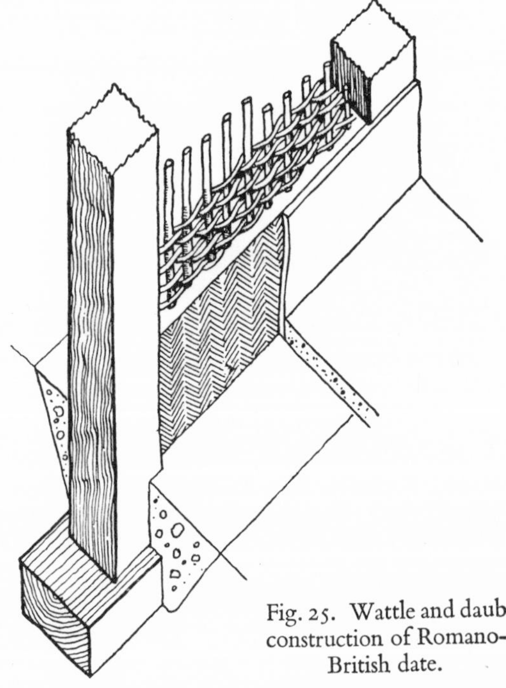

Fig. 25. Wattle and daub construction of Romano-British date.

covered the wattles of the infilling, and in consequence samples of daub retain the impressions of the wattle, and often the herringbone rouletting which had originally been applied to the soft daub to form a key for a finishing coat of lime mortar. Chopped straw or grass or other vegetable materials were often added to the clay daub to help to bind it, to assist the drying process, and to distribute the shrinkage cracking.

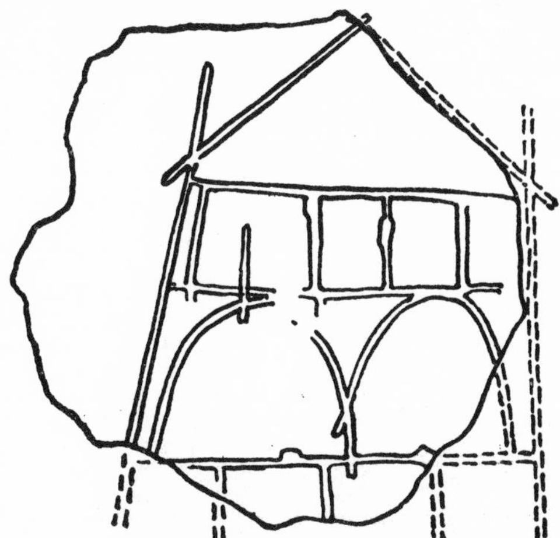

Fig. 26. Graffito on wall plaster in a Roman building at Hucclecote, near Gloucester, thought to represent the gabled end of a half-timbered house (after R. G. Collingwood).

The risk of fire was great and the results catastrophic, as demonstrated at Verulamium when the city was fired by Boudicca in A.D. 61. Vitruvius[15] spoke feelingly about the grave risk when he said, 'I could wish that walls of wattlework had not been invented. For, however advantageous they are in speed of erection and for increase of space, to that extent are they a public misfortune, because they are like torches ready for kindling. Therefore, it seems better to be at greater expense by the cost of burnt brick than to be in danger by the inconvenience of wattlework walls: for these also make cracks in the plaster covering owing to the arrangement of the uprights and the crosspieces. For when the plaster is applied, they take up the moisture and swell, then when they dry they contract, and so they are rendered thin, and break the solidity of the plaster'. An interesting graffito on wall plaster found in a Roman building at Hucclecote, three miles north-east of Gloucester, was thought by Collingwood[16] to represent the gabled end of a half-timbered house. The interpretation of this sketch, reproduced in Figure 26, is by no means clear.

Fig. 27. Lower Brockhampton Gatehouse, Herefordshire. Straight-braced frame with post and pan construction.

At first the timber uprights of the frames were closely spaced and reached from floor to ceiling, being mortised top and bottom into horizontal wall-plates and sills. Buildings with these close-timbered frames were common in England throughout the fifteenth and sixteenth centuries. The Brockhampton Gatehouse, Herefordshire, Figure 27, is a simple example of this type. However, demands for timber for shipbuilding and fuel, apart from that required for buildings, led to

Fig. 28. Buttas Gateway, Kings Pyon, Herefordshire.

increasing shortages. Even as early as the thirteenth century timber was being imported from Norway. The square-panelled construction, which used less timber, had come into general use by the end of the sixteenth century, and an example of this type is the Buttas Gateway, Kings Pyon, Herefordshire, Figure 28. The upright timbers were more widely spaced and horizontal timbers were introduced which divided the framework roughly into squares.

The close-timbered framework and the square-panelled framework are illustrated in Figures 29 and 30 respectively. The method of infilling was rather different in the two cases, however. In the former the sides of the uprights were grooved from top to bottom, and into these grooves were wedged pieces of split oak laths which were subsequently completely embedded in daub consisting of clay with organic binding material such as flax stems, straw, or tow incorporated in it. This was left to dry out thoroughly, but in doing so the clay mixture naturally shrank and cracked. A thin lime-plaster coating applied to the surface sealed these cracks and produced a good finish.

In the square-panel framework four split oak staves were usually 'sprung' into holes in the top and bottom of each frame panel. The outer two staves were generally rather thicker than the inner two, and in consequence stronger. Between these staves hazel branches were woven to form wattle or basketwork; but sometimes plaited laths were used instead. The panels were finished with clay and plaster in the same manner as for the close-timbered framework. Before the plaster was applied the surface of the clay was scored or impressed while still moist, to provide a key. This kind of work has been variously known in different parts of Britain as

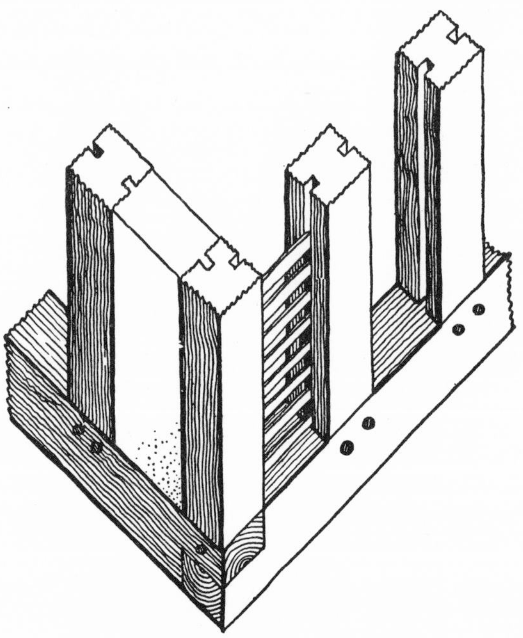

Fig. 29. Close-timbered framework.

'wattle and daub', 'reddle or raddle and daub' or 'red and dab' in Lancashire and Cheshire, 'daub and stower' in Lincolnshire, and 'stud and mud' in the North Country.

As much protection as was possible had to be given to the wattle and daub if it was to last very long. This was achieved by having good overhanging eaves to the roof, and, if the

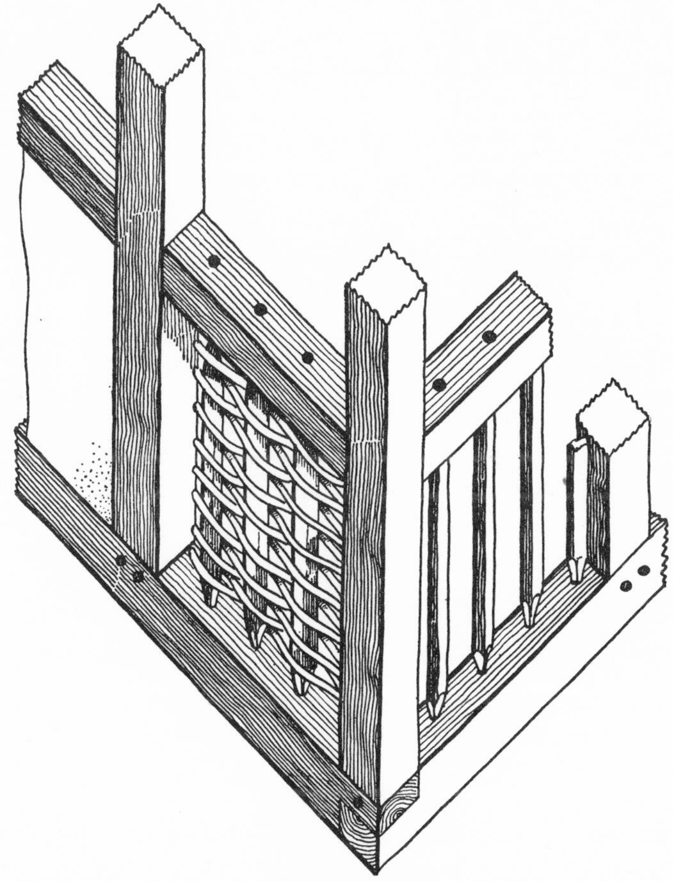

Fig. 30. Square-panelled framework.

building was of two storeys, by also extending the floor beams of the upper storey outwards so that the upper walls overhung or 'oversailed' the lower and kept them dry.

Sometimes lumps of clay mixed with straw, or 'cats', were worked into balls or rolls and laid between the laths in timber studding, the whole then being rendered to provide a smooth surface. In Newcastle-on-Tyne the workmen who undertook this work were called 'catters and daubers.' A later alternative method of filling the panels was to use brick sometimes laid in herringbone pattern.

Apart from the simple huts with continuous walls and roofs of curved and interwoven

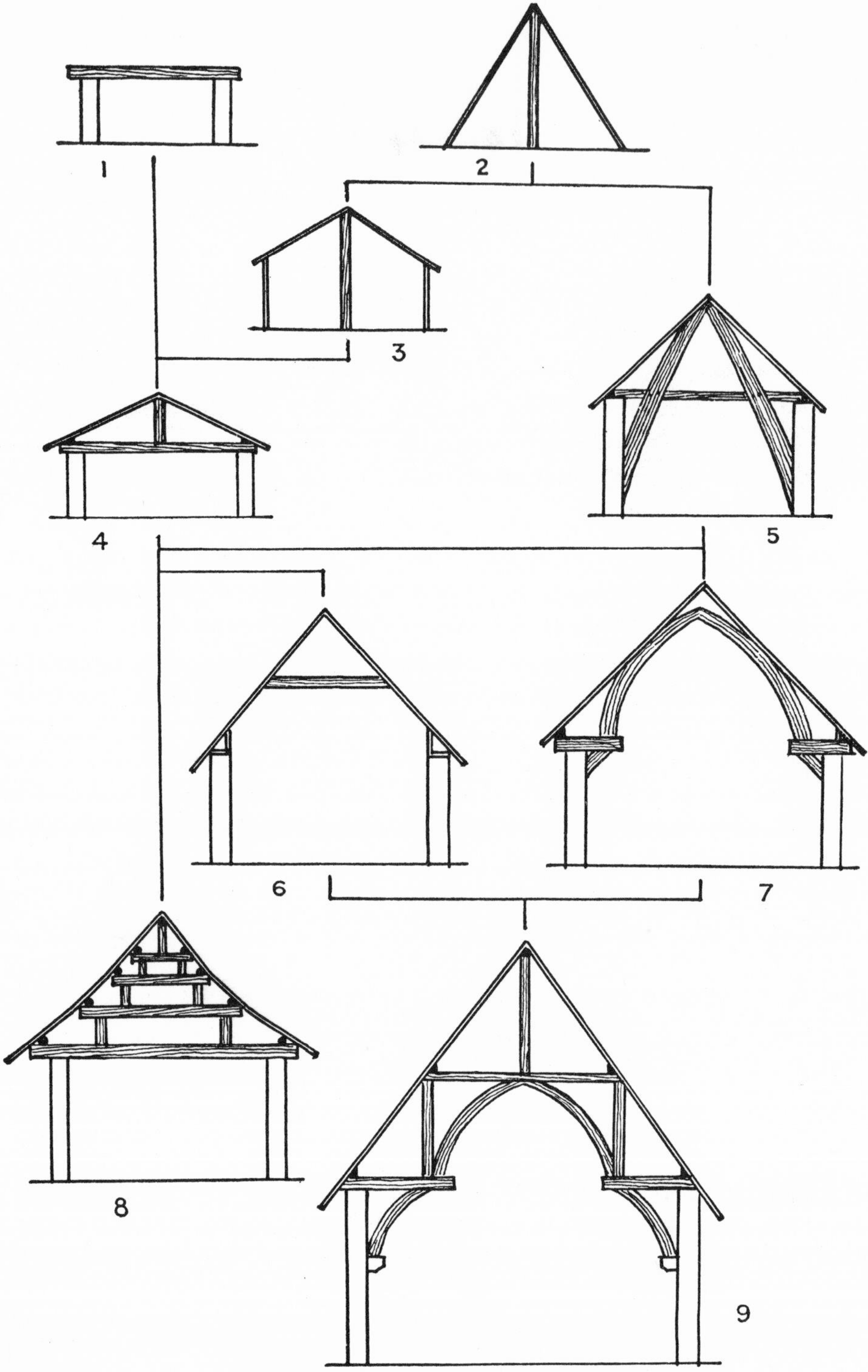

Fig. 31. Simple forms of timber construction.

branches, the most elementary forms of roof supports were either a simple wooden beam, spanning from wall to wall as in Type 1 (Figure 31), or poles, or rafters, leaning against a central post, or against a horizontal ridge tree supported on two or more posts—Type 2. From these two simple forms can be traced a progression of types, each one attempting to gain more usable floor space and headroom. The first and perhaps obvious way to attain more headroom was to rest the rafters on walls built to a convenient height. Two methods of constructing this Type 3 are known to have been used. The first was to erect the wall and the taller central post and to lay a series of radiating rafters from the top of this post to the top of the wall. The second method, which resulted in a building with a much more steeply pitched roof, was to set up a series of rafters in conical fashion, bound at the top. Wall posts were then inserted and bound to the rafters, at their points of intersection, and a coil of interwoven branches or wattles wound round the framework at this eaves level. The lower portion of the rafters was then cut off close to the eaves. The effect of this was to produce a hut with a very steeply pitched roof. The building depicted by the Iron Age hut-urn from Königsaue, near Aschersleben,[17] shown in Plate XXIV, may have been erected on the same principle.

A further development was the combination of Types 1 and 3 to produce Type 4. In this the central post located on the ground was replaced by a much shortened central post, later to be known as a 'king post', supported on the main beam. This type of roof was common throughout Classical times, and was made robust enough to support heavy stone and ceramic tiling. In wooded areas it was often possible to obtain tree trunks that could either be matched in shape and size with one another, or be split to form two matching principals or 'crucks' as shown in Type 5. The lower ends of the crucks were often built into the side walls near floor level, or rested on stone pads, and they were connected at their tops in a variety of ways, by crossing them to provide a cradle in which to rest the ridge tree, by halving and pegging them, or by joining their tops with a bridging piece—a collar beam or yoke, which supported the ridge tree. The side walls were built up to give adequate headroom for the ground floor, and beams spanning across from wall top to wall top provided the necessary supports for the upper floor. The rafters were laid from the apex of the crucks to a wall plate on the top of the walls. In Type 6 a collar beam was introduced, spanning between the principal rafters. This type gave considerably greater headroom, and unobstructed storage space, and is the traditional type of roof used, for example, in the great barns of Germany. The timber collar beam is possibly the first structural member deliberately designed as a tension member or tie, and its use soon led to the more elaborate open trusses, which were later copied in comparatively recent times in iron and steel.

A combination of Types 4 and 5 led to Type 7. Here the transverse beam was replaced by two short hammer-beams, cantilevered out from the walls on brackets, and these supported a matching pair of curved timbers. Many of the great halls and churches of medieval England embodied this type of roof structure; and it finally emerged in almost perfect form and proportions in the hammer-beam roof of Westminster Hall, constructed by Richard II at the end of the fourteenth century. At various times since 1663 repairs and alterations have been made in the roof, including the substitution of slates for lead at some time between 1760 and 1782. Examination of the timbers in 1912 showed them to be very seriously decayed by the larvae of the bettle, *xestobium tessellatum*, and during the first World War a scheme of strengthening was undertaken which involved the insertion of a steel structure, which is practically invisible from below.

Type 8 is the Far Eastern development of the beam and post construction. This traditional Chinese roof truss differs from the Western in that to gain height, it repeats the post and beam construction of Type 4 on a smaller scale. Instead of a central king post the beams carry a pair of short vertical queen posts, or short spacing blocks, each placed at about quarter span. This construction is repeated several times and each time the beam is shortened so that the roof truss increases in height in a series of steps, until the required height is reached. The last diminutive beam carries a king post which supports the ridge tree. The final shape of the roof depends on the spacing of the queen posts, but if as is usual they are placed at approximately the quarter points of each supporting beam, then the roof acquires the attractive concave form, so characteristic of Chinese building. Another type of Chinese building is illustrated in the model of the Han Dynasty (Plate XXII) now in the museum of the Art Institute of Chicago. It shows a three tier pagoda-like structure, and longitudinal stepped brackets, that have also remained a feature of Chinese building for over two thousand years.

Veneer (or overlay), intarsia (or inlay), marquetry

The art of overlaying and inlaying woodwork with a decorative veneer was well established in Egypt in the second millennium B.C. It was essentially intended to make the most economical use of rare woods often imported from other countries at considerable cost. In modern usage the word 'veneer' is often used in a rather derogatory sense to suggest a superficial layer or surface applied to hide an ugly interior. This most certainly was not the ancient intention. The art is a highly honourable and traditional one, and its universal use today throughout the woodworking industry is in every way sensible and desirable in order to conserve the world's dwindling supply of decorative timbers. Up to about a hundred years ago, veneers were usually applied to a solid timber base. Nowadays, again to conserve timber and to produce, weight for weight, a stronger product, the base for the veneer is itself made up of several thin laminae of wood, so placed one upon the other, that the direction of the grain in each lamina alternates in direction at right angles. The laminae are bonded together with animal or vegetable glues, or with synthetic resins. The composite board is known as plywood, and has found many uses in building.

Early evidence of the practice of veneering comes from the famous mural painting in the Tomb of Rekhmara at Thebes, in Egypt, of the time of Thothmes III (*c.* 1500 B.C.). Part of a drawing of the mural is reproduced in Figure 124, and shows veneers of contrasting types of wood being glued and then pressed into contact with the base board with bags of sand. The worker on the right-hand side is apparently brushing glue on to the back of the veneer; the glue itself is seen in the background being heated in a pot on a fire. A finished veneered cabinet is also shown, together with various tools used in the process.

Pliny[18] records that the proudest possession of Caesar was a table beautifully veneered. He devotes a whole chapter to the art of veneering, and comments that 'the best woods for cutting in layers and employing as a veneer for covering others, are the citrus, the terebinth, the different varieties of the maple, the roots of the elder and the poplar'. This last reference to the use of roots is interesting for even today some of the most attractive veneers are obtained from the stumps or butts of trees. It is also clear from what Pliny says that veneering was considered as a means of conserving timber: 'In order to make a tree sell many times over, laminae of veneer have been devised.'

The process of inlaying, or 'intarsia', from the Latin *interserere*—to insert, is also of remote antiquity. The Egyptians and Assyrians used various materials as inlays, not only woods, but ivory, metals, and vitreous pastes. The Greeks and the Romans also used many different kinds of wood for the purpose, which they called *sectile laminae*, including ebony, cypress, oak, cedar, willow, lotus, citron, maple, palm, olive, and white poplar.

The period of greatest development of the art of 'intarsia' was in the fourteenth and fifteenth centuries and was mainly centred in Siena in Italy. Among the woods used were pear, box, maple, walnut, pine, and cypress, and some woods artificially coloured with various substances, such as verdigris to produce green, cochineal for red, and sublimate of mercury for yellow. Shadow effects were produced by scorching the inlays with molten lead, or with a hot iron. Mastro Vanni di Zura dell Ammanato headed a team of twenty-eight artists who worked on the stalls in Orvieto Cathedral in 1331. Domenico di Nicole continued the work in 1414, Pietro di Minella and his brother Antonio in 1431, and finally Giovanni di Lodovico di Magno. Domenico di Nicole was one of the best Sienese masters of the craft and worked for thirteen years on the inlays in the chapel of the Palazzo Publico at Siena. Excellent examples of intarsia work can still be seen at Perugia, in the Sala del Collegio della Mercanzia (A.D. 1500), in the Sala del Notari (A.D. 1462), and in the Collegio del Cambio, Sala d'Udienza.

In marquetry, a later development, the pieces produce an all over pattern, often a pictorial character, and it is in the nature of a veneer over the whole surface, rather than of pieces inlaid into a lighter or darker ground as in intarsia work.

REFERENCES

(1) BRUNHES, JEAN, 1922, *Human Geography*, trans. T. C. Le Compte, Harrap.

(2) LUCAS, A., 1948, *Ancient Egyptian Materials and Industries*, Arnold (3rd revised edition).

(3) THEOPHRASTUS, *On the History of Plants*, IV, ii, translated by Sir Arthur Hart, Loeb Classical Library, Heinemann.

(4) CHILDE, V. GORDON, 1944, 'Archaeology in the U.S.S.R.', *The Anglo-Soviet Journal*, V, No. 2.

(5) CHILDE, V. GORDON, 1949, 'Neolithic House-types in Temperate Europe', *Proceedings of the Prehistoric Society*, CX (new series), 77.

(6) LAWRENCE, A. W., 1957, *Greek Architecture*, Pelican Books.

(7) PETRIE, W. M. FLINDERS, 1901, 'The Sources and Growth of Architecture in Egypt', *Journal* of the Royal Institute of British Architects, VIII (3rd series), 341.

(8) BULLEID, A., and GRAY, H. St G., 1911–17, *The Glastonbury Lake Village*, Chambers, 2 Vols.; BULLEID, A., 1924, *The Lake Village of Somerset* (Somerset Folk Series No. 16), Folk Press.

(9) VAN GIFFEN, A. E., January 1936, 'Der Warf in Ezinge Provinz Groningen, Holland und sein westgermanische Häuser', *Germania*, Vol. 40.

(10) BUTTLER, WERNER and HABEREY, WALDEMAR, 1937, 'Das bandkeramische Dorf, Köln-Lindenthal', *Germania*, XXI, 213–17.

(11) SCHMIDT, R. R., 1937, *Jungsteinzeitliche Siedlungen im Federseemoor*, Filser, Augsburg and Stuttgart.

(12) GODWIN, 1905, *Mediaeval Architecture in Essex.*

(13) VITRUVIUS, *De Architectura*, Book II, I.

(14) YURCHENKO, P. G., 1945, 'Methods of Construction and of Heat Insulation in the Ukraine', extract in *Journal* of the Royal Institute of British Architects, LII (3rd Series), No. 10.

(15) VITRUVIUS, *De Architectura*, Book II, VIII.

(16) COLLINGWOOD, R. G., 1934, 'Roman Britain in 1933', *Journal of Roman Studies*, XXIV, 231, 221.

(17) KÜHN, H., 1935, *Vorgeschichtliche Kunst Deutschlands*, Berlin.

(18) PLINY, *Natural History*, Book XVI, LXXXIV.

6

Reed and Straw

THERE ARE VARIOUS distinct species of reed or so-called 'reeds' that have found their use in building construction. The common, or water reed (*phragmites communis* or *arundo phragmites*) is the most widespread and occurs along the margins of lakes, streams, fens, and marshes from the Middle East to the Arctic. Other useful species are the sea reed or marram grass (*ammoplula arenaria* or *psamma arenaria*) growing along the sandy shores of Europe and North Africa, the pampas grass (*gynerium argenteum*), and some plants belonging to other orders such as reed mace (*typha*) and bur-reed (*sparganium*) belonging to the Typhaceae family, and bulrush (*scirpus*) belonging to the Cyperaceae family.

These and many other types of reed and grass have been woven by man to form mats and screens. He has tied them in bundles to form strong structural pillars and ribs when no other suitable timber has been available, and he has used them for thatching. In the Nile valley in Egypt, for example, reeds plastered with mud have been found during the excavation of Predynastic dwellings,[1] and a model of a house (Plate XXIII), now in the British Museum, from El Amarna gives an idea of the possible appearance of these early dwellings before 3000 B.C. The house represented was composed of reeds and mud.

Before the quarrying of stone in Egypt there was little material available for building other than the reeds and rushes, the alluvial mud of the Nile valley, and a few precious date palm stems and branches of acacia. With these materials the ancient Egyptians built their simple dwellings—with these same materials many of the modern Egyptians build today. When stone was quarried, possibly in the fourth millennium B.C., and new stone buildings were erected it seems that their architects strove to preserve the timber building tradition. Essentially the buildings embodied the simple post and lintel principle of construction, and the columns suggested natural vegetable growth, often like the sheathed stalks of the papyrus or lotus plant, a distinctive and peculiar feature of Egyptian work which persisted for over three thousand years. Some columns, incurving at the foot, appeared as a bundle of budding reeds or flowering stalks, often seemingly tied together near the top and at the base. The sketch in Figure 32 illustrates a rather late example of this, but serves well to show how long the tradition persisted. It is the head of one of the columns in the great Temple of Isis at Philae, built by Nekhtnebf about 350 B.C. The

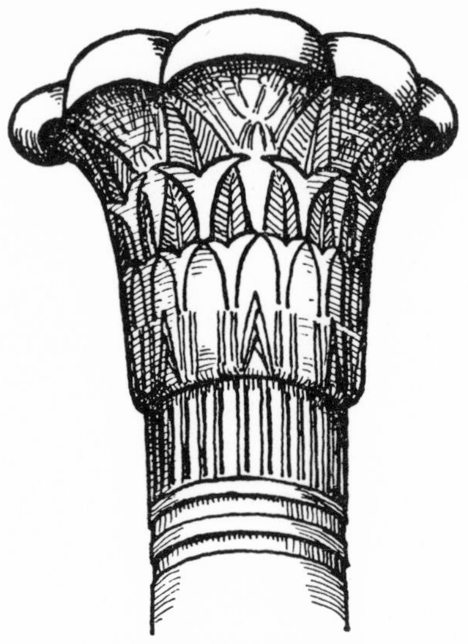

Fig. 32. Papyrus capital at Philae.

temple was reconstructed by Ptolemy Philadelphus and Ptolemy Euergetes I, but was mostly destroyed by flood, as the islet of Philae stood in the Nile just above the first cataract.

Even in the form and decoration of other building components the tradition persisted. A faience tile from Abydos for example, now in the British Museum, and dated about 3000 B.C., is made in imitation of reed matting, and a piece of ivory is shown carved in the form of the giant reed (*heracleum giganteum*). Later tiles from El Amarna, dating about 1380 and 1360 B.C. are shown inlaid with glazed faience, to represent lotus flowers and papyrus flowers

In Mesopotamia in the Al'Ubaid Period (early fourth millennium B.C.) the houses were at first built of reeds and mud.[2] Curved bundles of reeds were set up head to head to form high parabolic arches, and the spaces between were filled with more reeds woven into matting. The effect outside was that of rough buttresses and recesses. The principle has, however, survived for six thousand years and can be seen in the most remarkable reed dwellings of modern times in the Mesopotamian marshes built by the Ma'dan or Marshmen of Southern Iraq. Here the giant reeds (*phragmites communis*) grow to heights of up to 20 feet. They are tightly bound into bundles to form long tapering pillars and these are set in the ground opposite to each other, as shown in Figure 33, in two parallel rows, the width of the dwelling apart, and inclined outwards. The tops of the bundles are then pulled inwards and spliced at the top to form a series of parabolic arches of great strength. These arches are then linked by longitudinal bundles of reeds, and the framework so formed is overlain with matting. More tapering pillars of reeds are set up at the ends of the structure, to support the end walling of alternating matting and trelliswork.

Maxwell[3] gives a very clear account of how he saw these huts made in the marshes at Abu Malih, 15 miles south-east of Amara. Three or more men worked on each house, and they began by digging, with a spade much like that of the peat cutters of the Scottish Highlands, two parallel rows of holes for the feet of the reed arches. Into these holes, 2 feet 6 inches deep, they set the base of the 20-foot columns in such a way that they leaned outward from the floor space at an angle of about seventy degrees. Next they made from cut and bound reed bundles a tripod 5 or 6 feet high. Standing on this firm and rigid structure a man reached up and caught with the foot-edge of a spade the upper part of the reed column, bent it down to his own level, and held it there while he or an assistant reached for the other half of the arch. These two he bound securely together with twisted lengths of sedge leaf, and moved his tripod along to the next column. When the row of five arches was complete, more slender bundles of horizontals, fourteen of them in all, connected the whole structure together ready for its covering of reed matting.

There are longer buildings used as guest houses—or *mudhifs*—built in the same way. One described by Maxwell was 65 feet long by 20 feet wide, with nine arches 15 feet high and each tied with 120 double rings of rope—nearly 500 yards of rope to every arch for the average circumference from the yard-thick base of the columns to their tapering tops was not less than 6 feet. The arches carried 120 reed bundles, 4 inches thick, laid horizontally and tied every 4 inches of their whole length, employing another 1,000 yards

Fig. 33. Reed dwellings in course of erection in the Mesopotamian marshes.

of rope. These horizontals continued to within 3 feet of the floor, below which there was a bare skirt of matting that could be lifted to relieve the heat.

The Romans used reeds in the construction of curved ceilings in a rather different way. According to Vitruvius,[4] parallel laths of cypress wood were placed not more than 2 feet apart and bent to the shape of an arch. He says: 'When the ribs are in their place, Greek reeds are to be bruised and bound to the ribs with cords of Spanish broom, as the shape of the curve requires. . . . If there be no supply of Greek reed, thin reeds are to be collected from the marshes, and are to be made up in bundles with cords of rough thread to the right length and of equal thickness, provided that not more than two feet separates the knots of the bundles. These then are to be fixed with cord to the ribs as already described, and wooden pins are to be driven through them. . . . When the arched surfaces are fixed

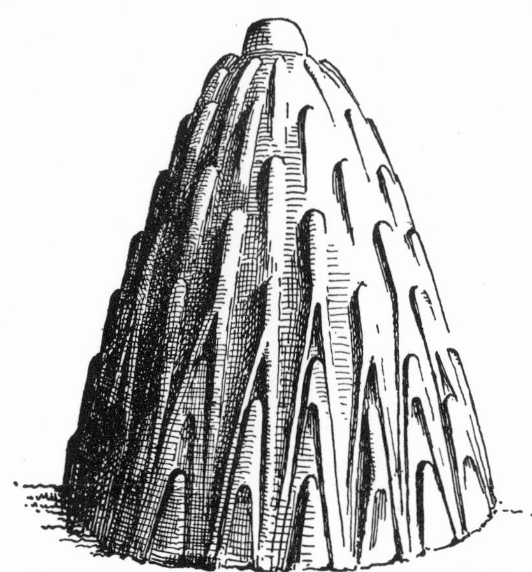

Fig. 34. Reed and mud hut of the Tchad region of Africa, 15 feet in height and formed with protruding shoulders which enable it to be climbed.

and interwoven with the reeds, the under surface is to be roughcast, then sand is to be applied and afterwards finished with hair mortar or marble. . . .'

Many different forms of reed and mud huts are built in Africa at the present time. Some remarkable ones are in the Tchad region. They are often 15 feet or more in height and like that shown in Figure 34 are provided with protruding shoulders which form convenient steps by which to climb.

Reeds have also been used for reinforcing flat roofs, floors, and ceilings for over five thousand years. Mallowan[5] records that there was a flat roof made of reeds and mud weighted down with pebbles on a prehistoric temple of the Halaf Period (late fifth millenium B.C.) at Aswad in the Balikh valley of the Euphrates. Lawrence[6] has described the construction of the ceiling of a middle Helladic House at Eutresis (*c.* 1700 B.C.). It consisted of closely spaced timbers spanning the main beams, and upon them a layer of clay reinforced with reeds, as shown in Figure 35a. This type of roof has survived in various forms in the Near and Middle East, and a modern Persian example is shown in Figure 35b. Upon the secondary beams is placed some 'chattai' matting followed by a layer of reed and a second layer of matting, then 'mutty', a mixture of mud and chopped straw ('tibben'), rendered water-tight by a sandwich layer of bitumen.

The plaster floors used in England up to the middle of the nineteenth century are essentially similar. As indicated in Figure 36 a layer of reeds or straw was laid across the floor joists and secured to them by battens, and on this layer lime or gypsum plaster was placed to a thickness of about 3 inches. It seems likely that in England the use of lime mixtures is more ancient than that of gypsum mixtures. The latter is also confined geographically to areas roughly twenty miles or so around the gypsum producing centres of Gotham and Newark. The composition of the mixture varied greatly, the lime varying from the high calcium type to hydraulic lime, and the gypsum according

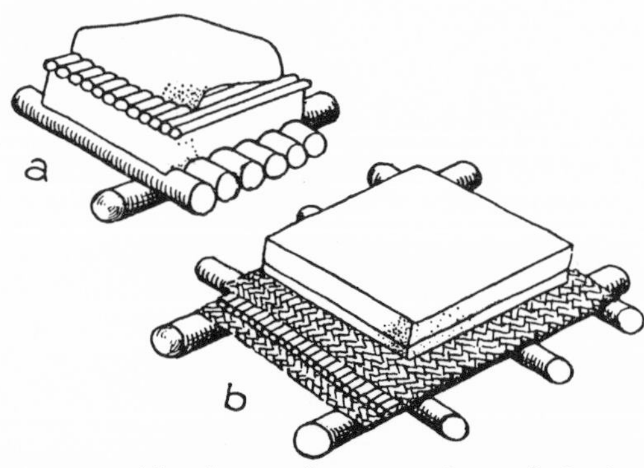

Fig. 35. (a) Flat roof construction of Ancient Greece (after Lawrence). (b) Modern roof construction in south Persia.

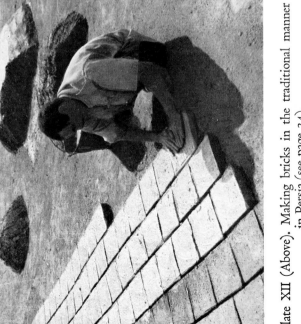

Plate XII (Above). Making bricks in the traditional manner in Persia (see page 24).

Plate XIII (Right). Mud bricks used in the wall of a Roman building at Leicester (see page 25).

Plate XIV. A building of circular plan of Prepottery Neolithic 'A' period, Jericho (see page 22).

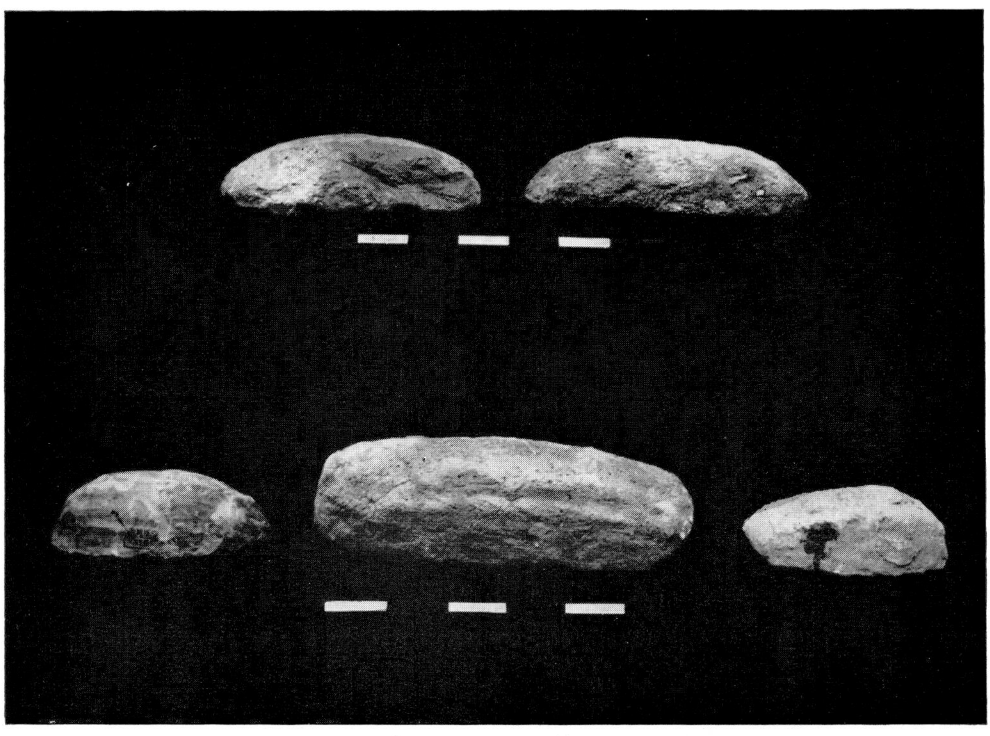

Plate XV. 'Hog-back' bricks of Prepottery Neolithic 'A' period, Jericho (see page 22).

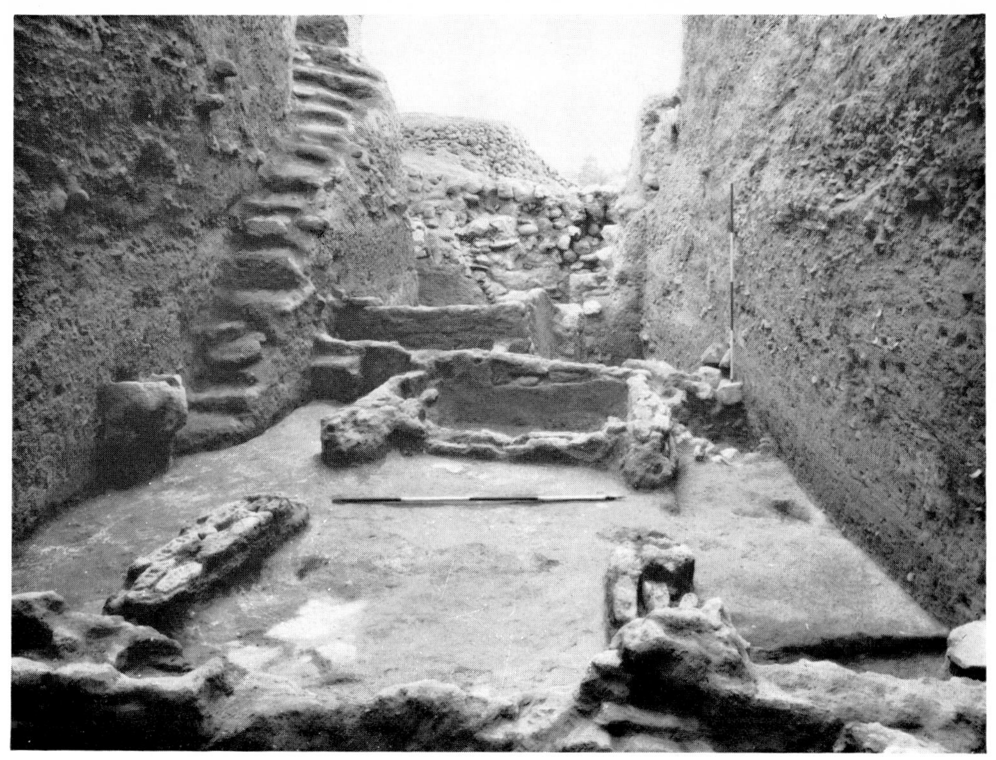

Plate XVI. A building of rectangular plan of Prepottery Neolithic 'B' period, Jericho (see page 22).

Plate XVII. 'Cigar-shaped' bricks of Prepottery Neolithic 'B' period, Jericho (see page 22).

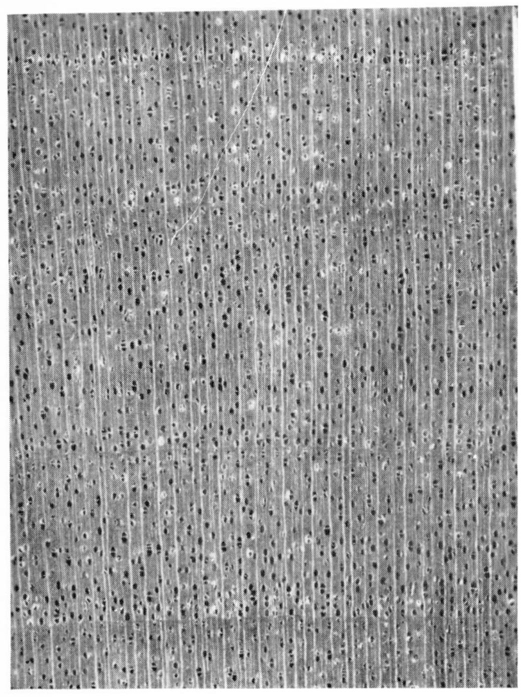

1. European Birch (*Betula pubescens*).

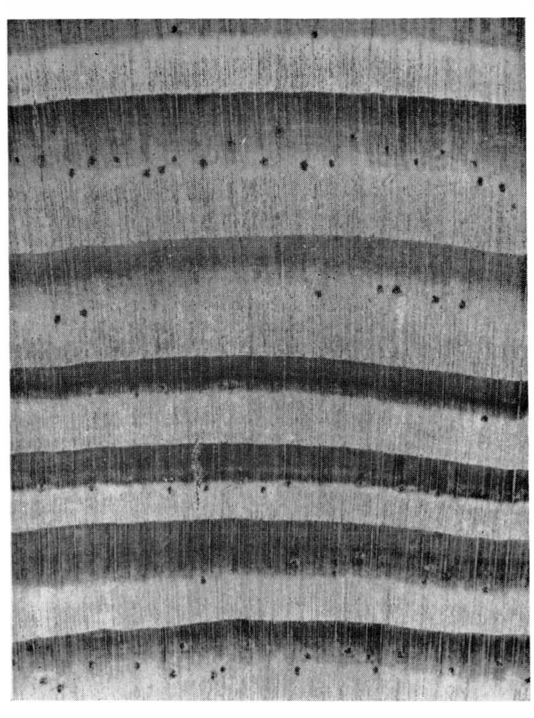

2. Scots Pine (*Pinus sylvestric*).

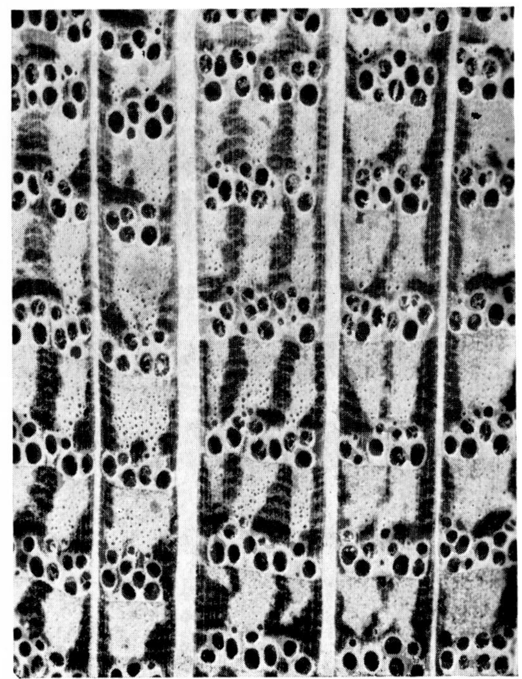

3. European Oak (*Quercus robur*).

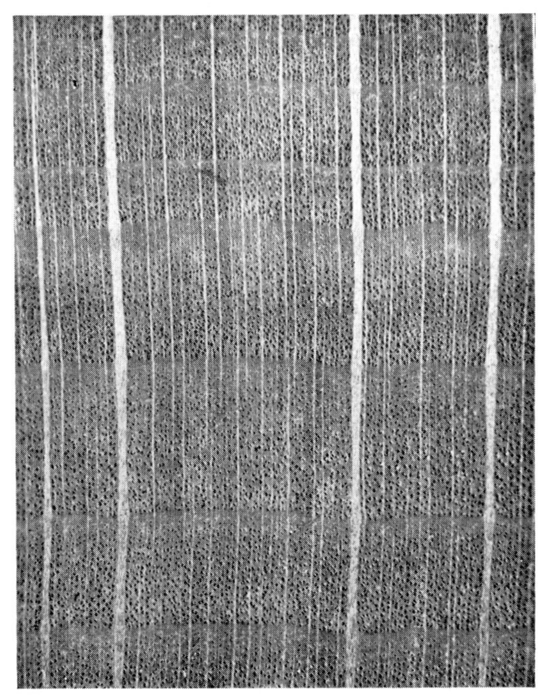

4. European Beech (*Fagus sylvatica*).

Plate XVIII. End-grain microphotographs of four predominant timbers used for constructional work.

to its degree of calcination, and containing differing amounts of unburnt gypsum, plaster of Paris, and anhydrous calcium sulphate. Ashes, sand, and crushed brick rubble were often incorporated in the mixture.

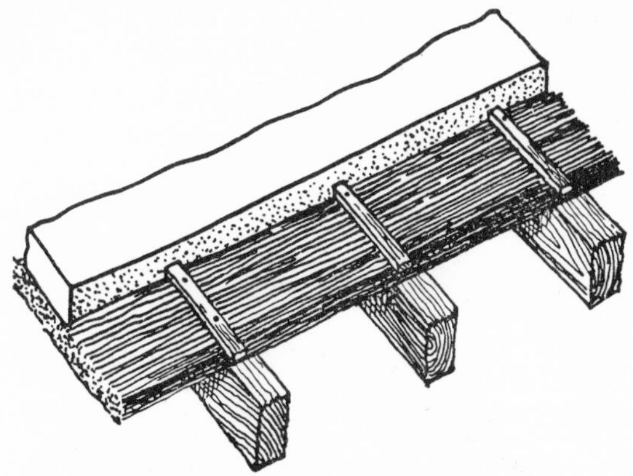

Fig. 36. Gypsum floor on reed or straw used in the Midlands of England in the eighteenth and nineteenth centuries; but sometimes lime was used instead of gypsum.

Reeds and straw have also found their use for wall construction. Very interesting examples occur in the Russian Ukraine.[7] Although in timber-framed building the panels are often either filled up solidly with clay or filled with plaited wattles, or with split timbers placed horizontally between the upright posts of the frame and daubed with clay as in other countries, it is not

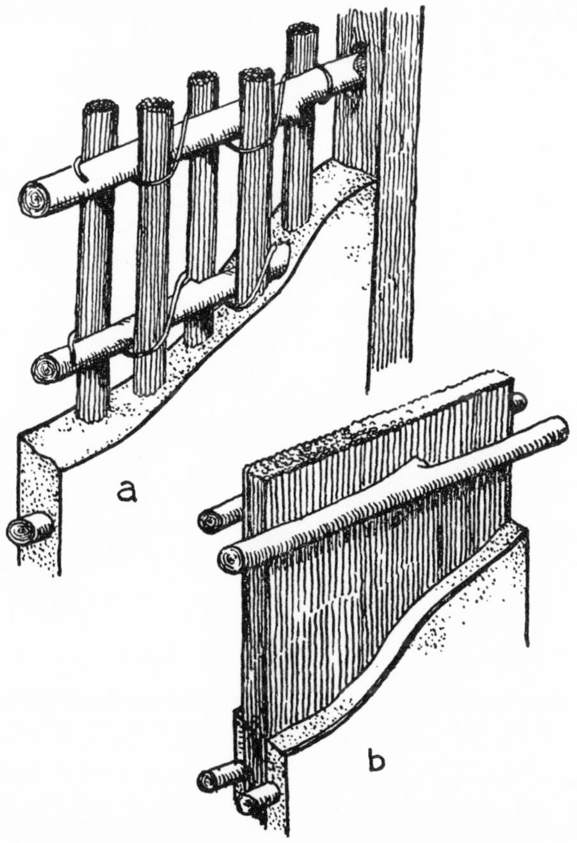

Fig. 37. Ukrainian use of reeds for walling.

uncommon to find bundles of reeds placed vertically, as shown in Figure 37a, and secured with cords to horizontal poles about 2 inches in diameter which have their ends located in prepared openings in the upright posts of the main frame. The bundles of reeds are arranged in staggered fashion. Clay mixed with chopped straw is pressed into the gaps between the bundles of reeds on both sides and the wall surface then finished off smoothly with a coating of clay.

Sometimes the space between the upright posts of the main frame is filled with reeds placed vertically, as shown in Figure 37b, and compressed between two poles, the ends of which are located in holes in the upright posts, the wall being finished in the same way as before. A modern development of this technique is the fabrication of sheets of compressed straw or reed, about 2 inches thick, stitched together with wire. This product, made in convenient sizes, is used for ceiling and wall construction.

REFERENCES

(1) Brunton, Guy, and Thompson, G. Caton, 1928, *The Badarian Civilisation*, Quaritch, 82–3.

(2) Directorate General of Antiquities, Government of Iraq, 1942, *A Guide to the Iraq Museum Collections*, Baghdad.

(3) Maxwell, Gavin, 1957, *A Reed Shaken by the Wind*, Longmans Green.

(4) Vitruvius, *De Architectura*, Book VII, III.

(5) Mallowan, M. E. L., *Twenty-five years of Mesopotamian Discovery (1932–1956)*, The British School of Archaeology in Iraq.

(6) Lawrence, A. W., 1957, *Greek Architecture*, Penguin Books.

(7) Yurchenko, P. G., 1945, 'Methods of Construction and of Heat Insulation in the Ukraine', extract in *Journal* of the Royal Institute of British Architects, LII (3rd series), No. 10.

7

Thatch

THE MOST PRIMITIVE method of thatching a structure was to cover the rafters and purlins, or the beams in the case of flat roofs, with brushwood, grass, bracken, heather, or other vegetable material held in place by stones, ropes, or poles, or interspersed with layers of mud, with or without chopped straw or animal dung. Unfortunately thatch, even if it is of the very best reed, cannot be expected to last more than seventy or eighty years without partial renewal. We have, therefore, very little direct knowledge about the ancient methods of thatching, but a study of present-day methods will give an indication of them.

The term thatch or 'thack' was used originally to describe an outer protective layer of some suitable vegetable material, not necessarily straw, put on to the roof of a building. It was only later that the term thatch became more specifically associated with straw and reed. It will be used here, however, in its wider sense to cover the other types of material as well.

From simple beginnings the skilled craft of thatching was evolved. The house models[1] known as 'hut-urns' illustrated in Plates XXIV and XXV suggest that the craft of thatching was well developed several centuries before Christ. In the model from Obliwitz (Plate XXV), near Lauenburg, dating between 750 and 400 B.C., it would seem that the roofing was held down by rope sways, or wooden ledgers, or rods arranged to form a pattern, while in the other, from Königsaue, near Aschersleben (Plate XXIV), of Iron Age date, the thatch appears to have been held down by longer rods or poles, passing from eaves to ridge, a method still practised in Germany, Esthonia, and Russia.

Humfrey Payne, who directed the excavations at the Heraeum of Perachora near Corinth, concluded that the roofs depicted in the two temple models from Perachora, dating about 800 to 750 B.C., were thatched, the thatch being fixed by a twisted rope along the ridge of the roof.[2] The model (Figure 38), 14 inches long, represents a simple apsidal building with an entrance door between *antae*, above which are three small square windows. Before each *anta* stand two slender columns side by side on a single base. The exterior, painted with a large meander, is marked above by a row of small impressed triangles which are probably primitive windows. The fragments of four other models enabled Payne to restore the very steep roof, along the spine of which runs a twist of rope, confirming his belief that the original building must have been thatched. The open pediment indicates that it had a ceiling, above which was the loft. It was from this type of thatched cottage that after an interval of only three hundred years Greek architecture produced the Parthenon.

These three examples of 2,500 years ago suggest that thatching had already become a highly developed technique. They are each different in style and finish. So today we find an infinite variety of methods used throughout the world, and it is not possible in one chapter to deal with many of them. Concentration will be mainly on the traditional methods used in the British Isles.

Fig. 38. Model of the Temple at Perachora.

Thatching was also used as a temporary protection to important buildings under construction. A fifteenth-century example of this is shown in Plate XXVI from a print in the British Museum.[3] It shows temporary thatching over the nave and porch of a church to protect it during the inclement winter weather. Thatch is also shown on the tops of unfinished walls.

Materials for Thatching

Many vegetable materials, found close to hand, have been used for thatching. Those commonly used in the British Isles have been heather, sally, or sallow, a willow of a low-growing and bushy habit (*salia repens*), broom, marram grass, oat straw, barley straw, flax straw, rye straw, wheat straw, various reeds, and tall sedge (*carex pendula*). Heather and sally are commonly used in Ireland, the north of Scotland, Orkneys, and Shetland, but not often in England. The weeds and rubbish are first of all removed, and heather or sally is tied in bunches to the roof timbers with stout twine, and held flat with runners and spars. Marram grass (*ammophila arenaria*), a poor substitute for straw, is found mainly on the sand-dunes in coastal areas. Broom, cleaned in the same way as heather, is easier to lay on the roof as the stems are straighter. Both heather and broom have often been fixed in position by pushing the tied ends of bunches through grass turves laid on the roof. Boswell[4] records that the house he visited in 1773 in the Hebrides was built of thick turves and thatched with thinner turves and heather.

Rye straw and flax straw have been used extensively in Ireland and elsewhere, but the practice of thatching roofs in Ireland is diminishing rapidly, particularly as flax is now comparatively little grown there. Oat and barley straw are soft and easily broken and are in consequence less durable than wheat straw, which is the most commonly used straw in England. Straw that has passed through a mechanical thresher, however, is of little use, as the stems may be crushed and broken. Straw that has been well matured in the stack is often considered to be better than newly thrashed straw. The trusses of straw are broken and shaken up lightly with a fork into layers, each layer being thoroughly damped by sprinkling with water, beaten down gently, and left for several hours. The straw is then pulled sharply in handfuls from beneath the heap, a process called 'drawing' which removes loose material, broken stems, flags, and rubbish. The cleaned stems are then laid out straight and close together and tied into small sheaves or bundles (known variously as 'yealms', 'bottles', 'gavels', 'bunches', or 'bats').

Another ancient method of cleaning the straw described by Hennell,[5] was to lay about two dozen wheatsheaves along the threshing floor and to beat the ears with a flail. The sheaves were taken two at a time with their heads brought together, and then hung up by a rope. They were combed through with a hand comb about a foot wide with long tines set an inch or more apart, firstly from heads to butts, then from butts to head.

Red standard wheat which has stems of bright yellow colour, about 3 feet to 3 feet 6 inches long, is the most suitable, and when prepared for thatching is often called 'reed' in the West Country, but is not to be confused with the marsh and river reed of East Anglia which is by far the toughest and most durable of the thatching materials.

The most common of the thatching reeds is *arundo phragmites*, which grows in Cambridgeshire and Norfolk to a height of 5 to 8 feet. It is, however, sometimes grown mixed with the lesser reed mace, *typha augustifolia*, but the latter does not usually exceed one-fifth part of the whole mixed reed, or 'mixed stuff' as it is called. The reeds are harvested between the end of December and the end of March. Sedge, *cladium mariscus*, is used for forming a roof ridge or 'cap' to the thatch.

Rushes and reeds of all sorts must have been used for thatching from the earliest times. Bede,[6] for example, records that during the visit of St German to the tomb of St Alban, about A.D. 450, fire broke out in houses 'covered with marsh reeds'. The term 'marsh reeds' probably referred to a natural mixture of sedge, mace, rushes, iris, etc. The material may have been just spread over the roof timbers and held down by timbers or ropes.

Underlay for Thatch

There are four main methods of fixing thatch:

(*a*) by sewing directly to battens or nailing to the rafters;
(*b*) by holding the thatch by rods laid across it;
(*c*) by securing with ropes stretched over the surface, with ends tied or weighted, or by ropes fixed by pegs to the thatch;
(*d*) by knotting the end of the yealm and thrusting it into or between turves.

Sometimes the yealms of thatch are laid on turves, sometimes called 'divots' or 'scraws'. The yealms are held down by rods which in turn are secured by 'broaches' (also called 'scoubs', 'brotches', and by other local names) driven into the turves. The turves themselves are laid directly on the battens and purlins of the roof timbering. In Ireland they are often cut in long strips, 20 feet or more in length and up to 2 feet in width, and about 2 to 3 inches thick, long enough in fact to extend from one of the eaves up to and a foot or so beyond the ridge. They are sewn with grass upwards on to the roof timbers. An alternative method is to interlace the battens with twigs to form a foundation for the thatch. It was customary in Saxon and medieval times to cover the roof timbers with wattles before applying the thatch. An early reference to this practice is given by Bede,[7] who records that while people were feasting in a house near Maserfield, 'a great fire having been kindled it happened that sparks flew up and the roof of the house, which was wattled and thatched with hay, was filled with sudden flame'. Many of the early and devastating fires in London and elsewhere resulted from the burning of thatch roofs, and in A.D. 1212 building regulations were issued in London which stipulated that after that date no roofs were to be covered with reeds, sedge, straw, or stubble, but only with tile, shingles, boards, or lead or plastered straw, and that existing reed and sedge roofs were to be plastered over. The regulations do not seem to have been rigorously enforced, however.

Where there were no battens it was not unusual to apply a layer of long straw, sometimes woven to form a mat or 'waistcoat' to which the yealms were secured. In Northern Ireland a thick layer of flax waste has been used for the same purpose, while another method used in East Anglia and elsewhere, is to weave reeds in basket fashion over the rafters as shown in Figure 42b—a process which is called 'reed flaking'.

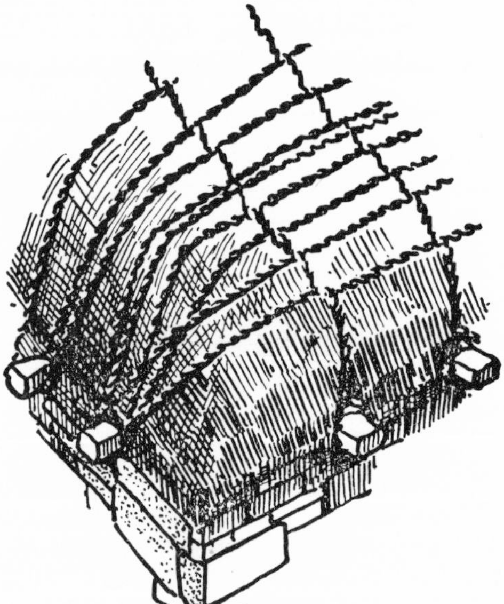

Rope thatching is the most primitive method still practised in the North of Scotland, Orkneys, Shetland, the Outer Isles, Isle of Man, and Ireland. In its simplest form straw was heaped on the rafters, which were almost horizontal, and the straw held down by ropes, the ends of which were weighted with stones. In better work the thatching material, often of heather, flax, or rye straw, is placed in layers in a more orderly fashion, on a pitched roof, and held down by ropes, or bonds ('sugans') of straw, heather or bog-fir, crossed at right angles. The ends of the ropes are sometimes tied to stone pegs projecting from the wall of the building, as shown in Figure 39, just below the eaves and the verges, or the ropes may be weighted with stone either hanging loose over the

Fig. 39. Thatch held by ropes tied to stone pegs at the eaves and verges.

eaves, or resting on the roof above the eaves. In the two former cases the ropes passed over a horizontal board placed just above the eaves to distribute the pressure evenly along the roof. A comparatively recent example of pegged rope thatch on the roof of a 'stitched house' at Portballintrae on the North Antrim coast, is shown in Plate XXVII. The straw is held down by horizontal ropes twisted and pegged to the thatch at frequent intervals. The thatch is shown mortared down at the verges of the roof to prevent the wind entering at this point and lifting it. Mud copings and stone copings are often used for the same purpose.

Many of the Etruscan hut-urns depict roofs in which the thatch was held down by poles crossing at the ridge of the roof. This ancient method of straw thatching has persisted for at least two thousand years throughout Western and Central Europe and far eastwards into Russia, from Denmark and Germany, to Czechoslovakia, Esthonia, and the Ukraine. Sometimes the poles are short but often they extend to the full height of the roof. The two Ukrainian examples shown in Figure 40 are based on details given by Yurchenko.[5] The surface of the roof is covered with small bound sheaves of straw placed with the ears downwards, except at the eaves where the sheaves are placed with ears upwards. The sheaves are tied to the battens with twisted straw. The ridge cap is held down by short rods crossing over at the ridge (Figure 40a). The alternative method is to open each bound sheaf fanwise at the ridge so that one half comes down on one slope and the other half of the sheaf down the other. The very attractive finish shown in Figure 40c is obtained.

The methods of thatching in straw and in marsh reed still in use will be described in more detail. The terms used in thatching vary very considerably throughout the country and are indeed quite confusing.

Long-Straw Thatching

A double layer of yealms or sheaves of straw 14 to 18 inches wide and 4 inches thick are laid wet at the eaves of the roof starting at one corner of the building, and working from verge to verge. They are tied tightly near their tops to the battens, the bottom ends hanging well over the eaves. Adjacent yealms are lapped together so as to form a compact mass about 10 to 12 inches thick and 2 or 3 inches thicker than this at the eaves. Tarred twine is now used for tying the yealms, but previously straw bands were used and even earlier in medieval times, the wrung vines of the blackberry. The yealms are also laid in double thickness at the verges, and the top of the roof is finished off by laying bundles of straw longitudinally along the ridge and tying them to provide a good foundation for the 'crown' or 'cap' of the thatch. Sometimes one end of a pointed stick, called a ledger, is thrust into the straw and carried across three or four yealms, and the other end tied to the rafters. Another ledger is pushed under the first one overlapping it for a few inches, and this also is tied or pegged in the same way. The cap is formed by placing a final row of yealms with their centre exactly across the top of the ridge, and bending the ends of the yealms down on either side, and securing them with horizontal rods or

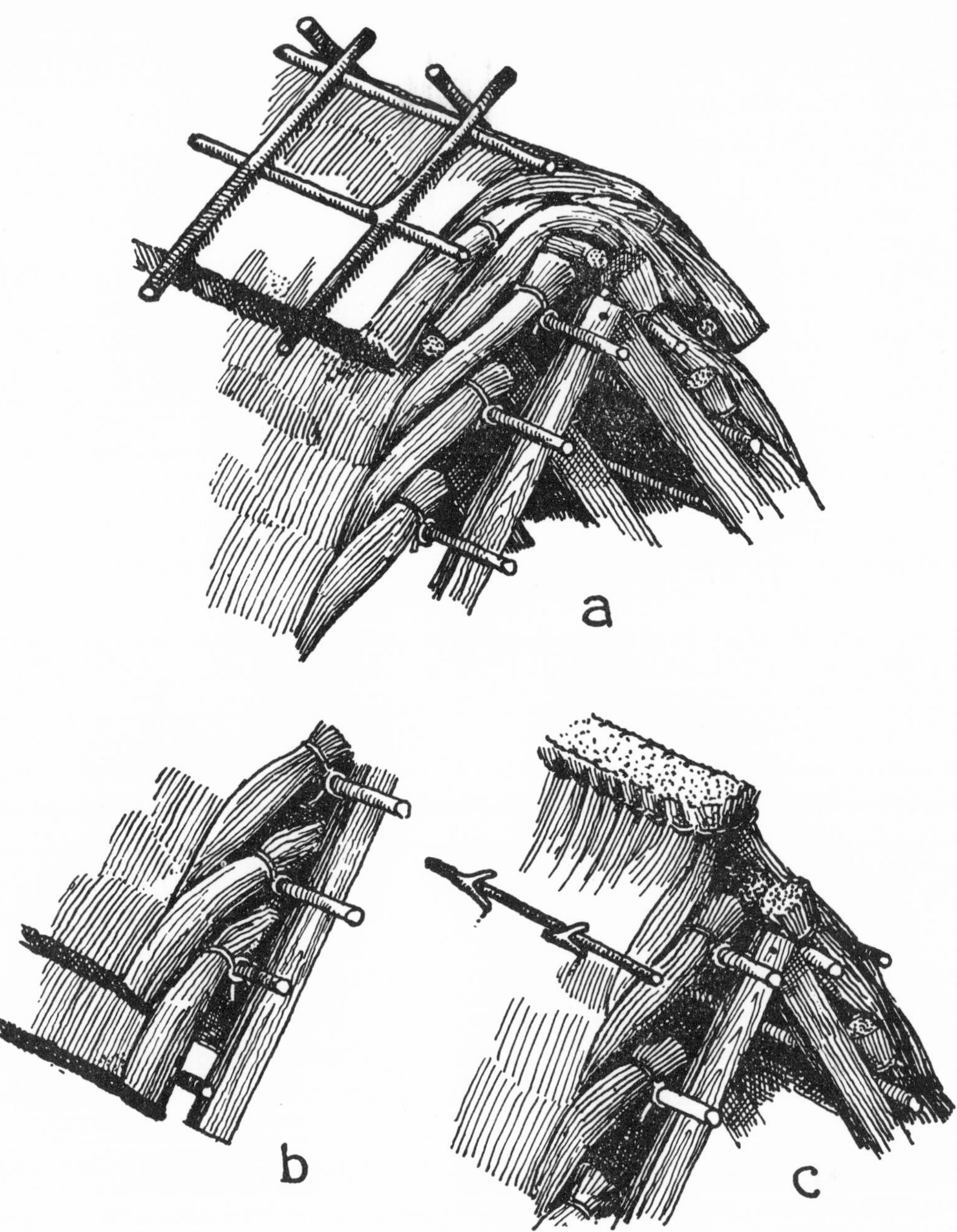

Fig. 40. Ukrainian examples of thatching.

Plate XIX. Nomadic peasants in Greece building a hut (see page 32).

Plate XX. Mortised timber framework and timber floor of an Iron Age rectangular hut at Meare, near Glastonbury (see page 36).

Plate XXI. The galleried storehouse of the Alvros farmstead, dating from 1666, re-erected at Skansen, Stockholm (see page 39).

runners of split hazel, and pegs made from short rods of hazel or withy, with ends sharpened, and twisted and bent over like a hairpin. The twist imparts springiness which gives them a better hold when driven into the thatch. The method is illustrated in Figure 41.

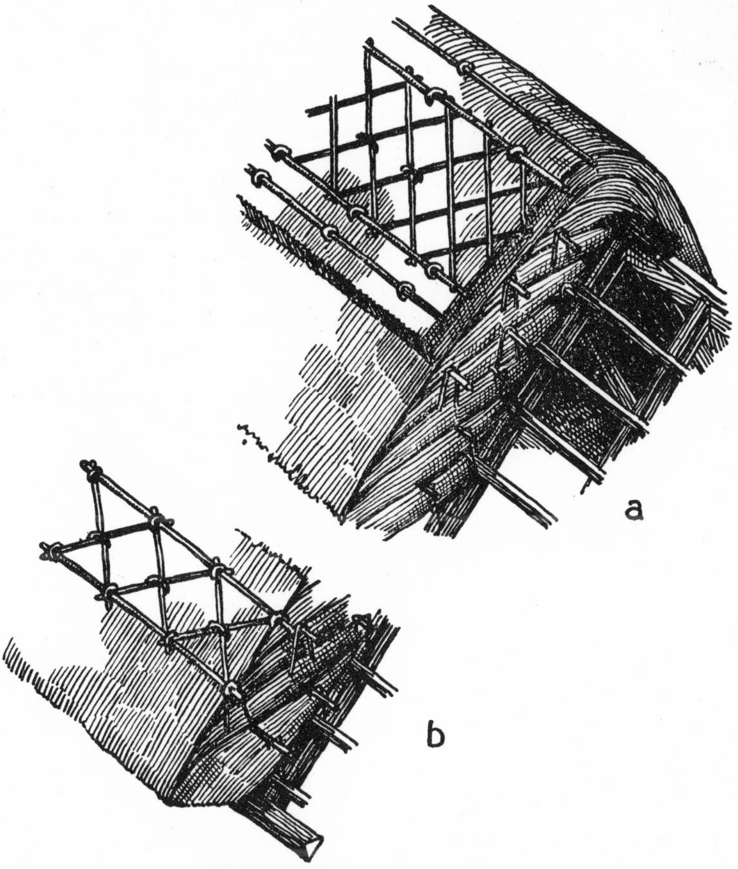

Fig. 41. Long-straw thatching.

In Northern Ireland the hazel rods were usually replaced by straw, heather or 'bog-fir' ropes, but more recently manilla rope has been used. The eaves and verges are usually reinforced with a double line of runners all round the roof spaced 9 to 12 inches from its edge; and the thatch is trimmed by cutting off loose ends of straw with a long-bladed knife. The surface of the thatch is gently beaten during laying with a flat mallet called a 'legget' or 'leggat' to consolidate it into a firm mass, and is occasionally combed with a hand rake.

Combed Wheat Reed

Wheat straw instead of being threshed can be passed through a reed combing machine, and being unbroken can be used for thatching in the same way as reed.

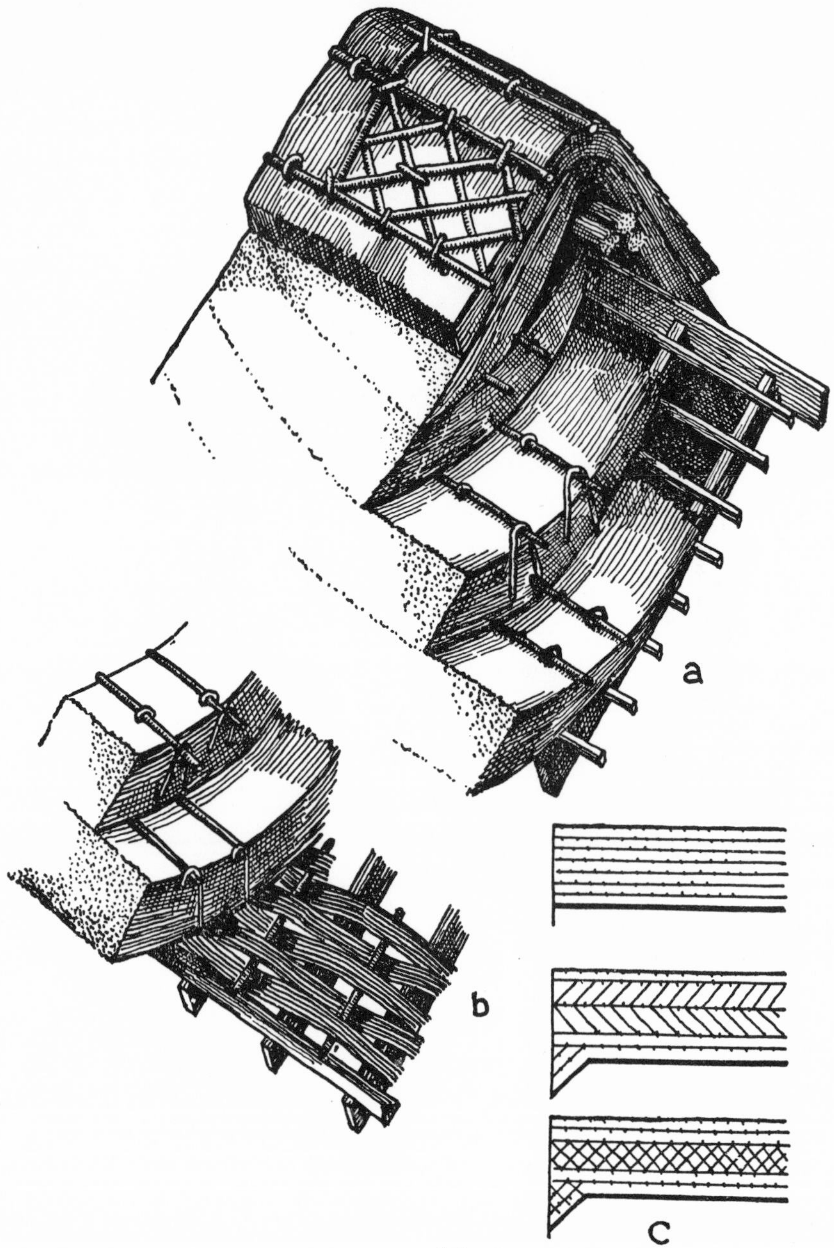

Fig. 42. Reed thatching.

Reed Thatching

The method of fixing the bundles of reeds is similar to that used for straw roofs, but the laying proceeds from eaves to ridge. The reeds are laid vertically up the roof, as shown in Figure 42a, b, and held down by horizontal hazel rods or sways 5 to 8 feet long, secured to the rafters by means of iron hooks driven into the latter. Often the reeds are tied—or stitched—to the battens with tarred manilla rope. Each bundle of reed is gently tapped into place by hand, the sway placed in position and fixed down tightly with more hooks driven into the rafters. The process continues, layer by layer up to the ridge of the roof, where the last layer of reed will project 2 or 3 feet above it. This is the only place at which the reed is cut, and this is done with a large knife 2 or 3 feet long, with a handle of similar length. The knife has to be razor sharp to cut the tough reed. A sedge 'cap' is then put on. The bunches of sedge are arranged so that the stems all lie one way, and after soaking with water to make them pliable, they are carried up the roof in bundles, placed across the ridge, half on each side, and fixed by rods of hazel or sallow of two lengths. The longer ones, called 'liggers' or runners, are about 4 feet 6 inches long and placed horizontally on the sedge. The shorter ones, called spars, are about 2 feet 6 inches long and are tucked under the liggers in a criss-cross or herringbone pattern. The liggers are held down by broaches which are short lengths of split hazel or sallow, twisted at the centre to form springy pegs. These are thrust into the reed, by squeezing the points together. As this is done the points open and hold tight in the sedge and reed. They are hammered home with a wooden mallet. The sedge is finally trimmed with a very sharp knife. The whole roof is then driven back with a 'legget', the face of which is covered with metal ribs or with horse nails. The final thickness of the reed is 10 to 14 inches. The liggers and spars are arranged to form attractive patterns; typical examples often seen in Norfolk are shown in Figure 42c.

Four stages in the process of reed thatching are shown in the photographs in Plate XXVIII. Plate XXVIII, 1 shows a bundle of reed being placed in position on the roof before the bond or tie is cut. Plate XXVIII, 2 shows the reed being driven with the hand after the bundle is cut so that the reed is practically in its final position. The reed is next driven up as shown in Plate XXVIII, 3, after the sway or rod has been firmly fixed, while in Plate XXVIII, 4 the sedge capping on the ridge is being trimmed.

Thatching tools are illustrated in Figure 133.

REFERENCES

(1) KÜHN, H., 1935, *Vorgeschichtliche Kunst Deutschlands*, Berlin.

(2) PAYNE, HUMFRY, (ed.), 1940, *Perachora—The Sanctuaries of Hera Akraia and Limenia*, Oxford University Press.

(3) Cottonian MSS. British Museum, Aug. A X fol 416.

(4) BOSWELL, JAMES, 1773, *Tour to the Hebrides.*

(5) HENNELL, T. B., 1931–2, 'Men of Straw: an account of surviving straw handicraft', *Transactions* of the Newcomen Society, XII.

(6) BEDE, *Opera*, Book I, 37.

(7) BEDE, *Opera*, Book III, 10.

(8) YURCHENKO, P. G., 1944, 'Narodnoe Zilische Ukraine gosudarstenoye', *Artchitekturnoye Izdatelvsto Akademii Arkhitekurni*, Moscow.

8

Burnt Brick (I)

THERE ARE MANY kinds of clayey material suitable for making bricks and tiles. They may be almost pure and plastic clays, products of the natural decay and disintegration of igneous rock and shale, or they may be alluvial and wind-blown materials with appreciable amounts of sand and silt. The best materials for brickmaking are often this latter type with up to 30 per cent of sand and silt, as the presence of sand in particular reduces the shrinkage that occurs when the plastic clays are burned. Clays are composed principally of hydrated oxides of aluminium and iron, and hydrated silicates of aluminium, but may also contain impurities such as humus, calcium carbonate, pyrites, and gypsum.

Some clays have been transported great distances by water, glaciation, or wind, and re-deposited in river valleys, and may in the process have become contaminated. For example, the alluvial clay that has for many centuries been used for brickmaking in Iraq and Persia is very silty, containing not only water-borne materials carried down the great rivers Tigris and Euphrates and their tributaries, but also wind-blown sand and limestone dust. The presence of this limestone, or calcium carbonate, is mainly responsible for the familiar cream and beige colour of the bricks. There is also an appreciable amount of gypsum or calcium sulphate brought down from the interior and re-deposited in the clay. This gypsum is undesirable as it subsequently leads to efflorescence on the face of the brickwork, and may even cause the bricks themselves to crack. The local people have always appreciated these possible defects and have been careful in their choice of clay, avoiding those clays with an excessive quantity of gypsum. It occurs in crystal form, often in nodules, and can be felt when the clay is kneaded in the hand. Only the weathered, and in consequence less contaminated, clay within a foot or so of the surface is used. It is thoroughly mixed and left exposed for up to two weeks depending on the weather and time of year. Water is then added, the clay well kneaded in the hands, any nodules of gypsum crystals being removed at the same time, and the clay formed to shape in wooden moulds. The bricks, which measure 9 inches square and 2 inches in thickness, are laid flat on the ground to dry for three days and then are stacked on edge for a further five days, after which they are transferred to the kilns for firing. Tests by the author in Southern Persia showed that whereas surface clay produced a sound brick when fired at

950°C., that of clay taken from 2 feet down and containing more gypsum was of poor quality and fissured.

The colour and texture of bricks depends on the iron oxide impurities in the clay, and on the conditions of firing. Products of many shades of colour can often be produced from one site. This was demonstrated by tests on a kiln site at East Runton in Norfolk[1] where products ranging from cream, pink, red, purple, and grey to black were made.

The majority of clays for brickmaking, however, burn to a red colour when fired at between 900° and 1000°C., in an *oxidizing* atmosphere. Above this temperature the colour often changes to darker red or purple, then to brown or grey at about 1200°C. Some clays cannot be heated to such a high temperature as this as they may melt. Under-fired material may be pink or pale dull brown and of poor durability. In a *reducing* atmosphere in which the supply of oxygen is restricted or cut off, for example by reducing the draught through the kilns, purple-brown or bluish bricks, often with black cores, are produced. The effect of a high iron content in the clay is to produce ferric oxide in an oxidizing atmosphere, making the brick salmon pink in colour at 900°C. and darker red or reddish brown at 1100°C., and ferrous oxide and ferrosic oxide in a reducing atmosphere, making a bluish brick. When lime or chalk is present in addition to iron in the clay, calcium ferrite, which is green, and ferric oxide, which is red, are formed in an oxidizing atmosphere. As green and red are complementary colours they tend to neutralize and cause the clay to burn to a pale cream or even a white brick. The well-known Yellow Gault bricks of Bedfordshire made from lias clay are of this type; so also are some of those from the Middle East.

When vegetable matter is present in the clay, this will burn black and the carbon so produced may be sealed in the brick, resulting in a black core; particularly so if the temperature of firing is raised too quickly, in which case an outer, relatively impervious red skin is formed which seals in the carbon. This condition is often seen in prehistoric and primitive pottery.

Bricks are burned either in heaps or clamps or in specially constructed kilns. Both methods are of great antiquity, and the basic methods have changed but little during the course of time. In clamp-burning, a foundation consisting of a layer or two of burnt brick is formed as a level site to protect the clamp from damp rising from the ground beneath. Channels may be arranged in this foundation in such a way as to form a number of fireholes or flues running the length and breadth of the clamp. These flues are filled with fuel. The green bricks, with more fuel between them, are then stacked and spaced so that the fire can penetrate throughout the whole mass. Burnt bricks and mud are laid over the top of the stack to protect it from the weather and to reduce heat loss. The clamp is set on fire and allowed to burn itself out, a process that might take several weeks.

Large kilns or clamps must have been necessary to produce the vast numbers of bricks that have been found on ancient sites. The remains of one such kiln is shown in Plate XXX. It was excavated at Lothal in the Ahmadabad district of Bombay State, India, and dates from about 2000 B.C. The Lothal culture was akin to that of Harappa and Mohenjo-Daro. The large mass of brickwork which forms the base of the clamp is intersected by a series of flues, which when excavated contained cinders and burnt clay lumps. Burning bricks in large quantities could only have been done where there was a good supply of brushwood, reeds, or other vegetable material for fuel. In many countries, as in Egypt for example, timber has always been too scarce to be used to any appreciable extent as fuel for brick-burning, and in consequence practically all the bricks made there up to Classical times were sun-baked. Bricks made from a mixture of mud and chopped straw already contained enough fuel to enable them to be burned in heaps or clamps, with perhaps a

Fig. 43. Roman brick-kiln near St Albans.

small amount of additional fuel, but the average temperature attained was probably not much more than 600°C., and the bricks as a whole were not very durable.

The second method of burning clay bricks is in up-draught kilns, in which much higher temperatures, 1000°C. or more, are obtained. The quality of material produced, being vitrified or partially so, is of much higher quality, more durable, and more resistant to the penetration of water. The kilns consist of two chambers, one above the other, the lower in which the fuel is burned, and the upper, the oven, in which the products are stacked for firing. A very early example was excavated at Khafaje[2] dating from the third millennium B.C. It was roughly circular in plan with four flues beneath the oven floor, and was very similar in construction to the up-draught kilns used by the Romans two thousand years later.

A reconstruction of a Roman brick-kiln of this type is shown in Figure 43. It is based on one of middle second century date excavated by the author near St Albans.[3] The structure, composed of pieces of brick and tile bonded with clay, was built below the natural level of the ground. In this way the structure was solid and better able to withstand the stresses set up in it by the great heat, and the heat losses from the kiln were greatly reduced. As the level of the oven floor was approximately the same as that of the ground, the stacking of bricks in the oven was easy. The kiln, as was usual, was built on the windward slope of a hill and the fire tunnel was lengthened to increase the draught. The oven floor, built of clay and tile fragments, had vent holes by means of which the hot gases could be drawn upwards from the flues below. The oven had straight-sided walls and, as is customary in the Middle East to this day, the products to be fired would have been surrounded and covered by pieces of burnt brick and tile and smeared with clay, to protect the new products from the weather, and to prevent the heat from escaping too quickly.

A fine series of Roman tile-kilns, dating between A.D. 90 and 150, at Holt, in Denbighshire,[4] were operated by the 20th Roman Legion and bricks made there bore the legion stamp. Precisely similar kilns, but larger in size, are still operated in the Middle East.

Once the art of pottery firing had become established it was not long before other simple products like tiles, drain pipes, and troughs were made. Being vitrified they were impervious to water. They were, however, costly to make and in consequence remained comparatively rare until larger kilns were built, and the products were only used in damp situations for floors and foundations, at the base of sun-dried brick walls, or as an external veneer to it for weather protection. By the end of the third millennium B.C. much building was carried out in Sumerian cities such as Erech, Eridu, Lagash, and Ur, with kiln-baked bricks. The bricks were of the plano-convex type 8 to 11 inches long (occasionally up to 13½ inches long) by 6 to 6¾ inches wide and 1¼ to 2½ inches thick (occasionally up to 3 inches thick), with characteristic finger impressions on the upper surface. The camber on the convex surface was about ⅝ inch. Sometimes the bricks were trapezoidal, about 11 inches long, 6 inches wide at one end and 4¾ to 5 inches wide at the other. These had a finger impression on the surface. Equally large cities such as Harappa and Mohenjo-Daro also used vast quantities of burnt brick, and many houses there were built on platforms of brick to raise the floors above flood level.

The Babylonians and Assyrians attained a high degree of proficiency in brickwork and a particularly fine example of the skilful use of burnt brick comes from Nimrud where Professor Mallowan[5] excavated a superbly built well just over 83 feet deep. Many of the bricks were inscribed with the name of Assurnasir-pal (883–859 B.C.). Burnt bricks during this period varied from 12 to 18 inches square (occasionally up to 24 inches square) and 2 to 3¼ inches thick. Perhaps the best example of all is the famous Ishtar Gate in Babylon built by Nebuchadnezzar II (604–562 B.C.), which led to his palace. It was faced with kiln-baked bricks bedded in bitumen. What remains of this wonderful structure is shown in Plate XXIX; of particular beauty are the animals moulded in relief with bricks made for the purpose (Figure 44). Nebuchadnezzar records that the earlier brickwork at Babylon built by his father Nabopolassar, did not resist the waters of the Euphrates, so he rebuilt it with burnt brick bedded in bitumen. A translation[6] of an inscription left by Nebuchadnezzar which records some of his building activities reads:

> In Babil, my favourite city that I love, was the palace, the house, the marvel of mankind, the centre of the land, the dwelling of majesty, upon the Babil place in Babil, from Imgur-Bel to the eastern canal Libil-Higalla; from the bank of the Euphrates to Aiburshabu, which Nabopolassar, King of Babylon, my father, my begetter, built of *crude bricks*, and dwelt in it. In consequence of high waters, its foundations had become weak, and owing to

Fig. 44. Glazed brick panel from the Processional Street at Babylon; Nebuchadnezzar II, end of the seventh century B.C.

> the filling up of the streets of Babil, the gateway of that palace had become too low. I tore down its walls of *dried bricks*, and laid its cornerstone bare, and reached the depth of the waters. Facing the water I laid its foundation firmly, and raised it mountain high with *bitumen and burnt brick*. Mighty cedars I caused to be laid down at length for its roofing. . . . For protection, I built two massive walls of *asphalt and brick*, 490 ells beyond Nimitte-Bel. Between them I erected a structure of bricks on which I built my kingly dwelling of *asphalt and bricks*. This I surrounded with a massive wall of *asphalt and burnt bricks*, and made upon it a lofty foundation for my royal dwelling of *asphalt and burnt bricks*.

Marking bricks with a distinctive stamp or inscription had been practised in Mesopotamia from the third millennium B.C. Numerous examples can be seen in the British Museum. They often bear the name of a particular king and give an inscription relating to the particular building in which they were to be used, or a record of some important event. A brick of Sin Gashid, King of Erech, records the building of his palace in that city (*c.* 2400 B.C.); another, of Ur-Nammu, King of Ur, records the building of a Temple for Nannar the moon god and the fortifications of the city of Ur (*c.* 2300 B.C.); another, of Samsi-Adad, Governor of Assyria, records the building of a temple to Ashur in the city of Ashur (*c.* 1700 B.C.); one (Plate XXXI) of Adad-Nirari I, King of Assyria, is from the quay wall which he built along the river Tigris in the city of Ashur (*c.* 1300 B.C.); another (Plate XXXII) is stamped with the name and titles of Nebuchadnezzar II, King of Babylon (604–562 B.C.) and of his father, Nabopolassar, and another (Plate XXXIII) of Cyrus the Great, King of Persia and of Babylon, celebrating his universal conquests and his peaceful rule (539–529 B.C.). There are many more, each recording in permanent manner some vital scrap of history. These inscribed bricks were laid in the foundations of buildings, or in pavements.

Both the Babylonians and the Assyrians from the ninth to the sixth century B.C. made patterned bricks and wall tiles with coloured glazes, and the Palace of the Achaemenid Kings of Persia at Susa had brick friezes decorated in relief in this manner. A particularly fine example is the 'Frieze of the Archers' from Susa, dating from about 500 B.C., depicting figures of the royal bodyguard (frontispiece), now in the Louvre, Paris. A figure from this frieze is in the British Museum, London.

The technique of decorating brickwork died out after the eastern conquests of Alexander the Great in the fourth century B.C., and neither the Greeks nor the Romans made use of decorated glazed bricks and tiles.

Burnt brick did not appear in Greece before the middle of the fourth century B.C., and was then used only rarely. As in Babylonia, the first burnt-clay products were the more specialized forms such as roof tiling and antefixes. Burnt bricks followed in Hellenistic times. The earliest burnt-brick constructions in Italy were probably the Etruscan walls at Arezzo. Up to the second century B.C. unburnt brick only had been used and although kiln-burnt brick was used in Rome in the Sullan period (138–78 B.C.) it did not become common until about the time of Julius Caesar. Here again, roof tiles of burnt clay seem to have established themselves before burnt-clay bricks. The waterproofing of roofs seemed to be a more urgent requirement than the protection of walls. Even broken pieces of roof tiles were always useful and were repeatedly re-used in wall construction, either in association with or instead of sun-dried bricks. The tiles were generally laid in the wall with a flange, measuring approximately 17 inches long and 1½ inches thick, exposed on the surface of the wall. In due course the walling bricks, the *lydium* and the *sesquipedales*, were made of similar length and thickness to match this existing work. It is not easy when looking at a Roman wall to distinguish between re-used roofing tiles and the true bricks. Rarely were walls made entirely of brick, but generally the brick was used as a thin facing or veener to a concrete backing (Figure 45a). In Rome itself there was a marked preference for bricks of triangular shape, perhaps for reasons of economy, and they were in common use by the time of Emperor Claudius in the first century A.D. They were used in the manner shown in Figure 45b with the apex of each brick embedded in the concrete. Occasionally the triangular bricks were reversed as shown in Figure 45c to produce a textured finish to the wall. This can be seen at the Basilica of Constantine in Rome. The triangular brick rarely appears in the Western Empire where the square and rectangular bricks, either whole or in broken pieces, were sometimes used with broken roofing

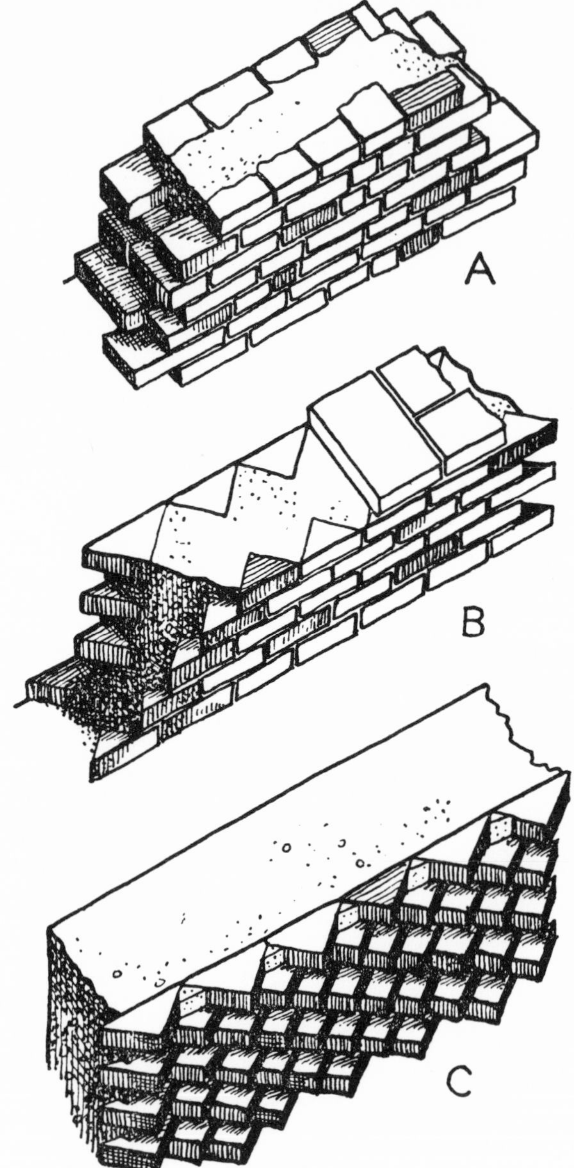

Fig. 45. Brick-faced walls of the Roman period.

tiles for the facing of walls. Broken material was re-used again and again until the end of the Empire.

The lime concrete in the interior of the walls hardened very slowly, and to reduce the load on it as much as possible during construction, bonding courses of rectangular brick were inserted every 3 feet or so to span across from one brick facing to the other. It was these brick facings which carried the main load during the construction period. The bonding courses also had the added advantage of providing a good level surface on which to build the next section of the wall. They were also used, alternating with courses of squared stone, in walling known as *opus mixtum*, a type which became very common in the third and fourth centuries A.D. In arch construction also bricks were used as a veneer to the concrete core, and were usually only narrow strips embedded in the concrete for a

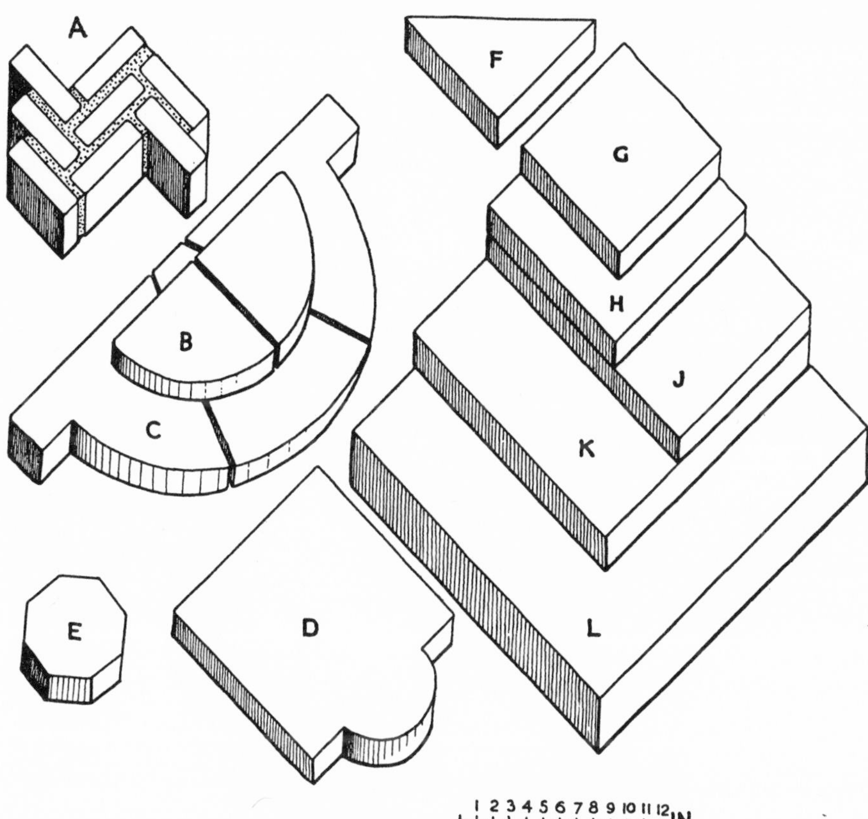

Fig. 46. Various types of Roman bricks.

few inches. Again, whole rectangular bricks were inserted at intervals to provide a more efficient bond between the brick veneer and the concrete.

The earlier brickwork in Rome was generally of a much better quality than the later, the mortar joints being much thinner in relation to the brick thickness. From the middle of the first century B.C. to the middle of the first century A.D., for example, the thickness of joint varied up to one half of that of the brick, the brickwork being very neatly laid with close joints. By A.D. 200 the joint often increased to about three-quarters of the brick thickness, and by A.D. 300 it is not unusual to find the mortar joint as thick as the brick. This was largely due to the increasing re-use of brick and tile in wall construction, and the incorporation of broken rubble in the mortar, generally leading, as it did in other parts of the Roman Empire, to coarser and more irregular work.

It is in Roman times that the size of bricks became more standardized, but there were many different shapes for special purposes. Some are shown in Figure 46, but it is not possible to give very precise measurements. Shrinkage of clay on burning can be as much as 10 per cent or more of its original volume depending on the characteristics of the clay and on the temperature of burning, and bricks of somewhat varying sizes are therefore often produced from the same kiln depending on their position in the kiln during burning.

Type A is a small brick used for floors; Type B are sectors of various angles for constructing columns; Types C and D are for making half columns; Type E, an octagonal brick for constructing small pillars; Type F, triangular tiles (*lateres trigones*) popular in Rome for wall facings; Type G, small bricks about 8 inches square (*laterculi besales*) for building pillars; Type H, tiles of 'four palms' square (*tetradoron*); Type J, rectangular bricks, very common in the Western Empire (*lydium*, the prototype of which may have been the much earlier Minoan brick which was approximately the same size in plan but twice as thick); Type K, square bricks a foot and a half square (*sequipedales*); and Type L, bricks 2 feet square (*bipedales*).

Many Roman bricks and tiles from the middle of the first century B.C. onwards were impressed by seals or trademarks or bore a decorative motif such as an animal's head, a bird, or an insect. These markings, like those on the Babylonian bricks, are of very considerable interest in that they often reveal the source from which the clay was taken, and the place and time of manufacture. A collection of over five thousand of these stamps was made by Gaetano Marini (*Locrizioni antiche dolari*, published under the direction of G. B. de Rossi, Rome, 1884). They ranged in date from 76 B.C. to as late as A.D. 554.

An interesting series of building tiles was found in 1957 on the site of a Roman bath building at Cottesford Place, Lincoln, in the north-eastern quarter of the Colonia (Lindum).[7] Forty-three tiles with a complete or broken stamp were found. The stamps formed part of an alphabetical series—LVLA, LVLD, LVLE, and LVLF. Presumably LVL was the manufacturer's mark and the letters A, D, E, and F the particular works or kiln from which they came. A similar series of stamps occurs on tiles found on Roman sites around Cirencester (Corinium) in Gloucestershire[8]—TPF, TPFA, TPFB, TPFC, and TPFP. This method of marking is very like the modern method used by some manufacturers who imprint not only the initial letters of the firm, for example L.B.C. for London Brick Company, but also a number which identifies the particular works whence the bricks came.

Bricks have been found in London bearing an official stamp P.P.BR.LON or variations of it (Figure 47). The exact title of the Government Department or officials concerned is in doubt, whether Publicani (tax collectors), Procuratores (financial officials) or Portitores (customs officers), but whichever it was it was abbreviated by the letter P., followed by some words such as P(rovincial) Br(itanniae) Lon(dini). The Royal Commission on Historical Monuments in its report on Roman London suggests that the stamp presumably implied that the structure for which the bricks were originally intended was the Chief Customs

Fig. 47. Roman bricks bearing official stamps.

House of Britain. Tiles were also made by various military legionary establishments at York, Caerleon, Chester, Leicester, and other places. It has already been noted that the bricks and tiles from the legionary kilns at Holt, in Denbighshire, were impressed with the mark and symbol of the 20th Legion, Legio XX Valeria Victrix. A roof tile antefix with the Legion's sign—a wild boar—is illustrated in Figure 94. A tile found in Leicester, the Roman town of Ratai Coritanorum, in 1855, bore a stamp of the Legio VIII,[9] while in the British Museum there are stamps of Legio VI which was stationed at York (Eburacum).[10] Wheeler[11] records that three or four tiles with the stamp of Legio II Augusta were found at Caerleon Castra Legionum, or legion's camp, known to the Romans as Isca Silurum.

Tiles were also made at naval establishments, particularly the forts of the Saxon Shore. Their marks vary in form (Figure 47), but they have been found at Richborough (Rutupiae), Dover (Portus Dubrae), Pevensey (Anderida), and Lympne (Portus Lemanae), and on the other side of the Channel at Boulogne and Desvres. The more usual form of stamp is CL.BR.—CL(assis) BR(itannica)—, the British Fleet, but other forms occur, such as CLAS. and CLASIS BRIT. Tiles made by naval establishments on the Gaulish coast were stamped CL.SAM.—CL(assis) SAM(brica). They have been found in the neighbourhood of Etaples.[12]

Occasionally tiles bore an Imperial mark such as HON. AUG. ANDRIA, which occurred on a tile from Pevensey, and it seems to suggest that the fort there may have been restored after the succession of Emperor Honorius A.D. 393–423.[13]

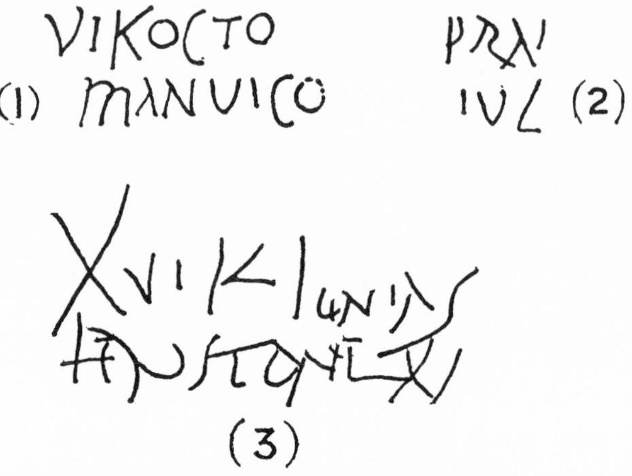

Fig. 48. Date marks on Roman tiles.

It is clear from the good quality of the Roman bricks that the clay was well prepared and very plastic. Having been moulded, the bricks were left on a bed of sand to stiffen until they could be handled into the kiln. Much might happen to them during this period. Stray animals and even human beings trespassed upon them. Occasionally their foot marks were impressed upon the bricks, as shown in Plate XXXIV, 1, 2, 3. A brick is shown in Plate XXXIV, 4 with a face drawn upon it. Sometimes the date on which the tiles were made was scratched upon the soft clay. Three examples are shown in Figure 48, recording dates in the summer and autumn, June, July, and October: (1) reads VIKOCTO MANVICO—VI K(alendas) OCTO(bres)—the 6th day before the kalendo of October, Manvico probably being the name of the maker; (2) reads PRN IVL—PR(idie) N(onas) IVL(ias) —the 6th of July;[11] and (3) reads XVI K(al) IUNIAS HRISTON LXI.[11] Another in Figure 49 has an inscription scratched with a stick, which reads AVSTALIS DIBVS XIII VAGATVR SIB COTIDIM—'Austalis has been going off by himself every day for these 13 days'. It would appear that a workman is calling attention to the continual absence of a fellow workman. A tile from

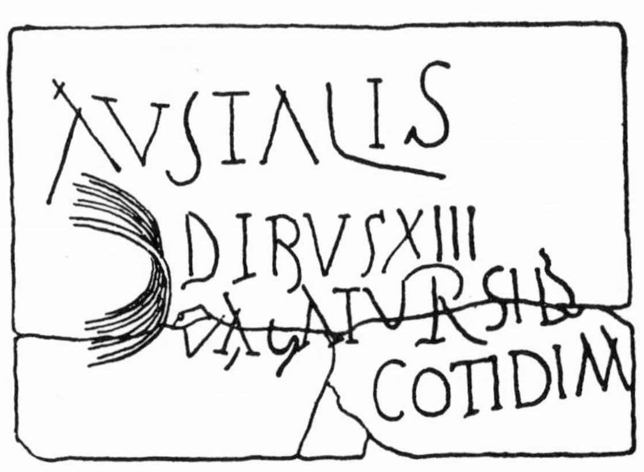

Fig. 49. Inscribed Roman tile. Guildhall Museum, London.

Silchester, now in Reading Museum, has SATIS written with a finger on it (Figure 50). SATIS—'enough'—may mean either that the brick was the last of a particular batch, or that it may have been an idle remark of the workman meaning 'I've had enough' or 'I'm fed up'.

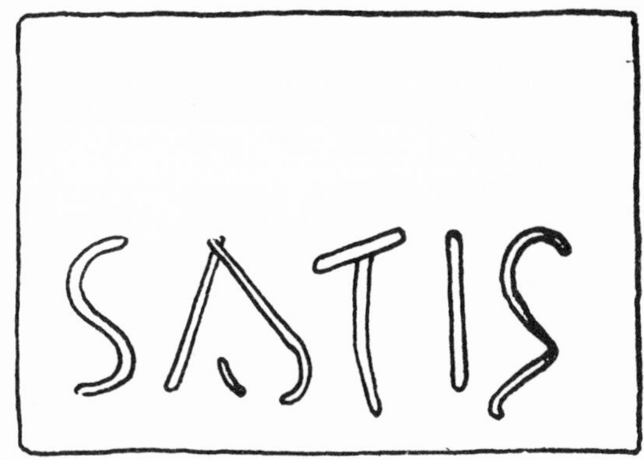

Fig. 50. Inscribed Roman tile. Reading Museum.

REFERENCES

(1) DAVEY, N., 1941, 'Pottery Kilns at East Runton, Norfolk', *Transactions* of the Norfolk and Norwich Archaeological Society, XXVII, 308–14.

(2) FRANKFORT, H., JACOBSEN, T., and PREUSSER, C., 1932, 'Tell Asmar and Khafaje—the first season's work in Eshnunna 1930–31', Chicago University Oriental Institute Communication No. 13.

(3) DAVEY, N., 1932, 'Roman Tile and Pottery Kiln, near St. Albans', *Transactions* of the St Albans and Hertfordshire Architectural and Archaeological Society, 212-14.

(4) GRIMES, W. F., 1930, 'An Aspect of the Romano-British Pottery Industry', *Y Cymmrodor*, XLI.

(5) MALLOWAN, M. E. L., *Twenty-five years of Mesopotamian Discovery (1932–1956)*, British School of Archaeology in Iraq.

(6) DELITZCH, F., 1910, 'Assurbanipal und seine Zeit', *Der Alte Orient*, Jahr 11, *1*, 24.

(7) 1958, 'Roman Britain in 1957', *Journal of Roman Studies*, XLVIII, Parts I and II, 136, 153.

(8) CLIFFORD, E. M., 1955, 'Stamped Tiles found in Gloucestershire', *Journal of Roman Studies*, XLV, Parts I and II, 68–72.

(9) HAVERFIELD, R., 1918, 'Roman Leicester', *Archaeological Journal*, LXXV.

(10) BRITISH MUSEUM, 1922, *Guide to the Antiquities of Roman Britain*, 25.

(11) WHEELER, R. E. M., 1925, *Prehistoric and Roman Wales*, Oxford University Press, 243.

(12) MOTHERSOLE, J., 1924, *The Saxon Shore*, The Bodley Head, 36.

(13) BLUMLEIN, CARL, 1926, *Bilder aus dem Römisch-Germanischen Kulturleben*, R. Oldenburg, Munich und Berlin, 47.

9

Burnt Brick (II)

In Rome a very high standard in decorative brickwork was reached in the first and second centuries A.D. and the motives and composition of classical architecture were carried out in brick and terracotta as competently as they were in stone. Special bricks were cut to the desired shapes to form elaborate cornices with dentils, ovoli, and brackets, and capitals were carved in the various orders. Bricks were selected for their colour and arranged to produce polychrome effects in yellow, red, and brown. Many exquisite examples embodying these features remain in and around Rome. The craft, however, followed the rapid decline of the Roman Empire. But in the fifth century A.D. under Byzantine influence new developments took place in decorative brickwork which were eventually to have a profound influence on medieval architecture throughout Europe. Surviving early Christian churches at Ravenna illustrate these changes. The ornamentation was much less elaborate than in the earlier brick buildings in Rome. The bricks at first were large; in the mid fifth-century Mausoleum of Galla Placidia at Ravenna, for example, they varied in size up to 16 inches long by 6 inches wide and 4 inches in thickness, but in the following century they had generally become smaller, roughly 10 inches by 5 inches by 2½ inches, as in the adjacent Basilica of San Vitale (A.D. 547) and they were to remain much this size for many years. Very simple sawtooth ornament was made by laying bricks corner to corner, few carved or moulded bricks being used. Large flat

Fig. 51. The eleventh-century apse of the Church of Santa Fosca at Torcello.

Plate XXII. Model of a building of the Han Dynasty (206 B.C.–A.D. 220) (see page 46, 155).

Plate XXIII. Pottery model of an Egyptian house of reeds and mud. At one end is the door and at the other (not visible) are two small windows. From El Amarna; Predynastic period, before 3000 B.C. (see page 49).

Plate XXIV. 'Hut-urn', house model from Königsaue, near Aschersleben; 750–400 B.C. (see pages 45, 55).

Plate XXV. 'Hut-urn', house model from Obliwitz, near Lauenburg; Iron Age (see page 55).

Plate XXVI (Above). Temporary thatching to protect the walls during the construction of a church; fifteenth century (see page 56).

Plate XXVII (Left). Pegged rope thatch on a house at Portballintrae, Antrim, Northern Ireland (see page 59).

1. Placing a bundle of reed in position on the roof before the bond, or tie, is cut.

2. Driving the reed with the hand after it has been cut so that the reed is practically in its final position.

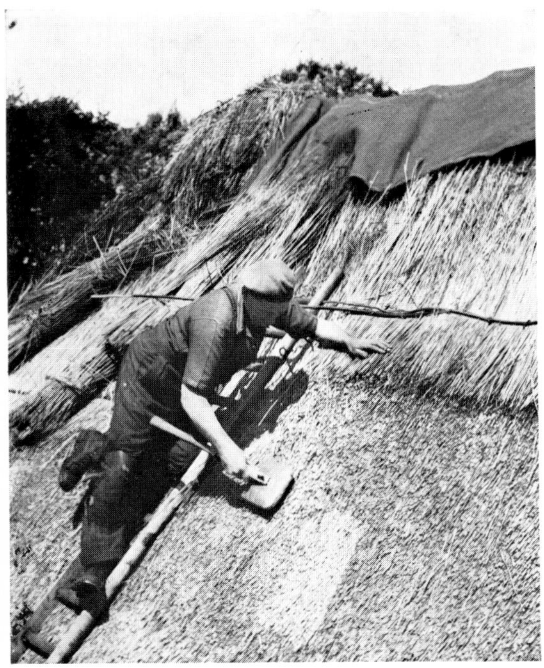

3. Driving up the reed after the sway, or rod, has been firmly fixed.

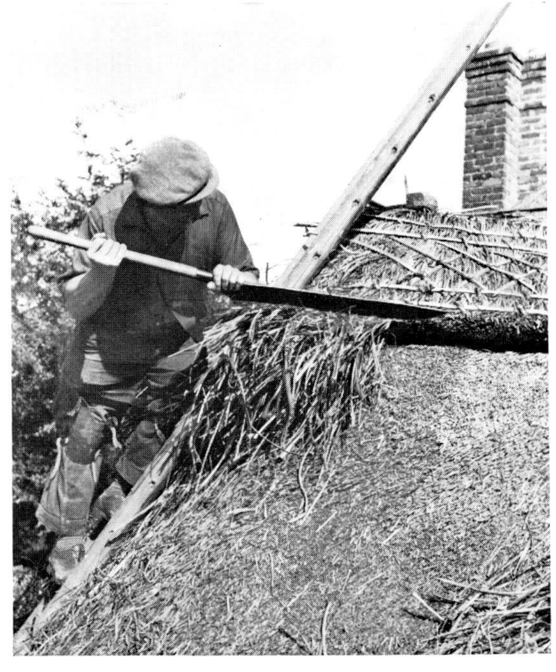

4. The sedge capping being cut and trimmed after thatching.

Plate XXVIII. Modern reed thatching technique (see page 63).

wall surfaces were often broken up with blind arches and small pendant arches, and in spite of their simplicity these modes of decoration remained distinctive features in later work. Sawtooth ornament and blind arches occur for example in the early eleventh-century apse of Santa Fosca, a church built in yellow and red bricks in Byzantine style at Torcello in Venetia. The large zigzag pattern beneath the white terracotta frieze, filled in this case with red tiles cut to shape, shown in Figure 51, is another feature which appears throughout Byzantium, as in the apse of the church of Santi Maria e Donato in the neighbouring town of Murano, in the church of the Holy Apostles at Salonika, and as far afield as Vladimir in Russia, where in the Cathedral of the Dormition (1158–61) the sawtooth ornament, the pendant and blind arches, and the zigzag ornament are all well developed features.

There is no more impressive example of the use of semicircular blind arches (Plate LIV) than in the great brick façade, over 100 feet in height, of the Sassanian Palace at Ctesiphon, near Baghdad, built in the sixth century. The Sassanians were competent builders with a capacity for combining the traditions of the past with their own ideas. Using the materials and techniques of construction that had been traditional in Iraq from Babylonian times, they seem also to have been ready to adopt ideas from others, including, it seems, the Romans, with whom they had contact and even defeated in battle. The Sassanians were themselves overwhelmed by the Arabs, and Ctesiphon fell in A.D. 637 and ceased to be the administrative centre. The Caliphate, however, passed in A.D. 750 to the Abbasid dynasty which lasted until its overthrow by the Mongols in the thirteenth century. From this period comes some of the finest decorated brickwork ever produced. Plate XXXV shows for example one of the cupolas in the Abbasid Palace at Baghdad, erected in the twelfth century A.D., richly decorated with

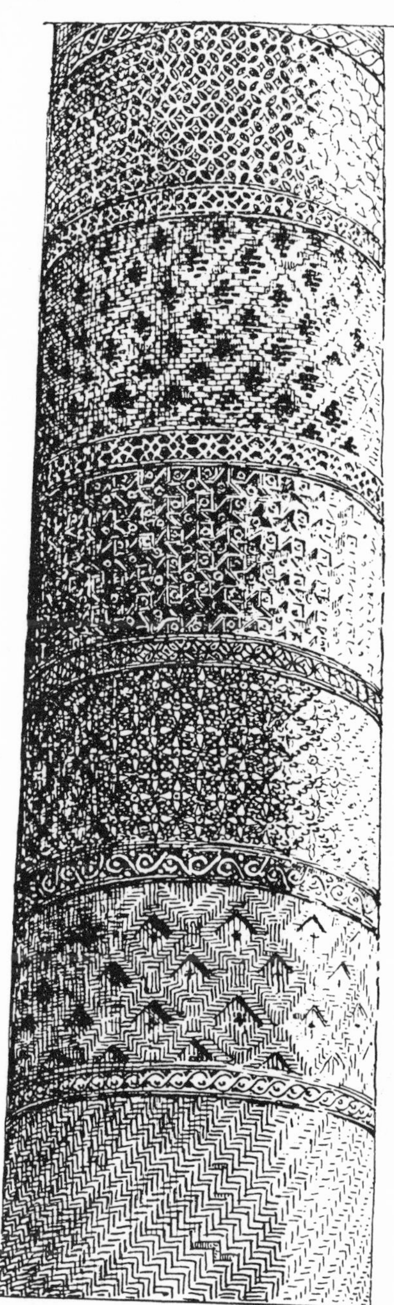

Fig. 52. Part of the minaret of the Great Mosque in Mosul, built in A.D. 1172.

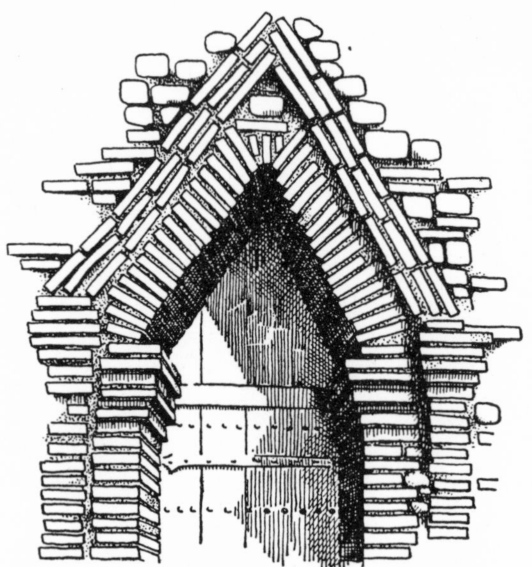

Fig. 53. Saxon doorway built with Roman bricks, in the tower of Trinity Church, Colchester, Essex.

carved and ornamental bricks arranged in pendants and squinches. The building has now been restored by the Department of Antiquities of Iraq and houses an important collection of Islamic works of art. During the last phase of the Abbasid dynasty, an independent dynasty, the Atabegs, emerged in Northern Iraq, centred on Mosul. They carried the ornamentation of brickwork to a peak of perfection, and the minaret of the Great Mosque in that town, built by Nur-ad-Din Zangi in A.D. 1172 is a superb example of their work. Part of this minaret is shown in Figure 52.

With the collapse of the Western Roman Empire brickmaking virtually ceased in Europe and Britain. The manufacture of burnt bricks was a lengthy process which could only be carried out efficiently under settled social and political conditions, in which buildings of a permanent character needing the products could be erected. The state of unrest in the West gave little encouragement therefore to the craft, but none the less it is highly improbable that the 'know-how' of brickmaking was ever entirely lost, as is so often assumed. Only in a few small townships, however, was there any incentive to erect buildings of a permanent character, and what few bricks were required could be gleaned from the nearby sites deserted by the Romans. Two of many examples have been taken to illustrate this. The first is the Saxon doorway in the tower of Trinity Church, Colchester, Essex, in Figure 53, built with bricks and tiles recovered from the Roman city of Camulodunum, upon which it stands. The triangular arch is characteristic of Saxon work. The second example is the Norman Tower of St Albans Cathedral in Hertfordshire, in Figure 54, a massive structure built of bricks and tiles from the adjacent Roman city of Verulamium. Ealdred and Ealmer, who were abbots, towards the close of the tenth century organized the systematic break-up of the structural remains of the abandoned Roman city, to gather together sufficient material with which to construct a new abbey church. The new church was not started, however, until after the Norman Conquest, when Paul de Caen was appointed abbot in 1077; it was consecrated in 1115. The eastern bays of the nave, the tower, and the transepts remain as important English examples of Norman work in brick. The fine west front and nave arcades of the Augustinian priory of St Botoph, Colchester, are also excellent examples of the re-use of Roman bricks and tiles in the twelfth century.

At some time in the next hundred years brickmaking started again in East Anglia, and some of the earliest brickwork of this revival is seen in St Nicholas's Chapel at Little Coggeshall Abbey (*c.* 1220). The bricks are quite different in shape from the Roman ones, but are generally larger than the Flemish type that was to follow, varying from $10\frac{1}{4}$ to $12\frac{1}{2}$ inches in length, 5 to 6 inches in width, and $1\frac{3}{4}$ to $2\frac{3}{4}$ inches in thickness. This large type of brick is found in various buildings in East Anglia up to the early part of the sixteenth century, when it was known as the 'Great' brick, and occasionally may occur up to 15 inches in length and up to $7\frac{1}{2}$ inches in width and correspondingly thick, as in the walls flanking the gateway at Waltham Abbey, Essex (*c.* 1370).

Fig. 54. The Norman tower of St Albans Cathedral, built with Roman bricks.

It may be significant that many bricks already in use in Northern Italy in the late eleventh century, as in the church of Santa Fosca at Torcello, fell within these limits of size. No doubt the very close intercourse in trade between the Venetians and the Flemings in the thirteenth century fostered the spread of the arts and crafts and there was a great deal of copying. Bruges was the great port uniting East and West. Motley[1] has pointed out that—'The trade of the Netherlands with the Mediterranean and the East was mainly through this favoured city of Bruges, which, already in the thirteenth century, had risen to the first rank in the commercial world. It was the resting-place for the Lombards and other Italians, the great entrepôt for their merchandize. It now became, in addition, the great market place for English wool, and the woollen fabrics of all the Netherlands, as well as for the drugs and spices of the East. It had, however, by no means reached its apogee, but was to culminate with Venice, and to sink to her decline. . . .'

Perhaps it is not surprising therefore, that as a result of this close intercourse between Venice, Flanders, and England the craft of brickmaking and other building crafts, and the use of a more or less uniform size of brick, eventually became common throughout practically the whole of Europe before the end of the thirteenth century from North Italy to the Low Countries and East Anglia.

The Hanseatic League started as an Association of merchants and before the end of the thirteenth century had become a federation of the great cities of the Low Countries and of the Baltic States. Many English ports joined the League and trading settlements were established at York, Hull, Ipswich, Norwich, Lynn, Boston, Yarmouth, London, and

Bristol. There was an influx of immigrants and new buildings were needed for warehouses and homes and it seems that in the first instance the settlers imported bricks from the Low Countries. It is recorded that great quantities of Flemish bricks were imported for use at the Tower of London in 1278.[2] Some bricks may have come to East Anglia in ships as ballast, in the same way that many Dutch bricks reached English ports and those of the

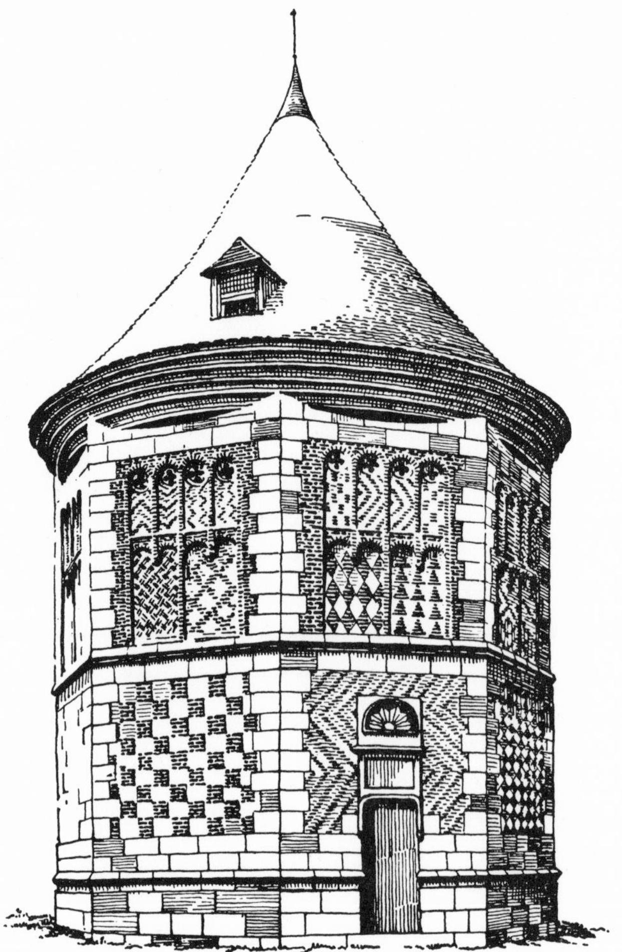

Fig. 55. Fifteenth-century dovecot, or *colombier*, at Boos, near Rouen, France.

New World in later years. It would not have been long before the new settlers and agents of the League started the manufacture of bricks to the sizes to which they were accustomed; probably about the middle of the fourteenth century. These so-called Flemish bricks were smaller than the local ones already in use, and varied roughly from 8 to $9\frac{3}{4}$ inches in length, from $3\frac{3}{4}$ to $4\frac{3}{4}$ inches in width, and $1\frac{3}{4}$ to $2\frac{1}{2}$ inches in thickness, and this type, known in the sixteenth century as the 'Statute' brick to distinguish it from the 'Great' brick, has remained more or less standard in Britain. One of the early examples of the use of Flemish bricks in East Anglia is at Little Wenham Hall, in Suffolk (*c.* 1260–80).

There was a marked development in brick building in England during the second quarter of the fifteenth century, in which period various castles were built embodying many features which their owners had evidently appreciated during their campaigns in France. Caister, Tattershall, and Hurstmonceux, all fine examples of brick buildings, were built between 1424 and 1449. Disputes between England and the Continental Hanseatic League cities in the middle of the fifteenth century did not encourage potential settlers to England and there appears to have been a slackening off in domestic building. However, the quarrels were patched up in 1474, prosperity returned to East Anglia, and almost immediately building received a great impetus. Certainly during the next fifty years many manor houses and churches were erected, mostly by wealthy merchants.

A new feature appeared however. It was the decoration of brickwork with diaper patterns in relief, a fashion that did not come from the Low Countries but from France, where it had already been set. Elaborate diapers were formed by darker vitrified bricks laid as headers and with bricks of various colours. A good example of this work is shown in Figure 55; it is the fifteenth-century dovecot, or colombier, at Boos Manor near Rouen. Some of the patterns used in France and copied in England are similar to some which occur throughout the Islamic world, and it may be that contacts with Islamic art and architecture across the Spanish border may have had some influence on the adoption of this type of decoration. The Bishop's Palace, Hatfield (*c.* 1480), has some of the earliest English examples of diaper work on its walls, but it is seen more highly developed in buildings of a slightly later date; at Layer Marney Towers, Essex (1500–25), Hampton Court Palace (1515–30), and Compton Wynyates in Warwickshire (1520). This period is also characterized by magnificent chimneys in carved and moulded brickwork, often of great beauty. The example shown in Figure 56 is of a pair of chimney shafts at St Osyth's Priory, Essex (1475). The chimney stack below is noteworthy as it shows the type of chequer pattern in knapped flint and ashlar used on the rest of the beautiful

Fig. 56. Chimney shafts at St Osyth's Priory, Essex; 1475.

gatehouse, and seen in many other East Anglian buildings. Another excellent example is the façade of the Guildhall at Kings Lynn. Tudor brickwork is characterized by rather thick mortar joints, as shown in the example in Plate XXXVI from Hampton Court Palace (*c.* 1520). The bricks also tend to be rather thin, in this case about 2¼ inches. This brickwork should be compared with that shown in Plate XXXVII, also from Hampton Court Palace, but the work of Sir Christopher Wren about 1690. The bricks are beautifully made, rather thicker, 2½ inches, than the Tudor ones, and laid with thin joints. Good examples of rubbed work by Wren also occur in garden niches at Hampton Court

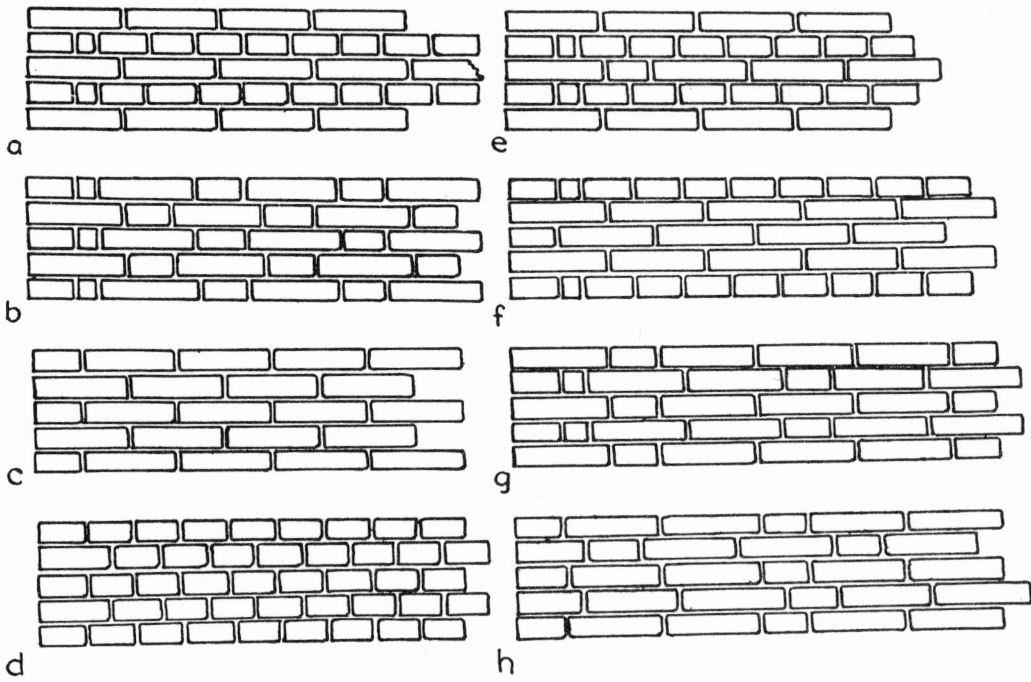

Fig. 57. Brickwork bonds: (a) English Bond. (b) Flemish Bond. (c) Stretcher Bond. (d) Header Bond. (e) English Cross Bond. (f) English Garden Bond. (g) Flemish Garden Bond. (h) Monk Bond.

Palace. This is probably the finest period of English brickwork. The bricks are laid in Flemish Bond with alternate headers and stretchers in the same course, which was introduced into English work about sixty years earlier. Kew Palace, built in 1631 by Samuel Fortrey and known for some long time as the Dutch House, is one of the earliest English examples of brickwork in the Flemish Bond. For the previous two hundred years or so Old English Bond of alternate rows of headers and stretchers was usual, and this seems to have been copied from France and is seen in the English castles already referred to, at Tattershall, Caister, and Hurstmonceux. Other different kinds of bond used in English brickwork are shown in Figure 57.

There are several other brickwork bonds less common than the English and Flemish.

For example, the English Cross Bond is similar to the English Bond, except that the stretchers break out, and is very like the Dutch Bond. The English Garden Bond has three courses of stretchers to one course of headers. The Flemish Garden Wall Bond, or Sussex Bond, has three stretchers then one header in every course. The Stretcher Bond has all bricks laid as stretchers, with the exception that there is a header at the quoins in alternate courses. Monk Bond has two stretchers then one header in every course. The Header Bond has all bricks laid as headers except in alternate courses at the quoins.

Numerous references have been made to the size of bricks at various periods in England but attempts to date buildings by the size and shape of bricks alone have not always been very successful. However, it is possible to make some rather broad generalizations. Up to the end of the twelfth century Roman bricks and tiles were re-used, and few, if any, bricks were made. From the early thirteenth century up to the early part of the fifteenth century locally made bricks of very variable size were used—10 to 15 inches long, 5 to $7\frac{1}{2}$ inches wide, and $1\frac{3}{4}$ to $3\frac{1}{4}$ inches thick. Flemish-type bricks were introduced about the third quarter of the thirteenth century, firstly by importation from the Low Countries and soon by local manufacture, the size being roughly, as already stated, about 8 to $9\frac{3}{4}$ inches long, $3\frac{3}{4}$ to $4\frac{3}{4}$ inches wide and $1\frac{3}{4}$ to $2\frac{1}{2}$ inches thick. From the fifteenth century onwards a relatively small quantity of Dutch bricks, about 6 to $8\frac{1}{4}$ inches long, 3 to $3\frac{3}{4}$ inches wide, and $1\frac{3}{8}$ to $1\frac{3}{4}$ inches thick, were imported. The imposition of a tax on bricks in the reign of George III (1784) had two effects, firstly, an increase in the size of the brick, up to roughly 10 inches by 5 inches by 3 inches or more, as a large brick paid the same duty as a small one, and, secondly, an increase in the use of weather tile to simulate brick-work. This increase in size was short-lived for in 1803 the duty on bricks having a volume greater than 150 cubic inches was made double (10*s.* per thousand) that of bricks with less than this volume (5*s.* per thousand). This discouraged the use of large bricks and the tendency then was to restrict the size to approximately 9 by $4\frac{1}{2}$ by 3 inches, or 121 cubic inches, well inside the limit of 150. This also allowed the manufacturers some tolerance, and the occasional brick, probably under-burnt, of about 10 inches by 5 inches by 3 inches, would escape the duty. However, in 1850 the duty was repealed. Well-fired bricks would be less than 9 by $4\frac{1}{2}$ by 3 inches and nowadays the accepted British Standard size is $8\frac{3}{4}$ ($\pm\frac{1}{4}$) inches by $4\frac{3}{16}$ ($\pm\frac{5}{32}$) inches by $2\frac{5}{8}$ ($\pm\frac{5}{32}$) inches or $2\frac{7}{8}$ ($\pm\frac{5}{32}$) inches, practically identical in size with the Flemish bricks imported seven hundred years ago. The brick tax of 1784 encouraged the use of tiles which, when hung on a vertical surface, had the appearance of normal brickwork. They had already been used before the tax was imposed and were variously described as 'mathematical', 'geometrical' or 'rebate' tiles. Being much lighter than bricks, they evaded the tax but on the repeal of the latter in the middle of the nineteenth century their use virtually ceased. One type is illustrated in Figure 58. Hussey[3] records their use by Soane at Sidney Lodge, Hamble, in 1786, by Wyatt at Belmont, Kent, in 1792, and by Holland for Brighton Pavilion in 1786 to 1788. Nathaniel Lloyd[4] records the use of this type of tile before the brick tax, in about 1755 at Lamb House, Rye, Sussex.

In America the common brick is rather smaller than the British Standard Brick, being about 8 inches by 4 inches by $2\frac{1}{4}$ inches. According to Harrington[5] it would appear that the first extensive use of bricks in the New World was at the settlement of Henricopolis on Farrar's Island in the James River, near the present city of Richmond. There, in 1611, Sir Thomas Dale laid out a town of three streets with several houses, the first storeys of which were of brick made on the spot by brickmakers brought from England by Sir Thomas Gates. There also had been brickmakers, limemakers, bricklayers, and other tradesmen at Sir Walter Raleigh's earlier settlements on Roanoke Island. In Plate XXXVIII is shown one of the two seventeenth-century kilns excavated by Harrington at Jamestown, Virginia. The kiln is similar in construction to the up-draught, or 'Scotch kiln' then in use in England, and the brick sizes were the same, $8\frac{1}{2}$ to $9\frac{1}{2}$ inches long by 4 to $4\frac{5}{8}$ inches wide, and $2\frac{1}{8}$ to $2\frac{5}{8}$ inches thick. He records that the fire chambers extended straight back to the rear wall of the kiln, being the same width as the arches. The sun-dried bricks were stacked on permanent benches, or bases, between the fire chambers. Such bases of well-burned bricks were often used to prevent moisture rising up into the bottom courses of the charge and damaging these bricks before they were burned. The benches of the kiln were three bricks wide, the bricks laid on edge, end to end, and like the walls, without mortar. The floors of the fire chambers were well-packed, natural clay, burned deep red to a depth of several inches. These floors were about an inch below the bottoms of the permanent bench bases, or roughly level with the bottom of the exterior walls. On each of these bases were found from one to five layers of incompletely fired bricks. The bottom four layers were stacked on edge at a slight angle. Corbelling over the fire chambers began with the fifth layer, which, unlike the first four, was laid at right angles to the chambers. Each corbelled course overhung almost half a brick, which would have formed a complete arch with the third course. It would appear therefore, that the fire chamber was seven bricks high, including the permanent base, or approximately 28 inches, which is roughly the same height as the arched openings in the front wall. There was no archaeological evidence indicating the original height of the kiln, but it was assumed to be between 12 and 15 feet high, the same as the contemporary English kilns.

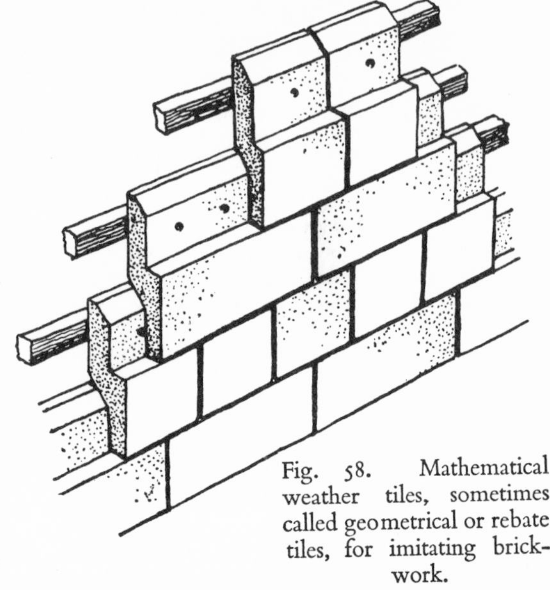

Fig. 58. Mathematical weather tiles, sometimes called geometrical or rebate tiles, for imitating brickwork.

It is interesting to note that the roofing tiles made in the kilns at Jamestown were also the same size as the English ones, 10 by $6\frac{1}{8}$ by $\frac{5}{8}$ inch, or very close to the statute size of 1477.[6]

REFERENCES

(1) MOTLEY, J. L., 1906, *The Rise of the Dutch Republic*, Dent, I, 41.

(2) Exch. K.R. Acts 467, 7 quoted by SALZMAN, L. F., 1952, *Building in England*, Oxford University Press, 140.

(3) HUSSEY, CHRISTOPHER, 1956, *English Country Houses—Mid-Georgian, 1760–1800*, Country Life.

(4) LLOYD, NATHANIEL, 1928, *A History of English Brickwork*, H. G. Montgomery, London, 244.

(5) HARRINGTON, J. C., Jan. 1950, 'Seventeenth Century Brickmaking and Tilemaking', *The Virginia Magazine of History and Biography*, LVIII, No. 1.

(6) 17 Ed. IV, c.4, 1477. See NATHANIEL LLOYD, 1928, *A History of English Brickwork*, H. G. Montgomery, London, 45.

10

Terracotta

TERRACOTTA MEANS LITERALLY *baked earth.* In material substance therefore, terracotta products differ but little, if at all, from other ceramic bodies—pottery, bricks, and tile. The main difference between these lies in the method of fabrication; they are modelled or sculptured from clay most carefully chosen and prepared, and every precaution is taken before and during burning to prevent distortion. This requires complete collaboration at all stages between the artist-modeller and the burner.

Unglazed terracotta is fired once, and glazed terracotta is fired once after the glazing mixture has been applied. If the terracotta is fired twice, firstly the body at a high temperature, and secondly the body and the glaze at a low temperature, the product is called faience (or fayence). The term faience is, however, a general one applied to materials of a pottery or porcellanic character, and composed of earthenware covered with an impervious glaze or enamel. True porcelains, like those developed in China and later in Meissen, produced their own glaze by fusion of the material at a high temperature, but the process called for great skill and very precise furnace control.

Unglazed terracotta varies greatly in quality, texture, and colour, depending on the particular clay used and on the temperature of firing, which for good quality ware should be in the range 1050° to 1200° C.

The majority of clays for terracotta have to be weathered to break them down; some may even require exposure to frost to do this satisfactorily. This process of weathering increases the plasticity of the clay considerably, and in doing so not only converts deleterious materials such as iron pyrites to the less objectionable hydrated ferric oxide, but also reduces alkalis, assists in the removal of soluble salts, and decomposes some of the constituent minerals such as felspar and mica.

Clay shrinks very considerably on drying and burning—often as much as 15 per cent—much too much to produce satisfactory terracotta. By adding suitable material called *grog*, which is usually fired clay or even sand, the shrinkage can be reduced to half this amount. The weathered clay and the grog are usually ground separately and then mixed in a pan mill, to produce a plastic mixture, which is then thoroughly kneaded. The primitive method was to do this by hand, but in more recent times the kneading has been done in a pugmill with revolving blades which churn the mixture and finally discharge it through an orifice, the operation often being repeated several times for important work. The mixture is then allowed to stand for some time before use, to *sour*. The old-fashioned way was to store the tempered material in a cool dark place. This souring process results in still greater plasticity, and a more intimate blending of the clay and the grog. The ideal condition is for the minute particles of grog to become thoroughly coated, or *slimed*, with the clay.

The mixture is then pressed into moulds, sometimes of burnt clay, but usually of plaster of Paris. This is done in a warmed room, and as the clay dries it shrinks slightly and comes away easily from the moulds. More thorough drying is carried out at a temperature of about 30° C., and then in a steam-heated chamber. Surface glazes, if required, are then applied. They consist of fluxes and colouring materials very finely ground and mixed with water to give a creamy consistence. Sometimes the glazes are applied after the clay has been given a preliminary light firing to a biscuit colour.

The firing process requires careful control. Unglazed ware is often fired in an *open kiln*—that is, one in which the ware is exposed to the products of combustion. Glazed ware on the other hand is protected from direct contact with the combustion products by firing in a *muffle kiln*, in which it is surrounded and protected by a muffle, or jacket. Alternatively the glazed ware can be fired in an open kiln provided it is placed within a *sagger*, a fire-clay container. A number of these saggers can be stacked one above the other. The first stage of firing is known as the *smoking period* during which the temperature is raised slowly to allow any residual free moisture in the product to be driven off gradually. This is the most critical stage since too rapid heating would result in warping and cracking. In the second stage the temperature is raised to the point where carbonaceous matter is burned off, ferrous compounds are oxidized to ferric, carbonates, if present, are decomposed, and the moisture, chemically combined with hydrated material, is driven off. In the final stage the temperature is raised to about 1000° to 1250° C. according to the type of clay, and further shrinkage takes place.

The temperature of firing and the rate and duration of heating affect the quality of the product, but the best conditions vary with different clays.[1] For some, a long heating period at a minimum temperature is preferable, for others a shorter period at a higher temperature, but generally the former is preferred.

The primitive terracotta objects of the ancient world—prehistoric and predynastic Egypt for example—were mainly small hand-modelled objects, often roughly pinched and manipulated to the desired shape. For repetitive work the original figure was first modelled in wax or clay, and from this a mould was formed by impressing clay upon it. This impressed clay mould was then baked, so that it could be used for making as many copies as were needed. Some of the earliest architectural products, however, were the Assyrian and Persian tiles and friezes like those at Susa.

Roof tiles of Ancient Greece were also of terracotta, early examples being those at the Temple of Hera at Olympia. They were flat and rectangular, almost square; there were also semi-cylindrical covering tiles and decorative end tiles, and coloured antefix ornaments of various designs, including heads and figures, but more usually in the form of palmettes. Cornices of terracotta were enriched with patterns of lotus and honeysuckle or meander designs in red, blue, brown, and yellow, while spouts to carry off the rainwater were often in the form of lions' heads. The seventh-century B.C. temple at Thermon in Acainania in Western Greece was constructed of terracotta and wood.

Fig. 59. Greek terracotta antefix from Lanuvium, Italy.

In Figure 59 is shown a very fine antefix excavated by the late Lord Savile[2] at Lanuvium in Italy, the site of a Greek colony. He considered the date of the antefix, which he presented to the British Museum, to be about 800 B.C. The hair, eyes, and eyebrows were painted brown, and the outer ornaments surrounding the head were coloured deep red and purple. Professors Dörpfeld, Graeben, Siebold, and Bowman in 1881 studied the use of terracotta in Greek buildings, particularly in Greece and Sicily, and they concluded that the difference between the early Greek and the Roman terracotta ornaments employed on roofs and exposed portions of buildings was in the manner of painting the ornaments. Whereas the Romans painted the decorations on a white ground prepared with stucco, which gave great brilliance to the colours, the Greeks laid the colours on the clay itself before the product was fired. The former method was much less satisfactory from the point of view of durability; the coloured decorations by the Greeks lasted for many centuries. Lord Savile gives as an instance of this the colours on the Geloa Treasury at Olympia (*c.* 900 B.C.). The colours in the Greek method were absorbed by the porous clay and on burning became integral with the body, but colours in the Roman method tended to flake off with the stucco undercoat.

The Etruscans became exceptionally skilled in terracotta work—their hut-urns of the third and second centuries B.C. being particularly interesting. The Romans used terracotta slabs decorated in relief for facing walls of buildings both internally and externally, but the practice seems to have been limited mostly to Rome itself. The panels measured about 18 inches by 9 to 12 inches and usually had holes through which they could be nailed to the house timbers; they often bore the name of the artist. For example, a panel in the British Museum bears the name of Marcus Antonius Epaphras. Like the Greeks before them the Romans used terracotta for many building purposes—for cornices, antefixes to mask the ends of ridges on roofs, troughlike gutters typical of Pompeian houses, and spouts ornamented with masks and animal heads for discharging rain water.

After the fall of the Roman Empire the art of making terracotta declined in Italy and elsewhere in Europe, but continued in Turkey, Persia, and countries to the east. In Europe there was a great revival in the fourteenth and fifteenth centuries, more particularly in Italy in the Po Valley and neighbouring regions, such as Pavia, Bologna, Cremona and Ferrara, and in Germany, and many beautiful examples exist in both countries.

It is to the Chinese that credit must be given for the development in the fourth and third centuries B.C. of glazed terracotta, practically a vitrified porcellanous stoneware, which was a great improvement on the earlier and more porous product. They achieved this by burning a white clay (china clay), which they called 'kaolin', and a fusible material called petuntse (china stone or felsite). By the time of the Han Dynasty (206 B.C. to A.D. 220) the craft was well established, and during the succeeding centuries the Chinese craftsmen produced some of the finest porcelain the world has ever seen. Many examples of Chinese work can be seen in the British Museum and elsewhere. The hollow brick or block shown in Plate XXXIX is in the British Museum and comes from a mortuary chamber of the Han Dynasty. It illustrates well the great skill of the craftsmen of this period; their ability to mould and fire hollow blocks as large and as finely decorated as this example is particularly noteworthy. They must be among some of the earliest hollow blocks ever made. The impressed decoration of the surfaces is excellent, and often includes representations of buildings, as the example illustrated here does.

Credit must also be given to Persian craftsmen who kept alive, through many adversities, the traditions of glazing and enamelling practised earlier by the Babylonians and Egyptians. They undoubtedly received much inspiration, however, from the Chinese, with whom they traded, and their ceramic work provides a link between Eastern and Western traditions. In turn the Islamic pottery and tiles traded in Europe influenced the work of medieval craftsmen there, and did much to encourage the development in Italy of tin-enamelled majolica ware, so named apparently after Majorca, which with Valencia and Malaga had become a centre of the Hispano-Moorish work after the invasion of Spain by the Moors about A.D. 710. Italian artists and craftsmen naturally became interested in the Spanish ware and by the fourteenth century they also were making tin-enamelled ware in Florence, but it was in the early fifteenth century under the patronage of wealthy families, particularly the Medici family, that products were eventually made comparable in quality with those from Spain.

Centres of production were established at Faenza, Florence, Rome, Venice, and elsewhere. Many great artists, including Donatello, Alberti, and Michelangelo, used terracotta for both internal and external ornamentation of buildings, particularly in the form of altar pieces, wall plaques, medallions, and other bas-reliefs. The famous Florentine sculptor Luca della Robbia (1400–82), Andrea his nephew (1435–1525), and Andrea's sons, Girolamo (1488–1566), Luca (1475–1550), and Giovanni (1469–1529), greatly extended the technique, and working under the patronage of the Medici family, and other wealthy families, produced some of the finest terracotta ornaments ever made. The enamel Luca used was formed of the ordinary ingredients of glass (marzcotta), made white and opaque by oxide of tin. A very beautiful example of his work is shown in Plate XL. It is the terracotta panel of the Madonna and Child, in the Basilica of S. Croce, Firenze. Stucco ornament eventually became more popular during the Baroque period, and the use of terracotta in Italy itself rapidly declined.

In the early sixteenth century some of the Italian majolica potters settled in France, in Lyons in particular, and during the next hundred years or so they and their followers developed the tin-enamelled ware which became known as 'faience' after Faenza, in Italy. Girolamo della Robbia went to France in 1528 and spent nearly forty years in the service of the French royal family. He set up kilns for burning terracotta at Suresnes, and produced many decorative features for the palace of Francis I—the Château de Madrid in the Bois de Boulogne.

The art reached England during the reigns of Henry VII and Henry VIII; it was Henry VIII who commissioned the Italian artist-craftsmen, like Torrigiano, to make the terracotta ornaments—parapets, gargoyles, crestings, trefoils, mullions, and fluted columns—which were to adorn the great houses of the period, such as Hampton Court, one of his own palaces, and Layer Marney in Essex, the home of Sir Henry Marney, Captain of the Guard to Henry VIII. English craftsmen did not seem to have the necessary skill, or inclination, to continue the art after the Reformation, and although Sir Christopher Wren used some terracotta about 1680 it was not until 1722 that Richard Holt and Thomas Ripley, an architect, established a factory for terracotta at Lambeth, where it operated for about thirty years. George and Eleanor Coade,[3] his wife, started to manufacture terracotta products on or near the site of Holt's works in 1767. The terracotta produced by the Coades soon acquired a good reputation and became known as Coade Stone. The early designs for their products were nearly all modelled by John Bacon the sculptor or carried out under his direction. After various changes of ownership the company ceased to exist in 1835.

Analysis of samples of Coade Stone[4] showed that there were appreciable amounts of potassium, sodium, and titanium present, indicating that possibly a fluxing material such as marl (chalky clay) or even felspar was added. The material had a long vitrification range with a progressive reduction in porosity as the temperature was raised from 950° to 1250° C.; 1300° C. was too high a temperature as it caused the material to *bloat*. The firing temperature used by the Coades was probably about 1100° C.

Plate XLI shows terracotta ornament in the gateway to Syon House, Brentford, built by Robert Adam for the Duke of Northumberland; the material which appears lighter in colour did not weather well and much of it was replaced by Coade Stone, which appears darker in the photograph and has weathered better.

There was a revival in the use of terracotta in the nineteenth and twentieth centuries; particularly during the so-called Gothic revival, when George Tinworth, of Messrs Doulton of Lambeth, produced excellent decorative architectural panels. He received much encouragement from Ruskin and George Edmund Street, and one of his best works is the large panel in the reredos of York Minster depicting the Crucifixion.[5]

The great reputation acquired by terracotta in Greek and Roman times and in the Renaissance period, when many great artists used it, did not survive the unfortunate production of much under-fired material of poor durability in the nineteenth century, and terracotta has unfairly fallen into disrepute.

REFERENCES

(1) McIntyre, W. A., 1929, *Investigations into the Durability of Terracotta and Faience*, Building Research Special Report No. 12, H.M.S.O., London.

(2) Savile, Lord, 1892, 'Further Excavations at Lanuvium', *Archaeologia*, LIII, 147–54.

(3) Hamilton, S. B., Nov. 1954, 'Coade Stones', *The Architectural Review*, vol. 116.

(4) London County Council, 1951, *Survey of London*, XXIII.

(5) Proctor, J., 'The Tinworth Panel in the Reredos of St. Stephen's Chapel, York Minster'. Private communication from Messrs Doulton, Lambeth.

II

Gypsum Plaster

GYPSUM PLASTER SEEMS to have been the earliest deliberately manufactured cement. Just when it was first used is not known, but in Egypt it was abundantly used from early dynastic times, for example in the pyramids at Giza and in the tombs of Saqqara. It most probably originated in the Middle East where there are extensive outcrops of rock gypsum. To produce it, the rock gypsum was broken into convenient lumps and stacked in a primitive kiln, often consisting of nothing more than a small hollow scooped in the hillside like the one in southern Persia shown in Plate XLII. The blocks were built up in beehive fashion and then burnt with wood or charcoal. Nowadays in Persia crude oil from neighbouring oil-fields is used for fuel.

Calcium sulphate plasters are made from gypsum ($CaSO_4.2H_2O$), or from mineral anhydrate ($CaSO_4$). By calcining the gypsum at a relatively low temperature, usually between 130° and 170° C., for about 3 hours, only about three-quarters of the chemically combined water in the gypsum is driven off and a material known as plaster of Paris, or hemihydrate plaster ($CaSO_4.\frac{1}{2}H_2O$) is formed. If burned at a temperature of 400° C. or more all the water in the gypsum is driven off and anhydrous calcium sulphate ($CaSO_4$) is formed. Material of much the same composition can be obtained by simply grinding the raw mineral anhydrite, without calcination.

Plaster of Paris sets very rapidly when mixed with water, and to make it usable for building work small quantities of keratin (made by cooking animal hair, horns, and hoof in caustic soda solution) or similar glue-like materials have to be added to retard the set. The material so produced is termed retarded hemihydrate plaster. The anhydrous calcium sulphate on the other hand does not set and harden in a reasonable time, and accelerators of various types have to be added. This has resulted in the production of a number of proprietary brands of plaster, such as Keenes', Parian, and Martin's.

Keenes' cement, patented by Keene in 1836, is a white plaster obtained by steeping plaster of Paris in warm water containing alum (a double sulphate of aluminium and potassium) or in an aqueous solution of aluminium sulphate, drying the product and recalcining it at a temperature of 400° to 500° C., and then grinding to a fine powder. Parian cement, patented by J. Keating, is made in a similar manner but a solution of

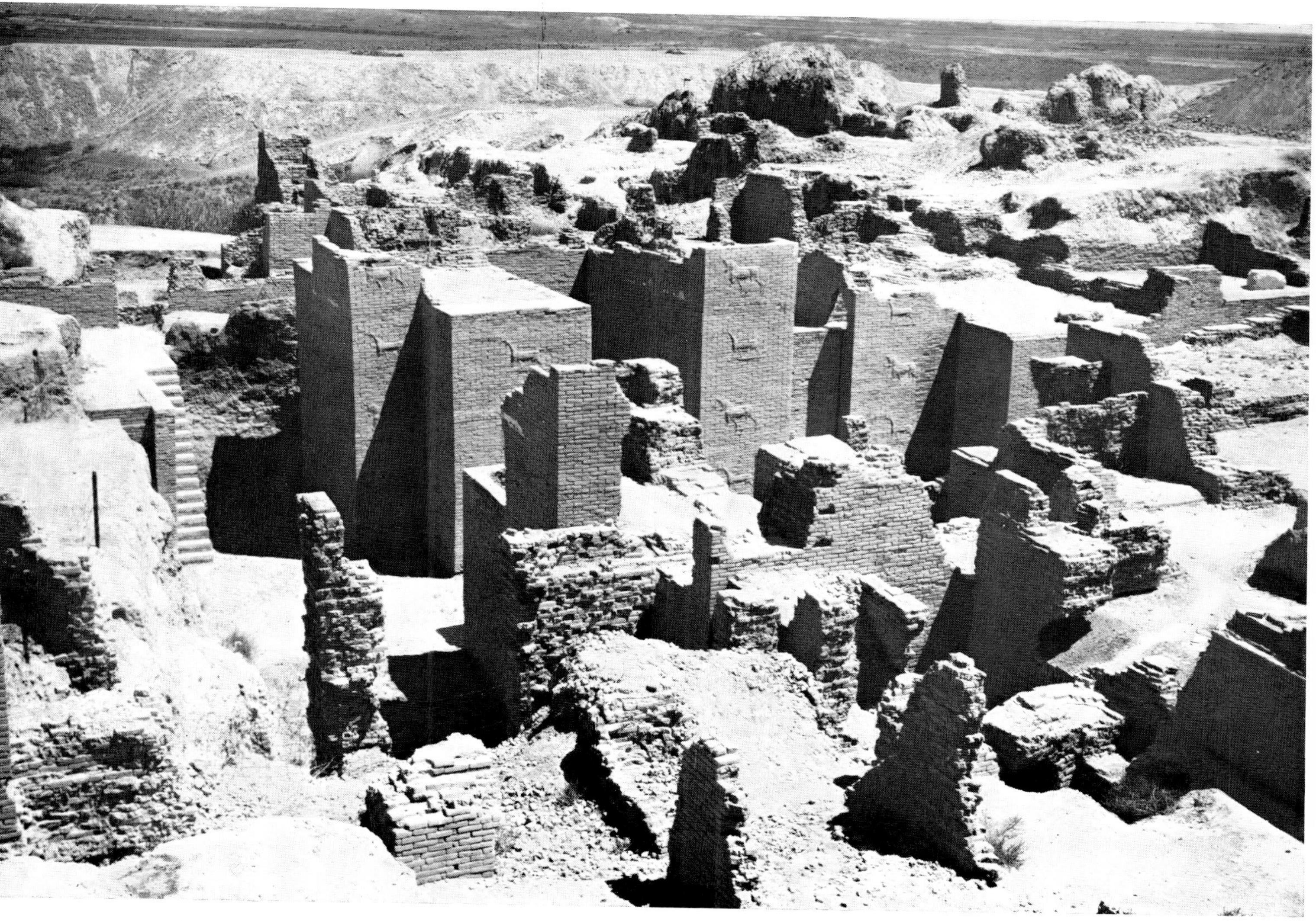

Plate XXIX. The Ishtar Gate at Babylon built by Nebuchadnezzar II; end of the seventh century B.C. (see page 67).

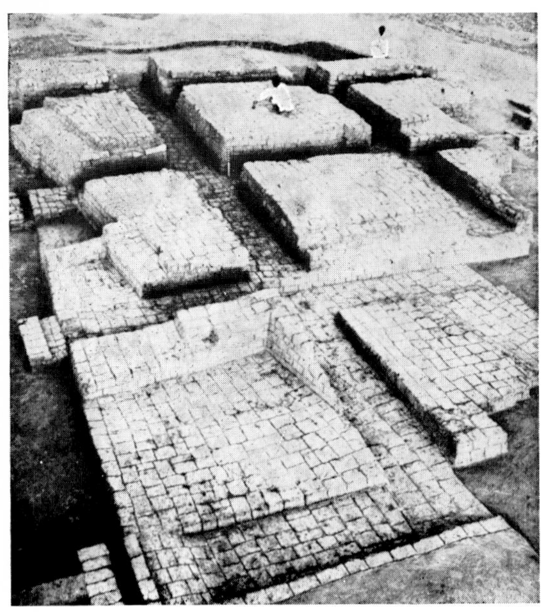

Plate XXX. A brick-kiln excavated at Lothal, Ahmadabad, India; *c.* 2000 B.C. (see page 65).

Plate XXXI. A brick of Adad-Nirari I, King of Assyria, from the quay-wall along the river Tigris, Ashur; *c.* 1300 B.C. (see page 69).

Plate XXXII. A brick stamped with name and titles of Nebuchadnezzar II, 604–562 B.C., and of his father Nabopolassar (see page 69).

Plate XXXIII. Inscribed brick of Cyrus the Great, 539–529 B.C., excavated at Ur (see page 69).

1.

2.

3.

4.

Plate XXXIV. Imprints on Roman bricks found in Britain (see page 74).

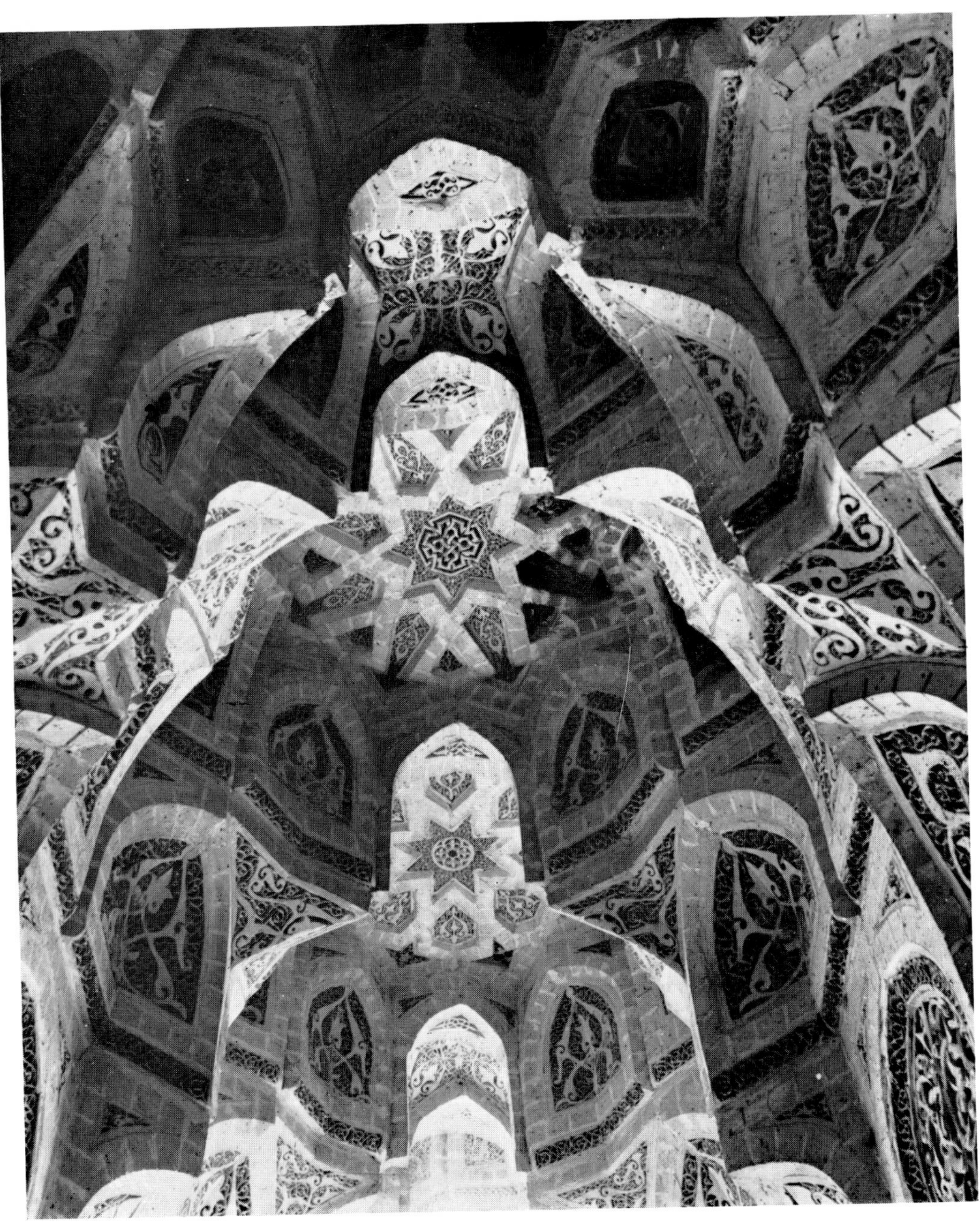

Plate XXXV. Richly decorated brickwork in the Abbasid Palace, Baghdad; thirteenth century A.D. (see page 77).

borax (biborate of soda) is used instead of alum; or it can be made by mixing finely ground gypsum and borax together in a dry state, calcining the mixture, and grinding. Martin's cement is made by mixing gypsum with potassium carbonate or carbonate of soda.

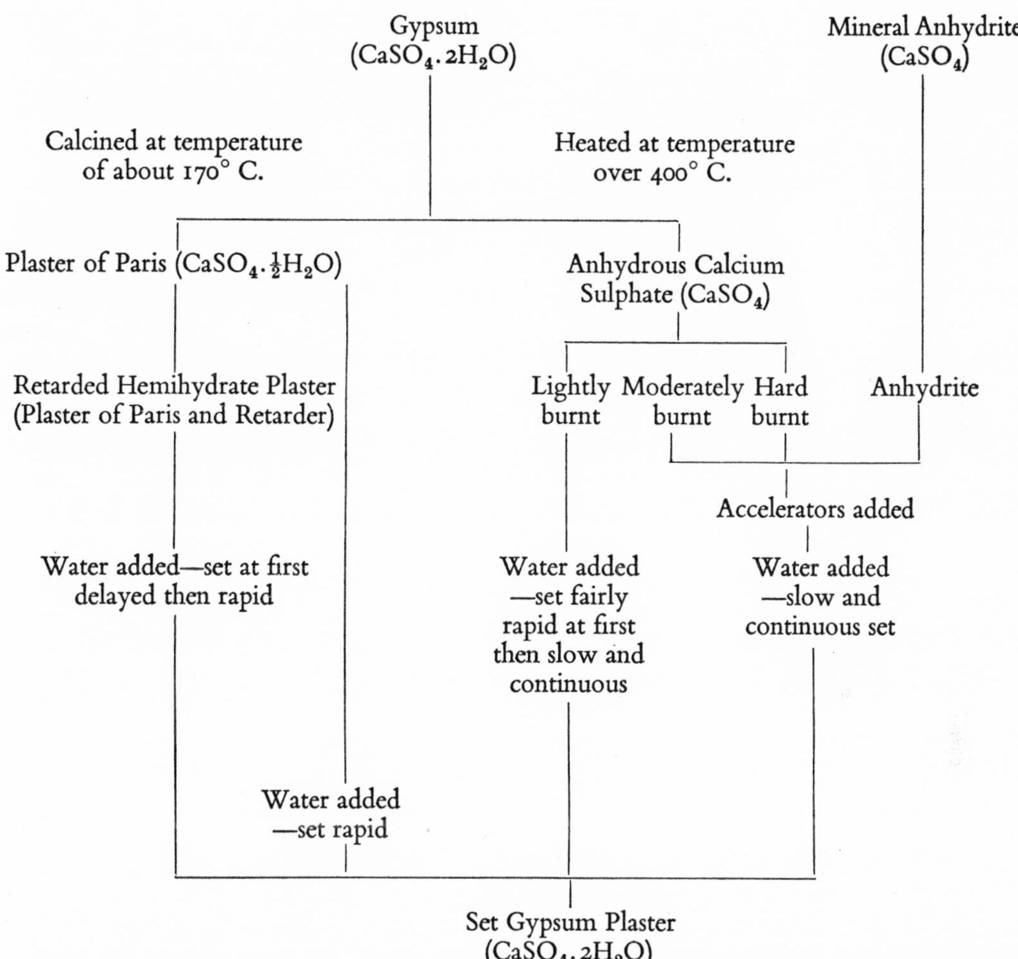

If the calcination of gypsum is carried out at temperatures of between 1100° and 1200° C. dissociation of some of the material occurs with the result that it contains anhydrite ($CaSO_4$) and a small amount of free lime (CaO) intimately dispersed throughout the product. It is used particularly in Germany under the name of 'Estrichgips' as a flooring plaster.

Selenitic lime or cement is composed of hydraulic lime with an addition of about 5 per cent. of plaster of Paris. This addition quickens the set and increases the strength of the lime.

Some gypsum deposits may also contain limestone, but the temperatures required for burning the gypsum are not high enough to reduce this limestone to quicklime, and it remains in the final product as calcium carbonate. In some ancient Egyptian samples of plaster there may be as much as 30 per cent, or even more, of calcium carbonate. Although limestone suitable for burning to lime existed abundantly in Egypt there is little evidence to suggest that lime plaster was used there before the Ptolemaic period. To calcine the limestone to produce quicklime the temperature had to be very much higher, and much more fuel, probably always in short supply, would have been needed.

There is no definite evidence yet of the use of gypsum plaster for building purposes by the Romans in Britain. Roman coffins at York and Malton have contained gypsum, but one cannot be quite sure that the bodies were not originally embedded in quicklime, which in course of time might have come in contact with sulphate-bearing waters which could have reacted with it to produce calcium sulphate.

Gypsum plaster, or plaster of Paris, was introduced into England from France in the thirteenth century when Henry III gave instructions for it to be used at Nottingham Castle. Matthew Paris[1] referring to King Henry's visit to Paris in 1254 records that 'he took note of the elegance of the houses which are made of gypsum, that is to say plaster'. The plaster of Paris was produced by burning gypsum obtained from the deposits around Montmartre. Burnell[2] writing in the middle of the nineteenth century gave a contemporary account of the process of manufacture from which the following is a quotation:

> The plaster is 'got' from the quarries, either underground or open, by picks and wedges; sometimes with gunpowder. The greater number of the quarries around Paris are underground; and at Montmartre, nearly the whole hill is thus dug out. The stone is broken up into small blocks about the size necessary for rubble masonry, before being carried to the kilns. The burning of the plaster stone at Paris, and throughout the Continent is managed in a very slovenly way. The kilns consist simply of three sides of a square enclosed by brick walls, covered with a rough tiled roof, in which spaces are left to allow the escape of steam. Under this sort of shed, as that is a more correct name than that of a kiln, the plaster is arranged by constructing firstly a series of vaults of the largest stones, filling in the haunches as the arches are carried up. Upon these the remaining stones are piled, paying attention only to the fact that the larger ones should be near the fire place formed by the vaults. These are subsequently filled with faggots, or other firewood, which is then lighted. The flames rise through the spaces left in the stones; they ascend gradually through the mass, and distribute as equally as may be, the heat in their passage. The system of calcination adopted, as might naturally be expected, leads to a great waste of raw material, owing to the very slovenly way in which it is executed. As much as one fifth is wasted in many kilns. After calcination, the plaster is reduced to powder, either by hand or in a mill.

Burnell records that there were several windmills in the Montmartre district, and that they originally ground flour for the city of Paris, but that later some, including the Red Mill (Moulin Rouge) were converted to another use—the grinding of plaster of Paris. By the end of the thirteenth century a similar material was being made from deposits of gypsum at Nore Down, Purbeck, and was known variously as Plaster of Purbyk, Plaster of Corfe, or Plaster of Nower.

The main deposits of gypsum in England are in the Keuper Marls, near Newark (Nottinghamshire), Fauld (Staffordshire), Chellaston (Derbyshire); in the Permian Beds in Cumberland and Westmorland; and in the Purbeck strata at Robertsbridge near Battle in Sussex. Up to the last fifty years or so plaster of Paris was relatively costly in England, and in consequence it was more usual to use a mixture of chalk lime and sand with cows' or calves' hair added to give it mechanical strength.

Gesso

Strictly speaking the term *gesso* refers to the white ground composed of calcined gypsum (plaster of Paris) and glue which Italian painters applied to wood or other rigid material to form, often in relief, a groundwork for gilding or for tempera painting. The term came to be more widely applied in north-west Europe—England, France and the Low Countries—to grounds prepared with other inert white materials such as whiting (chalk) or more recently zinc oxide.

Two mixtures were described by Cennino Cennini in 1417—*gesso grosso*, the coarser and thicker undercoat, being a mixture of glue and finely powdered calcined gypsum (made from the *gesso volterrano*, from the gypsum deposits at Volterra in Tuscany), and *gesso sottile*, a mixture of glue and calcined gypsum, which had previously been soaked for some weeks in an excess of water.

The word *gesso* is Italian for gypsum, and its use in Italy refers only to materials containing gypsum. Thus *gesso crudo* is unburnt gypsum (hydrous calcium sulphate) and *gesso cotto* is burnt gypsum or plaster of Paris. The coarse grade of plaster of Paris used by bricklayers and plasterers is *gesso da muratore*, and the finer plaster used by modellers and sculptors is *gesso per scultore*.

In England gesso plaster mixtures were largely replaced about 1820 by Hamelins' and Dehl's oil mastics, and cheaper composition mixtures, and the quality of the work seems to have suffered accordingly.

Scagliola

Scagliola is a coloured gypsum plaster made to imitate marble. It originated in Italy and reached England from France in the latter half of the eighteenth century. It was Henry Holland (1745–1806), architect to George III, who first invited artists from Paris to carry out this work in Carlton Place, London, which he was reconstructing as a town house for the Prince of Wales. The composition of the mixture used was finely powdered plaster of Paris mixed with glue and isinglass and this was applied to an undercoat of lime and hair which itself was often applied to a framework of laths. During the floating of the mixture (that is, when applying it to a surface and bringing it to a smooth finish) the artist incorporated the colours needed to imitate the marble and mingled them as necessary.

The surface was thoroughly compacted and when sufficiently hard was rubbed with a fine pumice stone and wiped with a wet sponge. It was then polished with tripoli powder and charcoal applied with soft linen, gently wiped with a piece of felt dipped in a mixture of oil and tripoli powder, and given a final application of pure oil. The effects were often very fine and the examples that can still be seen in splendid condition after a hundred and seventy years testify not only to the skill of the artist-craftsmen, but to the lasting quality of this type of work. Good examples can be seen in Home House, No. 20 Portman Square, built by Robert Adam in 1776 and now the Courtauld Institute of the University of London.

Sgraffito, or Graffito

Sgraffito, or Graffito, is a very ancient form of ornamentation produced by scratching the surface of the finishing coat of a plastered surface to expose the coloured stucco coat below. A notable example of its early use was on the façade of the Palazzo del Consiglio, in Verona (1476). The technique was greatly developed in Italy and spread to other parts of Europe, where it has been practised more freely than in England, where it was introduced early in the sixteenth century. The usual method has been to apply a coloured undercoat of cement and sand and to cover this with a skimming coat of lime, gypsum plaster, or selenitic plaster. When this surface has dried the design is transferred to it. The broad areas of the background are exposed by removing the skimming coat to reveal the coloured material beneath, and the outlines of the rest of the design are scratched with an iron knife or stylus. Sometimes undercoats of various colours can be applied, depending on the effect desired. Vasari (1511–74) mentions the use of 'travertino limewash' as the finishing coat.

REFERENCES

(1) PARIS, MATTHEW, *Chronicles* V, 481, quoted by Salzman, L. F., 1952, *Building in England*, Oxford University Press.

(2) BURNELL, G. R., 1856, *Limes, Cements, Mortars, and Concretes*, Weales' Rudimentary Series, 2nd ed., Crosby Lockwood.

12

Limes and Cements

WHEN AND HOW the process of burning limestone to produce quicklime was first discovered is a matter of conjecture. As a much higher temperature of burning than that required for burning gypsum was needed, it seems safe to infer that lime-burning was generally a later development. Lime is formed by burning chalk or limestone (calcium carbonate) at about 900°C. (1652°F.) to convert it into quicklime. For building purposes this quicklime is slaked with water to produce what is called hydrated lime, and sand is added to this as required to produce a suitable mortar. There are many different kinds of limestone which when burned produce limes that may have differing characteristics.

Lime falls into four broad groups:

(*a*) non-hydraulic limes, high calcium limes or 'fat' limes produced from carboniferous and pure oolitic limestone and white chalk;
(*b*) semi-hydraulic or moderately hydraulic limes from grey chalk, siliceous limestones, and argillaceous limestones (containing clayey matter—alumina and silica, in the form of hydrated aluminium silicate);
(*c*) hydraulic limes from lias limestone and chalk marl;
(*d*) magnesian limes from magnesian limestone including dolomite (with up to 40 per cent. of magnesian carbonate).

In Britain limestones burnt to produce limes of group (*a*) are mountain limestone of the Carboniferous (massive) Beds at Buxton, Forest of Dean, Mendips, North and South Wales; white chalk of the Upper Cretaceous Beds (Upper Chalk) of East Anglia, South-east England, the Thames Basin, and Yorkshire; and oolitic limestone from the Oolitic Belt (Bath, Portland, etc.). To produce group (*b*) are the greystones of the Upper Cretaceous Beds (Lower Chalk) of the Thames Basin, Dorking, Merstham, and Guildford. For group (*c*) are Blue Lias limestones of the Liassic Belt (Aberthaw, Bridgend, Lyme Regis, Keynsham, Shipton, Rugby, Barrow-on-Soar), and in Flintshire, Lincolnshire, and Yorkshire; chalk marl of the Lower Cretaceous Beds of Cambridgeshire and Carboniferous (shaley) limestone from the Glasgow district of Southern Scotland. For group (*d*) are used the high magnesian limestone (dolomite) of the Permian Belt (Durham, Mansfield, Nottingham, and South Shields, and Arden in Scotland).

Group (*a*) produces a white lime, which when slaked and used in mortar can only gain strength very slowly by taking up carbon dioxide from the atmosphere and so reverting extremely slowly to calcium carbonate. Such mortar has very little strength, and is described as non-hydraulic. Some other limestones, for example, those in groups (*b*) and (*c*), on the other hand, contain materials in addition to calcium carbonate, such as silica and alumina in various forms. The limes produced from these limestones are called hydraulic limes and mortars made from them gain considerably in strength. These semi-hydraulic or hydraulic limes, or cements, will set under water. Their quality depends on the relative proportions of calcium carbonate, silica, and alumina present in the raw materials, the care taken in preparing and blending the raw materials, and the temperature at which they are burnt or calcined. When the lime is hydrated, the silica and alumina present will combine with it to form insoluble compounds of cementitious value such as calcium silicates and calcium aluminates.

Two basic types of kiln have been used for a very long time for calcining limestone for producing lime, the Periodic, or 'flare', kiln (intermittent), and the Draw tunnel, or Running kiln (continuous). They are often built into the foot of the hill from which the limestone is obtained, so that the raw material can be fed into the kilns with the minimum labour. The walls of the kilns are often of stone masonry, but the more modern kilns are lined with firebrick.

In the Flare kiln, shown in simple form in Figure 60, the lime which is burnt does not come into contact with the solid fuel, but only with the heat and flames, and the method is used mainly for calcining white chalk to a pure white lime, very evenly burnt and uncontaminated. To load the kiln a rough arch of limestone lumps is formed over a framework or hearth of iron bars and further limestone is added to fill it completely. In modern practice a coal or coke fire is started on the hearth beneath the rough arch, so controlled to heat up slowly at first but then more rapidly. It takes about three to four days to burn all the limestone and to cool it sufficiently to enable the whole kiln to be emptied and reloaded. This method of burning lime is strangely similar to that described by Cato[1] (234–149 B.C.) over two thousand years ago.

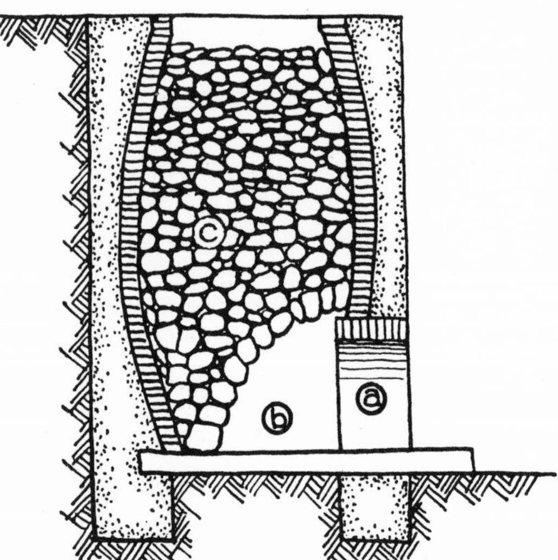

Fig. 60. Periodic, or 'Flare', lime-kiln. (a) Eye. (b) Fuel. (c) Limestone.

Make the lime-kiln ten feet wide, twenty feet deep, and reduce it to three feet wide at the top. If you burn with

SOURCES OF LIME IN GREAT BRITAIN

	(*a*) High Calcium Lime mainly $CaCO_3$			Hydraulic Lime $CaCO_3$ with varying amounts of clay matter (Al_2O_3, $2SiO_2$, $2H_2O$)				(*d*) Magnesian Lime $CaCO_3$ and $MgCO_3$
				(*b*) Moderately Hydraulic	(*c*) Eminently Hydraulic (i)	(ii)	(iii)	
Description	White Chalk	Oolitic Limestone	Mountain Limestone	Greystone	Blue Lias	Chalk Marl	Carboniferous (shaley) Limestone	Dolomitic Limestone (dolomite)
Geological Period	Upper Cretaceous (Upper Chalk)	Oolitic	Carboniferous (Massive)	Upper Cretaceous (Lower Chalk)	Liassic	Lower Cretaceous	Carboniferous (thin bedded)	Permian
Main Locations	Thames Basin, S.E. England and E. Anglia, Yorkshire	Oolitic Belt (Bath, Portland, Ketton, etc.)	Buxton, Mendips, S. and N. Wales, Forest of Dean	Home Counties and Thames Basin	Liassic Belt (Rugby, Aberthaw, Bridgend, and Somerset)	Cambridge-shire	Glasgow district of Scotland	Permian Belt (Nottingham, Mansfield, and South Shields)

> only one furnace entrance, make a large pit within it, large enough to hold the ashes so that they will not need to be taken out. Build the kiln well. See that the carrier [fortax] goes round the whole kiln at the bottom. If you burn with two furnace entrances, there will be no need of a pit. When it is necessary to throw the ashes out, throw them out at one entrance and there will be fire at the other. Beware of neglecting to keep the fire continually going, beware of neglecting this at night or at any other time. Put good stone in the kiln, as white as possible and as little mottled as possible. When you build the kiln make an opening straight down. When you have dug deep enough, then make room for the kiln. Let it be as deep as possible and as little exposed to the wind as possible. If you have a place where you cannot build a limekiln deep enough, build up the top with sundried brick or else with small stones and clay mortar and plaster the top [with clay] on the outside. If when you have set fire to it, flames come out anywhere except at the round opening at the top, plaster it with clay. Do not let the wind come to your kiln door, and in this respect beware especially of the South wind. This will be the sign when the lime is burnt: the stones at the top should be burnt, likewise the stones at the bottom will be burnt and fall down, and a less smoky flame will come out.

In the simple Draw tunnel, or Running kiln, shown in Figure 61, alternate layers of moistened limestone and coal are piled up to the top of the kiln. A fire is started at the bottom and as the lower layers of limestone become calcined the material falls through the grating at the base of the kiln, where it is withdrawn. Further layers of fuel and limestone are deposited in the top of the kiln to replenish it, and the process is for practical purposes continuous. It takes about a week for the limestone to pass from the top to the bottom of the kiln, but the lime produced is not so pure or so white and evenly burnt as that from the flare kiln, and may be intermixed with fuel ash. The temperature required for calcining the limestone is about 900° C., and to attain this temperature when burning chalk to produce 'fat' limes, 15 to 20 per cent of coal by weight of the chalk is needed, and when burning hydraulic limes about 25 per cent is needed in the type of kiln illustrated; but in more efficient modern kilns this figure is reduced to 20 per cent or less.

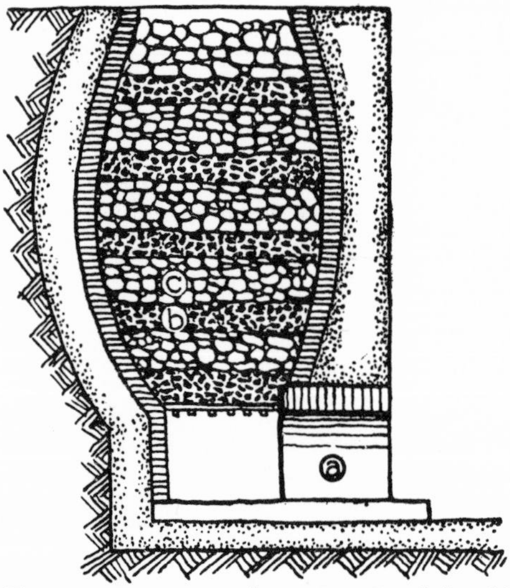

Fig. 61. Draw tunnel, or Running kiln. (a) Drawhole. (b) Coal, one part. (c) Limestone, four parts.

In ancient times timber was the usual fuel and often in lime mortars, of the Roman period for example, fragments of charcoal can be seen. Coal was not used as fuel for the purpose to any appreciable extent until the end of the thirteenth or the beginning of the fourteenth century. Lime-kilns of this period have been found at a number of places. Craster[2] has described one he excavated at Ogmore Castle in Glamorgan in 1949, and has compared it with others of the same period at Merthyr Mawr

Warren, St Catherine's Hill, at Niton in the Isle of Wight, Weobley Castle in Gower, and at Cilgerran Castle in Pembrokeshire. The kiln at Ogmore consisted of a circular pit with battered sides and had a diameter of 6 feet 8 inches at the top and 5 feet 8 inches at the bottom, enclosed by a thick dry-built stone wall now standing to a maximum height of 2 feet 9 inches. On opposite sides of the pit there are two flues with openings 4 feet 5 inches on the outside, narrowing to 1 foot 3 inches, where they enter the pit. The flues were 1 foot 9 inches high: only a small part of the roof of the flues, which were formed of flat slabs supported by corbelling out the course below them, now remains. On the floor of the pit and inside the flues coal and lime were found, while outside the pit there was a layer of coal and lime 18 inches deep.

The very similar but smaller kiln at Cilgerran, shown in Plate XLIII, was not completely circular but was built in the angle of two walls. This prevented the flues being placed on opposite sides as at Ogmore, so they were placed at right angles to each other.

One can only assume that it was soon found by experience that limestone from one place produced a better cement than one from another, but probably there was no very clear understanding of the reason as to why this should be. It was not until the eighteenth and early nineteenth centuries that a sytematic study of the subject was made, first on the Continent and then in England by Smeaton[3] (1724–92) and Pasley[4] (1780–1861).

Before the end of the thirteenth century, timber and perhaps peat were the fuels used for burning lime. Great quantities were required to reach the temperature of calcination. Burnell,[5] writing a hundred years ago, gave the following figures for the quantity of various kinds of fuel necessary to produce 35 cubic feet of lime—approximately one ton —in an intermittent kiln:

60 cubic feet of oak (about 28 cwt);
117 cubic feet of fir (about 38 cwt);
9 cubic feet of coal (about 4½ cwt);
117 cubic feet of peat (about 45 cwt).

In a continuous or running kiln less fuel was needed, for example, 7 cubic feet of coal (about 3½ cwt) as compared with 9 cubic feet.

Something equivalent to the amount of wood in an oak trunk 18 inches in diameter and over 30 feet long, or in two fir trunks of the same size, was therefore required to produce 1 ton of burnt lime. It is not surprising that grave concern was expressed in the thirteenth century at the denudation of forests for fuel not only for lime burning but for brick burning. For example, a presentment[6] was made in 1275 regarding Wellington forest where five hundred oak trees had been used as fuel for the King's two lime-kilns. Towards the end of the thirteenth century, however, coal was being used for firing the kilns. Even this innovation caused concern in towns as a result of the smoke nuisance. Salzman[7] records that in the early fourteenth century the growing use of coal for lime burning in London became so great a nuisance that its use was rigorously prohibited (Pat. 35 Edw. I m 5 d). Complaints had previously been made and commissions of inquiry appointed in 1285 (Pat. 13 Edw. I m 18 d) and 1288 (Pat. 16 Edw. I m 12).

A traditional method of preparing lime was to slake the freshly burnt lime with an excess of water in an upper basin and to allow it to flow in a creamy state into a lower one, where the excess could evaporate leaving the 'lime putty'. A grating placed between the two basins prevented any lumps of unburnt or unslaked material from passing. The lime was then made into mortar with sand, and hair was added if the mortar was to be used for rendering walls and ceilings.

The ancients discovered that they could also convert a non-hydraulic lime into a hydraulic or partially hydraulic one by adding suitable materials. Such additions, which we call pozzolanas, after Pozzuoli, the locality in Italy where a natural source of such material—a volcanic earth—exists, are those which, though not necessarily cementitious by themselves, possess the requisite compounds of silica and alumina which will combine with non-hydraulic or semi-hydraulic limes at ordinary temperature in the presence of moisture to form stable insoluble compounds of cementitious value, such as calcium silicates and aluminates. When mixed with lime mortar in addition to, or in partial substitution for, sand, they will impart hydraulic properties and greater strength. Pozzolanic materials fall into two categories: (*a*) natural and (*b*) artificial.

(*a*) *Natural:*

Italian Pozzolanas, e.g. from around Pozzuoli, near Naples, Civita Vecchia, and around Rome.

Santorin Earth from the Greek island of Santos.

Trass composed of pumice fragments from Andernach on the Rhine in Germany, and from Bavaria.

Volcanic ash from deposits in South-east France, Azores, Teneriffe in the Canary Isles, and Japan.

Diatomaceous Earth including Kieselguhr, infusorial earth, diatomite, tripoli, and rottenstone, etc.

(*b*) *Artificial:*

Burnt shale, burnt diatomite or pumicite, burnt clay, e.g. homra (Egypt) and surkhi (India).

Powdered tile and potsherds.

Certain slags.

The clays and shales are burnt to a temperature varying between 600° and 950° C., the optimum temperature varying rather critically with different types of material.

Crushed pottery has been observed in mortar of the Middle Minoan Period, but whether it was a deliberate addition or fortuitous is not known. It is clear that the knowledge of the use of lime mortar, and the benefits to be derived by adding pozzolanic material, spread from Greece to Rome. This in turn led to radical changes in building construction. Not only was it possible to erect more slender walls with the stronger mortar, but the construction of arches and vaults became possible. The cement also offered good resistance to seawater and in consequence was extensively used for marine structures. The Romans found that the volcanic clay or tufa consisting of clay and gravel, containing approximately 35 per cent. of soluble silica, from Puteoli in the bay of Naples, was excellent for producing hydraulic mortar. A good example of its use is shown in Plate XLIV, of a Roman wall near Naples which has been exposed to the sea, and in spite of the fact that the tufa blocks have been appreciably eroded, the pozzolanic mortar between them has successfully endured. The Romans called the material 'pulvis puteolanus'. It is at present variously called puzzolana, pozzolana and pozzuolana, and materials which possess similar properties have come to be described generally as pozzolanic. The trasses of the Eifel, the Moselle, Nette, and Brohl valleys played an important part in the magnificent waterworks of Gaul which were erected in the reigns of Emperor Trajan (A.D. 98–117) and Emperor Hadrian (A.D. 117–138) and supplied water to the various Roman fortifications near Cologne (Colonia Agrippinensis). In addition to the natural material from Pozzuoli and elsewhere the Romans continued to use crushed brick and tile. It produced a mortar with very much the same characteristics, and its use seems to have been preferred for some specific purposes throughout the Empire, and was, in fact, in some parts the only hydraulic cement available to them.

The Romans used these pozzolana mortars in positions where it was important to prevent the penetration of damp—for example, for lining the inner surfaces of channels, drains, baths, tanks, and aqueducts, for rendering walls in damp or exposed situations, for bonding masonry in waterlogged ground, for pavements, and for torching (sealing the spaces between) roofing tiles to prevent the penetration of driving rain. An early example of the use of lime mortar with crushed tile admixture is the lining of the *specus* of the aqueduct called Aqua Marcia near Rome (144 B.C.). In Britain, where no natural pozzolana such as pumice, trass, or volcanic earth was available, the Romans used the artificial ones, crushed brick, tile, or pottery.

In post-Roman times there seems to have been a reversion to the use of non-hydraulic limes, which were not so durable, and in England it was probably not until the sixteenth and seventeenth centuries that imported pozzolana ('Dutch tarras' or trass) and lime mixtures were used; the usual mixtures for works exposed to the action of water being composed of 1 volume of trass to 2 volumes of slaked lime. The so-called Dutch tarras (terras or trass) was dug at Andernach, Bockenheim, and Frankfurt-on-Maine in Germany and transported down the Rhine to Holland where it was ground for mixing with lime mortars. The export trade was very considerable. In Holland the material was mixed with a hydraulic lime (blue argillaceous lime) made on the banks of the River Scheldt. A layer of this lime, about 1 foot in thickness, was spread on the ground and moistened with water and covered with a layer of trass of the same thickness. After two or three days the material was thoroughly mixed together and well beaten, and left for a further two days before use. The cement so produced was the famous 'tarras mortar' used in Holland for the construction of sea defences and for aquatic work. Smeaton, after he had visited Holland and Belgium in 1754 and 1755 to see marine and hydraulic structures, was satisfied that a cement containing equal parts of lime and the so-called 'Dutch tarras' was the type most suitable for him to use in the construction of Eddystone

Lighthouse. However, he experimented with different limes and found that the siliceous limestone from the Blue Lias formation at Aberthaw, in South Wales, which also contained some clay, produced a cement which set hard when burned 'with a good deal of fire'. He deduced from these experiments that a good cement could be produced by deliberately mixing limestone and clay together and burning them. He also experimented with pozzolana from Civita Vecchia in Italy and finally decided that the cement he would use for the lighthouse should consist of equal parts of this pozzolana and the lime from the Aberthaw limestone.

In Ireland a hydraulic lime (roach lime) had been mixed with gravel and used by George Semple (*c.* 1700–*c.* 1782) for the foundations of the Essex Bridge over the River Liffey in Dublin.

Towards the end of the eighteenth century and in the first half of the nineteenth century a great need was created for dependable hydraulic cements. Firstly, the London Building Act of 1774 (14th of Geo. III) drafted by Sir Robert Taylor, architect of the Bank of England, gave great encouragement to the use of stucco as the Act virtually prohibited the use of exposed timber details on buildings, and laid down that external ornaments to fronts of buildings were to be of brick, stone, burnt clay, artificial stone, stucco, lead, or iron. Secondly, the great industrial revolution which was breaking on the country called for development of internal communications, canals, roads, bridges, tunnels, docks and harbours, and eventually railways. Great engineering works had to be carried out, and hydraulic cements which would resist the penetration of water were needed for their successful completion.

In 1796 James Parker of Northfleet discovered that he could make a hydraulic cement by calcining the nodules of argillaceous limestone, called 'septaria', 'cement stones', 'rock stones' or 'noddles', which were derived from the Tertiary clay beds and found lying along the foreshore of the Thames Estuary, mainly along the coast of the Isle of Sheppey. The septaria had been washed out of the London clay cliffs in the course of ages by sea erosion, and occurred in large accumulations not only at Sheppey, but at South Benfleet, Leigh, Southend, Shoebury, Mersea Island, Clacton, Frinton, Walton-on-the Naze, Dovercourt, and Harwich, but it was at this last place that the industry became mainly centred under the direction of James Frost. The removal of vast quantities of material from the foreshore at Harwich—over a million tons between 1812 and 1845—became a serious matter, and in 1845 the Government passed a regulation prohibiting the digging of stone within 50 feet of the cliffs. This soon led to the exhaustion of cement-stone from the foreshore, and it was then for some years dredged from the sea bed, until the time that 'Roman' cement was superseded by 'Portland' cement.

It is surprising that the Romans did not discover this source of hydraulic cement. At Chelmsford in Essex, for example, although the walls of the bath building were constructed with blocks of septaria, gathered from the estuarine deposits of the Essex foreshore, the blocks were bedded in white (chalk) lime mortar, and for a hydraulic cement for use in drains, etc., the Romans added powdered tile, not realizing that they could have produced an equally satisfactory hydraulic cement by burning the septaria. Parker called the product 'Roman Cement', a misnomer, but none the less a name by which it is still known. In his patent specification of 1796 Parker described his invention as follows:

> The principle and nature of the said invention consists in reducing to powder certain stones or argillaceous productions called noddles of clay, and using that powder with water so as to form a water [misprint for mortar] or cement stronger and harder than any mortar or cement now prepared by artificial means. . . . These noddles, on being burnt with a heat stronger than that used for burning lime, generally assume a brown appearance, and are a little softened, and when so burnt and softened become warm (but do not slack) by having water thrown upon them, and being reduced to powder after burning, and being mixed with just sufficient to make into a paste, become indurated in water in the space of an hour or thereabouts. Any argillaceous stone, then, corresponding with this description, whether known by the name of noddles of clay, or any other name, is the sort and kind only that I mean to appropriate to my own use in the fermentation [misprint for formation] of my cement. . . . . . . The stones of clay or noddles of clay are first broken into small fragments, then burnt in a kiln, or furnace (as lime is commonly burned) with a heat nearly sufficient to vitrify them, then reduced to powder by any mechanical or other operation, and the powder so obtained is the basis of the cement.

Until the middle of the nineteenth century the term 'cement' generally referred to 'Roman' cement. Since then the term 'cement' has commonly been understood to mean 'Portland' cement.

'Medina' cement, somewhat later, was similar to Parker's cement and was made from natural septaria found in and around the River Medina in the Isle of Wight, and in the Solent area, but much of the material for this cement also came from Lyme Regis, Dorset, and Weymouth Bay. Across the Channel a hydraulic cement was made from similar material found near Boulogne; and in the United States at Rosendale and Louisville. When the supply of septaria nodules dredged from the foreshore diminished, the cement manufacturers resorted to the artificial blending of suitable clays with chalk, finely ground together, in the proportions of $1\frac{1}{2}$ to 2 of clay to 1 of chalk. These were calcined and then re-ground, but the temperature of calcining was not so high as that needed later to produce Portland cement, which also contained a higher proportion of chalk.

Parker's cement was sometimes known as 'Harwich' cement or 'Sheppey' cement. Similar 'Roman' cements were 'Calderwood' made in Scotland from limestone at Calder Glen, near Barrhead, and Griffnock, near Glasgow, 'Whitby', 'Mulgrave', and 'Atkinsons' cement made from material from the Whitby shale beds of the Lias formation of Yorkshire. Houses in the neighbourhood of Whitby in Yorkshire, including Mulgrave Castle, were covered with stucco made from 'Whitby' or 'Mulgrave' cement. It was also used by John Nash[8] for making roofing tiles for a gate lodge at Ravensworth Castle, near Durham, the mixture being composed of cement and coarse grit in equal parts. The rebuilding of Ravensworth Castle in 1808 was carried out by John Nash for Sir Thomas Liddell, and these are probably the earliest cement tiles to be made in England.

The composition of these so-called Roman cements was variable, but they usually contained between 45 and 65 per cent of calcium carbonate, and up to 55 per cent of clay, silica, iron, etc. Vicat[9] classified cements used in France as:

(*a*) non-hydraulic, or rich limes, with less than 10 per cent of foreign matter;
(*b*) hydraulic limes, 10 to 34 per cent of clay and 90 to 66 per cent of lime;
(*c*) cements, 40 to 60 per cent of clay and 60 to 40 per cent of lime;
(*d*) pozzuolanic cements, 70 to 90 per cent of clay and 30 to 10 per cent of lime.

Thomas Telford (1757–1834) was quick to appreciate the properties of Parker's cement and used it between 1796 and 1801 in the construction of the Chirk Viaduct which carries the Ellesmere Canal across the River Ceiriog. The sides of the canal were built in ashlar masonry backed with hard burnt bricks laid in Parker's cement, and thus made watertight. Isambard Brunel (1806–59) used it for the construction of the first tunnel under the River Thames between Wapping and Rotherhithe. The tunnel was started in 1825, but in 1828 the walls collapsed at one point and a large quantity of Aspdin's Portland cement from the Wakefield works was used successfully to seal the breach. Work was suspended until 1835, however, when it was restarted and carried to completion in 1843. Robert Stephenson (1803–59) used it later in the construction of the London and Birmingham Railway. The cement was normally mixed with an equal part of sand for these works, but it was used neat by Stephenson in the Kilsby tunnel on the new railway.

In 1811 James Frost patented a hydraulic cement very much like that made previously by L. J. Vicat (1786–1861)[10] in France by calcining an intimate mixture of limestone (chalk) and clay which he ground together in a wet mill. The temperature of calcining was not high and the resulting product was considered to be inferior to Parker's Roman cement. In 1822, however, Frost took out a further patent (British Patent No. 4679) for a hydraulic cement in which the calcining was carried out at a higher temperature, high enough in fact to drive off all the carbon dioxide in the mixture. He called his new product 'British Cement' and it gained a better reputation in England and America than his earlier cement did.

To produce the modern Portland cement the same ingredients of chalk and clay are used, but the temperature of calcining is high enough to sinter or vitrify the material to form a clinker which is subsequently ground to a fine powder. It has long been a matter for discussion as to when and by whom cement of this type was first produced. Certainly Vicat and Frost were progressing along the right lines, and so was Joseph Aspdin (*c.* 1779–1855) of Leeds, a bricklayer who took out a patent (British Patent No. 5022) in 1824, and to whom most credit for the invention of Portland cement is given, and he was the first to call the cement 'Portland'. Aspdin described his method of making the cement as follows:

> . . . I take a specific quantity of limestones such as that generally used for making or repairing roads, and I take it from the roads after it is reduced to a puddle or powder; but if I cannot procure a sufficient quantity of the above from the roads, I obtain the limestone itself, and I cause the puddle or powder, or the limestone, as the case may be to be calcined. I then take a specific quantity of argillaceous earth or clay, and mix them with water to a

> state approaching impalpability, either by manual labour or machinery. After this proceeding I put the above mixture into a slip pan for evaporation, either by the heat of the sun, or by submitting it to the action of fire or steam conveyed in flues or pipes under or near the pan till the water is entirely evaporated. Then I break the said mixture into suitable lumps, and calcine them in a furnace similar to a lime kiln till the carbonic acid is entirely expelled. The mixture so calcined is to be ground, beat or rolled to a fine powder.

His first works were at Wakefield in 1825 and were continued by his son William, who later established works on the Thames. The boom in railway building and the great demand created for Roman cement led Sir Robert Peel in 1846 to express the fear that the supplies of septaria nodules (cement stone) might become exhausted, and that sufficient should be reserved for government works. He seems to have been assured by William Aspdin that he need not worry in view of his manufacturing of 'Portland' cement.

It appears to have been I. C. Johnson (1811–1911) who first fully appreciated the importance of vitrification in the burning of the raw materials, and in 1845 he produced the first reliable Portland cement, at Swanscombe, in Kent. Johnson's cement was exported to France and used in the government harbour works at Cherbourg, which were publicly inaugurated in the presence of Queen Victoria in 1858. It was in another cement works set up by Johnson at Gateshead that a Newcastle-on-Tyne plasterer named W. B. Wilkinson learned much about the application of Portland cement and was the first to patent, in 1854, a method of producing reinforced concrete and, particularly, concrete beams. Little could he know then of the tremendous impact his invention was to have on future building construction. Since that time great developments have taken place all over the world in the production of true and modified Portland cements, and Portland cement has assumed such importance in this century that a few brief notes on the various stages of development in its manufacture would seem justified.

Three types of kiln have been used for calcining cement:

(*a*) vertical intermittent, or 'bottle', kiln;
(*b*) vertical continuous, or shaft, kiln;
(*c*) horizontal continuous rotating, or rotary, kiln.

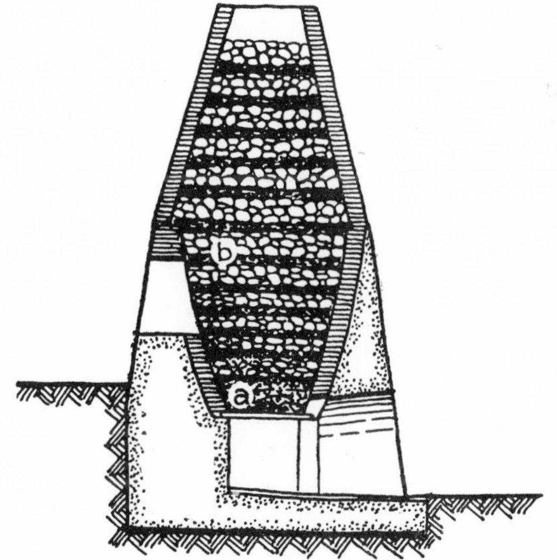

Fig. 62. Vertical intermittent, or 'bottle', kiln used for burning Portland cement. (a) Wood faggots (bavins), coal, and coke. (b) Layers of three parts cement stone, one part of coke.

Type (*a*) was very like that used for lime burning. The raw materials were placed

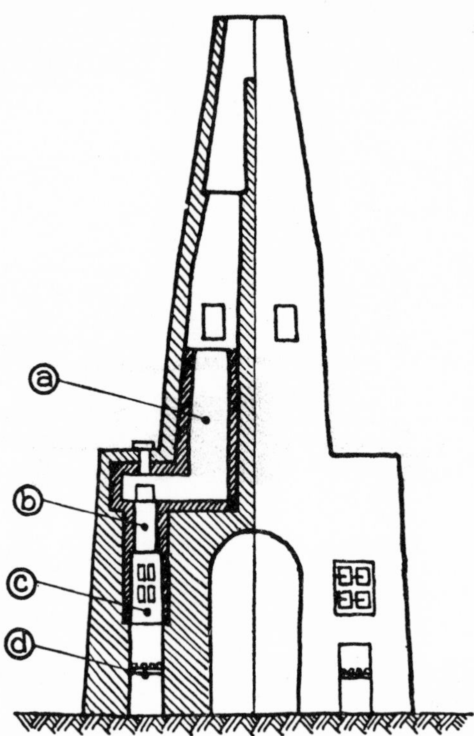

Fig. 63. Vertical continuous, or shaft, kiln (Dietsch type), for burning Portland cement; late nineteenth century.

in layers alternating with layers of fuel as shown in Figure 62—a layer of wood faggots (bavins), coal, and coke, followed by a layer of three parts of cement stone or dried slurry, and so on. The drawback of this method was that the kiln had to be recharged after each burning, and during the period of reloading the kiln itself naturally cooled down, and much new fuel was wasted in reheating the kiln structure. It was not long, therefore, before a modified type of this 'bottle' kiln, type (*b*), known as the Dietsch Kiln, was introduced. It was continuous instead of intermittent in operation. This occurred about 1880. The raw materials, in a dry state as before, were loaded with the fuel into the upper part of the kiln, *a* (Figure 63), but the interior construction was such that firing took place in a narrow firing zone, *b*, which on account of the higher temperatures attained had to be lined with refractory bricks. The cement clinker produced fell into the lower chamber, *c*, and was then removed by a movable grate, *d*. A forced draught was often admitted at the bottom of the kiln, and this air-cooled the clinker in chamber *c* and was itself preheated as it entered the firing zone *b*. The invention of the rotary kiln, type (*c*), in 1877 by Thomas Russell Crampton, a railway engineer, followed by improved designs by two civil engineers, Frederick Ransome in 1885 and Frederick Stokes in 1888, enabled the raw materials to be fed into the kiln as a wet slurry, without its having to be dried previously. The process came to be known as the wet process as distinct from the earlier dry process. As the kiln rotated in an inclined position, the slurry gravitated downwards towards the firing zone, where it was burned to clinker. This method of producing Portland cement, which was not a commercial success until about 1900, has remained essentially the same to the present day. Gooding and Halstead have given a good account of the early history of cement manufacture in England.[11]

Modern Portland cement is made from one of the following mixtures:

(i) high calcium limestone or chalk and clay or shale, giving a mixture with about 65 to 75 per cent of calcium carbonate, the rest being aluminium silicate and free silica;

(ii) argillaceous (clayey) limestone, or cement rock either alone or mixed with high calcium limestone;

(iii) blast-furnace slag and limestone.

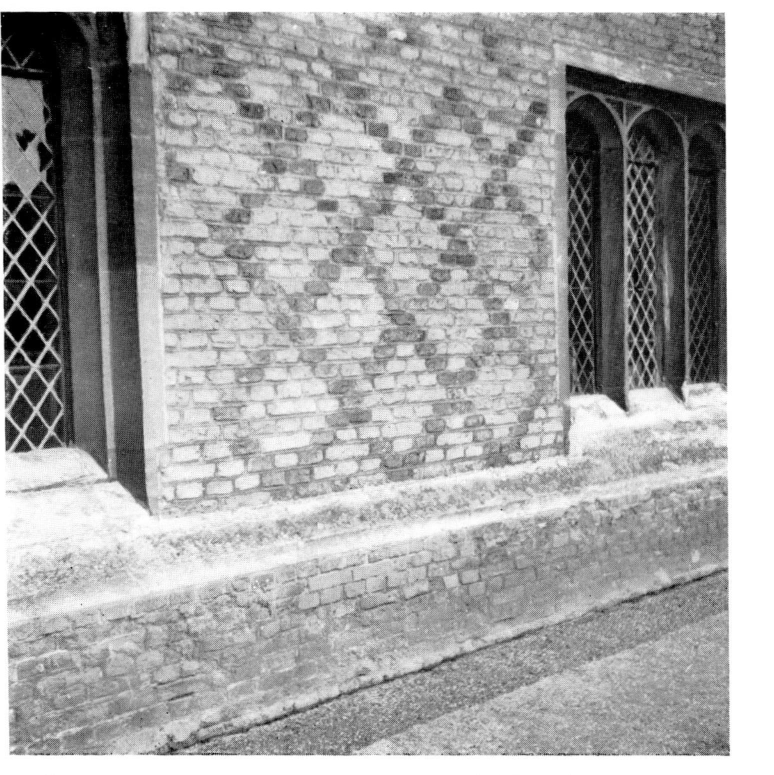

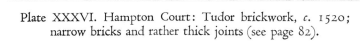

Plate XXXVI. Hampton Court: Tudor brickwork, *c.* 1520; narrow bricks and rather thick joints (see page 82).

Plate XXXVII. Hampton Court; Wren brickwork, *c.* 1690; fine bright red bricks with thin joints (see page 82).

Plate XXXVIII. Seventeenth-century brick-kilns excavated at Jamestown, Virginia (see page 84).

PRODUCTION OF BUILDING LIMES AND CEMENTS

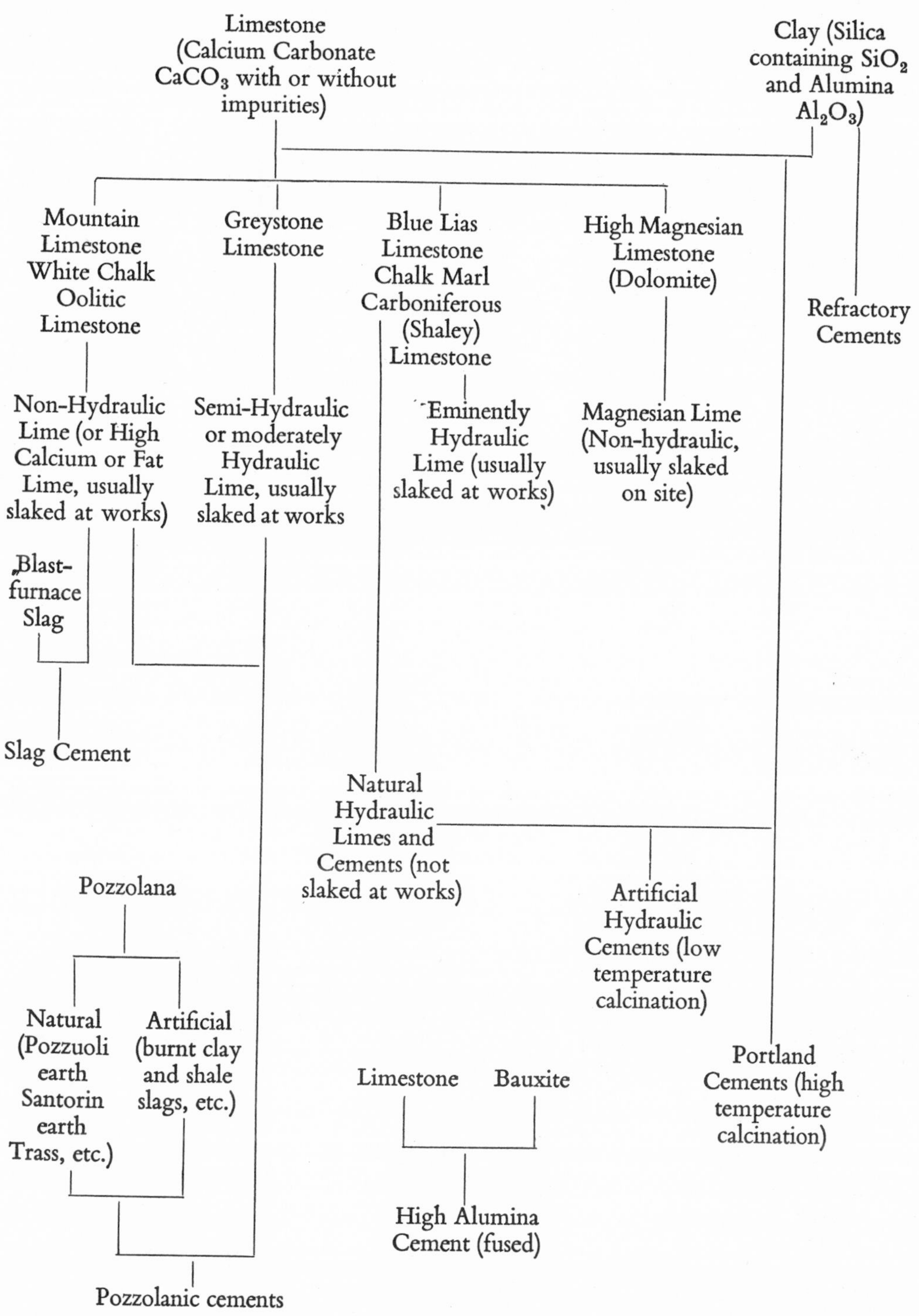

Limestone (Calcium Carbonate $CaCO_3$ with or without impurities)
Clay (Silica containing SiO_2 and Alumina Al_2O_3)
Mountain Limestone White Chalk Oolitic Limestone
Greystone Limestone
Blue Lias Limestone Chalk Marl Carboniferous (Shaley) Limestone
High Magnesian Limestone (Dolomite)
Refractory Cements
Non-Hydraulic Lime (or High Calcium or Fat Lime, usually slaked at works)
Semi-Hydraulic or moderately Hydraulic Lime, usually slaked at works
Eminently Hydraulic Lime (usually slaked at works)
Magnesian Lime (Non-hydraulic, usually slaked on site)
Blast-furnace Slag
Slag Cement
Natural Hydraulic Limes and Cements (not slaked at works)
Artificial Hydraulic Cements (low temperature calcination)
Pozzolana
Natural (Pozzuoli earth Santorin earth Trass, etc.)
Artificial (burnt clay and shale slags, etc.)
Limestone
Bauxite
Portland Cements (high temperature calcination)
High Alumina Cement (fused)
Pozzolanic cements

These raw materials are finely ground either dry or wet, and then sintered at a temperature of about 1,300° to 1,450° C. When ground to a fine powder and mixed with water the cement sets very quickly, too quickly in fact, for it to be of much use. A small amount of gypsum is added to the cement clinker during grinding and this acts as a retarder. Present-day methods of manufacture are most highly developed, and controlled carefully at every stage to ensure a very uniform product of high quality.

Towards the end of last century it was found that granulated blast-furnace slag had hydraulic properties and could be used as an addition to Portland cement. The slag occurs in molten form in the production of pig-iron in blast-furnaces, and it is granulated by quenching rapidly in water. If slowly cooled the slag has no hydraulic properties. The granulated slag is normally added to the Portland cement clinker and the two materials are finally ground together.

In England the cement is called Portland-blast-furnace cement and contains up to 65 per cent of granulated slag. In the United States of America the cement is called Portland-blast-furnace-slag cement, and contains not more than 70 per cent of slag. Slag cements have been used to a greater extent on the Continent, and in Germany the types are *Hochofenzement*, with up to 85 per cent of granulated slag, and *Eisenportlandzement*, with not more than 30 per cent. The corresponding names in the Netherlands for these same cements are *Hoogoven cement* and *Ijzerportlandcement*. In France and Belgium cements with up to 30 per cent of granulated slag are called *ciment de fer*, and *ciment de haut fourneau* with up to 70 per cent of granulated slag. The French also use a cement called *ciment de laitier au clinker*, which has no more than 20 per cent of Portland cement clinker and the rest slag.

Some inferior cements have been made on the Continent by mixing about 10 to 20 per cent of slaked lime, or 20 to 30 per cent of hydraulic lime with slag. The names given to these are *Mischbinder* or *Schlackenbinder* in Germany and *çiment de laitier à la chaux*.

Early in this century it was found that anhydrous calcium sulphate (anhydrite or estrichgips) could also be used with suitable blast-furnace slag to produce a good cement. In Germany it has been called *Gipsschlackenzement*, or more recently *Sulfat-Hüttenzement*, in Belgium and France *ciment métallurgique sursulfaté*, and in England supersulphated cement. It is particularly resistant to attack by sulphate groundwater and sea water.

High alumina cement, first produced in France in 1908 under the name of *ciment fondu*, has very rapid hardening properties and is especially useful in emergency work, and for making refractory concrete. It is made by melting a mixture of limestone and bauxite (aluminium ore).

For a detailed study of modern cements and their properties, the reader is referred to the revised edition of the work by Lea and Desch.[12]

REFERENCES

(1) CATO, *De Agricultura*, XXX, VIII, 1–4.

(2) CRASTER, O. E., 1950, 'A Medieval Limekiln at Ogmore Castle, Glamorgan', *Archaeologia Cambrensis*, LI, 72–6.

(3) SMEATON, J., 1791, *Narrative of Eddystone Lighthouse*, H. Hughes, London.

(4) PASLEY, C. W., 1838, *Observations on limes, calcareous cements, mortars, stucco and concrete*, London.

(5) BURNELL, G. R., 1856, *Limes, Cements, Mortars and Concretes*, Weales' Rudimentary Series, 2nd ed., Crosby Lockwood.

(6) Hundred R. ii, 56.

(7) SALZMAN, L. F., 1923, *English Industries of the Middle Ages*, Oxford University Press, 6.

(8) LOUDEN, J. C., 1842, *An Encyclopaedia of Cottage, Farm and Villa Architecture*, Longman, Brown, Green and Longmans.

(9) VICAT, L. J., 1828, *Mortiers et Ciment Calcaires*, Paris. English translation by Capt. J. T. Smith, 1837, London.

(10) VICAT, L. J., 1818, *Récherches experimentales sur les Chaux de Construction*, Chez Goujon, Paris.

(11) GOODING, P. and HALSTEAD, P. E., 1954, 'The Early History of Cement in England,' *Proceedings* of the Third International Symposium on the Chemistry of Cement, London 1952, published by the Cement and Concrete Association.

(12) LEA, F. M., 1956, *The Chemistry of Cement and Concrete*, (revised edition of Lea and Desch), Arnold, London.

13

Stucco

THE TERM *stucco* is applied rather vaguely to renderings of lime, gypsum, or cement mixtures applied as a coating to both internal and external wall surfaces, or used for moulding into architectural decorations. The word is probably derived from an old German word *stucchi* meaning a crust. The renderings are put on wet and on drying form a durable coating which can be decorated if required. The earliest materials for daubing on wattle screens, or for rendering and decorating walls were mud and clay, or mud and chalk mixtures, with or without the addition of vegetable material such as chopped straw, grass, or reeds, or animal dung. Unless well protected from the weather it was clearly not a very durable material, but in spite of this it is still used in many parts of the world. The Egyptians used a stucco mainly of calcined gypsum to level up the surface of sun-dried brick walls and masonry walls by filling up the hollows and providing a hard smooth layer about $\frac{1}{16}$ inch in thickness, which could be painted. The masonry in the chambers in the Great Pyramids was treated in this way and a sample of the stucco[1] from the pyramid of Cheops was found to consist of 82 per cent of calcined gypsum and about 10 per cent calcium carbonate probably derived from the impurities in the raw gypsum before it was burnt, and not an artificial addition.

Although in some countries stone was plentiful it was not long before stucco came to be applied to masonry as a cheap substitute for dressing and tooling, and for sculptured ornament. In other countries, however, where stone was not available in quantity, as in Iraq for example, stucco was valued as a material which served not only as an ornamental covering to rough walls often of mud, but greatly increased their durability.

In Crete by the middle of the Early Minoan period lime stucco was applied as a protective coating to rubble masonry. At Vasiliki buildings of this period built of sun-dried bricks and of loose rubble were rendered with about 2 inches of stucco, the top coat being about $\frac{1}{2}$ to $\frac{3}{4}$ inch thick. An analysis[2] of this mixture showed that there was about 40 per cent of silica, not in the form of sand, and some alumina, which suggested either that the raw limestone before calcining contained some other matter such as clay, or that after the limestone had been calcined, a clayey substance had been added. There were also in the mixture some small pebbles, fragments of pottery, and a considerable proportion of chopped straw. Rather later examples from Knossos of Middle Minoan date consisted of 70 per cent of carbonated lime, and the remainder clay with an admixture of fine pebbles and grit. In these samples chopped straw was absent. The proportion of carbonated lime in later samples towards the end of the Middle Minoan period ran as high as 95 per cent. Whether this stucco was made of pure hydrated lime without any addition, or whether a proportion of powdered limestone was added to the lime, cannot be determined. The latter is likely, as this kind of mixture was used later by the Greeks and the Romans. It was sometimes applied by the Minoans in as many as four coats. The underneath coat was of coarse stucco of lime, small pebbles, and crushed pottery, and this was followed by coats of lime stucco mixture, each worked to a smooth finish, giving a total thickness to the rendering of about $\frac{3}{4}$ inch.

The Greeks made great use of stucco, often adding marble dust to the mixture, for covering stonework. Dinsmoor[3] records that the Doric temples were usually built of soft limestone (*poros*) taken from various local quarries, as no suitable marble was readily available. This porous limestone was covered with a thin coating of stucco, not only to fill in the crevices in the stone, but to allow a greater smoothness and refinement to be given to flat surfaces and mouldings. The stuccoed surface also provided a suitable ground for enrichment in colour.

Ancient writers refer to the use of stucco. Pliny, for example, records[4] that no builder should employ lime which had not been slaked for at least three years; certainly the longer that the lime is slaked the better will be the product. It seems unlikely, however, that much lime could have been kept for as long as three years before use, but it certainly was the practice in England and other countries until recent times for plasterers to keep in stock, in casks, a supply of well-slaked lime putty, and it is still considered good practice in many places to allow the putty to stand for at least three months before use. Vitruvius[5] writing about 16 B.C. refers in detail to the preparation of the lime and the importance of ensuring that it is thoroughly slaked, since if unslaked particles find their way into the finished work, they are liable to damage the surface on subsequent hydration. Vitruvius also records that the Greek plasterers made a trough in which a gang of men mixed up the stucco with wooden poles. Caius Plinius Secundus (A.D. 23 to 79) reiterates what Vitruvius said earlier and adds that 'stucco always lacks brilliance unless the wall had received three coats of sand mortar and two of marble mortar. In damp places and those exposed to attack by sea air, it is wiser to lay on a first coat of mortar made with powdered earthenware'.

The Romans took great care in the preparation of their stucco mixtures. A mixing pit or trough, or *mortarium*, is depicted on Trajan's column in Rome, and the mixing is being carried out with a special hoe (*ascia* or *rutrum*) made for the purpose (Plate XLV). This type of tool has continued in use until modern times, and is now known as a *larry*. The trough shown in the relief is rectangular in shape. The discovery of one such trough during excavations several years ago on a Roman site in Chelmsford throws some light on the method of preparation. A hole was excavated in the ground and was lined with the boards as shown in Plate XLVI, both sides and bottom, to avoid contamination of the mixture. The side boards were retained by means of vertical uprights. An analysis of the mixture remaining in the trough showed it to contain the following materials:

Ordinary chalk lime and lump chalk	50·6 per cent by weight
Gravel and sand	16·3 ,, ,, ,, ,,
Crushed tile and burnt clay	14·7 ,, ,, ,, ,,
Silt, clay, etc.	18·4 ,, ,, ,, ,,

Another method of preparing the mixture was to excavate a shallow pit in the ground, into which the lime was deposited and then slaked with water. One such pit, shown in Plate XLVII, was uncovered during the excavation of a Roman villa at Park Street near St Albans, in Hertfordshire.[6] The mixing pit measured 2 feet 9 inches in diameter and was 12 inches deep. When found it was full of carbonated lime which on analysis at the Building Research Station was found to be of a semi-hydraulic type, similar in composition to the present-day local greystone cretaceous lime of the Luton-Dunstable area. This lime would develop some strength and hardness when mixed with sand, but very much more when used in conjunction with an admixture of crushed tile.

It is apparent that considerable care was taken in slaking the lime, and during the process it was probably protected from the weather by being covered with straw, or bracken, as is still done in parts of Europe, the object being to conserve as much as possible of the heat generated during the process of slaking, and so to ensure as complete hydration as possible.

Vitruvius, in describing the preparation of stucco (Book VII, C. II), said that if the lime which is being slaked in the pit is chopped with a hoe, and lumps are met with, then the lime is not properly slaked. If when the hoe is drawn out it is dry and clean, it shows that the lime is poor, but if the lime clings to the tool like glue then it is rich and properly slaked and properly mixed.

Roman lime stucco modellings in slight relief, of the first century A.D., were very delicate in design and execution. One of a number of examples, now in the Museo Nazionale in Rome from the Villa Farnesina, shown in Plate XLVIII, serves to illustrate this. The figure is only about 18 inches high but contains a wealth of detail. Decorative mouldings were also run in this material; examples excavated in Roman Britain have been examined and found to consist entirely of carbonated lime, but the type of organic binder, if such were used, could not be established.

After the collapse of the Roman Empire the art of stucco declined in Italy until its revival in Rome in the fifteenth century. Little seems to have been added to the craft by the Byzantine builders. The Sassanian Persians who overthrew the Romans in Mesopotamia in the third century A.D. and even pushed them back across the Euphrates to the Gates of Antioch, developed the use of stucco for the ornamentation of buildings to a very great extent, and kept the art alive long after it had declined in Rome. It seems to have received some inspiration from the East. The palace at Ctesiphon, which they built probably in the middle of the sixth century, was originally richly decorated with moulded gypsum stucco ornament, examples of which are in the Iraq Museum, Baghdad. This great structure, of which the main reception hall and one wing of the façade are still standing (Plate LIV), is roofed with a great parabolic vault of unreinforced brickwork, the largest in the world.

This palace was captured in A.D. 637 by the Arabs, but in 750 the Abbasids assumed control and Caliph Mansur built their capital at Baghdad. Later, one of the Caliphs, Al-Muctasim, in 833 chose a new site for the capital at Samarra, seventy miles north-west of Baghdad. The whole concept covered hundreds of acres of ground, and the buildings were elaborately decorated with fine gypsum stucco ornament, and it is recorded that the best craftsmen of that time were encouraged to live at Samarra. An example of modelled and carved stucco from the site of this town is shown in Plate XLIX. It is made of raw gypsum stucco, or more precisely of the indigenous 'juss'.

This craft spread throughout the Near East, to Syria, Armenia, and Turkey, and to North Africa. Hamilton[7] records that in Syria the earliest buildings known to have been extensively decorated with carved stucco belong to the Umayyad period (more precisely to the Caliphate of Al Hisham, A.D. 726–743). The stucco is made of gypsum plaster and is used in three main classes of work: modelled in the round or in three-quarter relief for ornamental statuary; incrusted and deeply carved on walls and vaulting; and lastly, made up in the separate slabs carved or pierced to serve as window grilles or balustrades. He concludes that it is natural to infer that the introduction of this new material into Syria was connected with the existence in Iraq and Persia of a long established stucco industry, which as can be guessed from early Islamic buildings at Hira and other sites, and later from Samarra, had not been seriously interrupted by the Arab conquest.

By Mohammedan law the representation even in ornament of any living thing was forbidden, and in consequence the designs are mainly geometric with interlacing straps, scrollwork, and inscriptions. Some of the earliest known examples in Egypt are in the mosque of Ibn Touloun, in Cairo, finished in A.D. 878. The Mosque el Azhar, also in Cairo, built in A.D. 973, has excellent examples of modelled stucco arabesque ornaments and Kufic, or African, friezes.

Marguerite van Berchem[8] excavated beautifully carved plaster at the Ibadite capital of Sedrata, a Moslem city of the tenth to thirteenth centuries A.D., five hundred miles south of Algiers in the heart of the Sahara. She found rooms of buildings lined with sculptured plaster. A complete chamber of the palace was retrieved for the museum of Algiers. It measured 42 feet by 7 feet and had carved plaster inscriptions in beautiful Kufic characters attributed to the latter half of the eleventh century. Miss Berchem comments that with the Hellenistic traditions still preserved at Sedrata are blended many Oriental elements, and the fusion of two great civilizations accounts for the wealth and variety of the ornamentations found there. Local grey gypsum plaster called 'timchent' was used in the stucco, and in the construction of the rubble walls. It still is to this day.

In 710 Mohammedan Moors overran Spain, which they held until the fall of Granada to the Christians in 1492. They took the craft of stucco-working with them to Spain, and the most beautiful examples of their ornamental work are in the Alhambra, part of the palace of the Moorish Kings at Granada, perhaps the most famous of all Saracen buildings. It was commenced in 1248 by the Sultan Ibn al-Ahman and finished in 1354.

It was not until the fifteenth and sixteenth centuries that there was a revival in decorative stucco work in Italy, reaching its peak of popularity in the period of Raphael (1483–1520). It had become fashionable to study the work of the Roman craftsmen, particularly that revealed by systematic excavations in Rome, for example, of the Golden House of Nero, and to base new designs upon it. The Italian plasterers at first modelled in fairly low relief following the Roman pattern, but the modelling soon became bolder in design and execution, and perhaps the finest examples of all are to be found in the seventeenth century in the work of the Bernini School. By the middle of the eighteenth century, however, stucco work had become rather commonplace in Italy.

The early Italian stucco was old air-slaked lime and fine marble dust. Occasionally fine sand and hair were added. The mixture was well beaten with sticks, and sometimes a small amount of burnt gypsum was added to give it a 'set'. The hardened product was called 'stucco-duro', or hard stucco. The most durable Italian stucco had pozzolana incorporated in the lime mixture similar to the Roman material. A typical recipe, now in the Bodleian Library at Oxford, of mid-sixteenth-century date, is given by the Italian, Pirro Ligorio,[9] who collaborated with Michelangelo in the architectural work at St Peter's, Rome. The recipe says:

> Take three parts of pounded Parian marble—easily got from among the ruins in Rome, and from broken statues; add one part of lime which is to be perfectly slaked by letting it lie in a heap covered with pozzuolana and exposed to the sun and rain for at least a year. The lime is to be made from pure white marble, not from travertine, or any other stone which is full of holes and yellowish in tint. Mix a day before use with sufficient water on a tile floor. The first or 'rendering' coat to be of stucco, made with coarsely-pounded marble, allowed to dry thoroughly, before applying the finishing coat of the finely powdered marble cement.

Ligorio's description of the stucco is very like that given by Vitruvius[10] for *opus albarium* or *caementum marmoreum*.

Andrea di Pietro, or Palladio, by which name he is better known (1518–80), was a great exponent of the art of stucco. He had studied the ancient monuments at Rome and for his own buildings borrowed freely from classical architecture. He seems to have followed closely the precepts of Vitruvius, and in fact prepared a new edition in 1556 of the latter's work, collaborating with the Patriarch of Aquileia in the task. Most of his buildings, although designed to be executed in stone, were mainly constructed in brick with a covering and ornamentation of stucco. The palaces of Porto Barbarano and Chiericati in Vicenza are notable examples of this work.

In the 1530's Francis I commissioned Francesco Primaticcio, of Bologna, and Giovanni Battista Rosso, of Florence, to decorate the many rooms and loggias of his new palace at Fontainebleau in what were probably the first stucco and frescoes of any account in France. Not to be outdone, Henry VIII in 1538, when building his palace of Nonsuch at Cheam, between Sutton and Epsom, also employed Italians to carry out the very elaborate stucco decorations. Among these artist-craftsmen were Luca and Bartholomew

Penni, Gerome of Trevisa, and Toto del Nunziato. Unfortunately the palace was demolished in 1670 and little is therefore known about their work. During recent excavations, however, samples of the stucco work have been found. Some of the material was in excellent condition in spite of the fact that it had been exposed to the weather for over a hundred years up to the time of the demolition of the building.

The entry in his diary records John Evelyn's interesting comments on the state of Nonsuch Palace in 1666. It reads:

> Jan. 3rd. I supp'd in Nonsuch House whither the office of the Exchequer was transferred during the Plague . . . and tooke an exact view of ye plaster statues and bass relievos inserted 'twixt the timbers and punchions of the outside walles of the Court; which must needs have been the work of some celebrated Italian. I much admired how they had lasted so well and intire since the time of Henry VIII, expos'd as they are to the aire; and pitty it is that they are not taken out and preserved in some drie place; a gallarie would become them. There are some mezzo-relievos as big as the life; the storie is of ye Heathen Gods, emblems, compartments, etc. The Palace consists of two courts, of which the first is of stone, castle-like, by ye Lo. Lumlies (of whom 'twas purchased), ye other of timber, a Gotiq fabric, but these walls incomparably beautiful. I observ'd that the appearing timber punchions, entrelices, etc., were all so well covered with scales of slate, that it seem'd carv'd in the wood and painted, ye slate fastened on the timber in pretty figures that has, like a coat of armour, preserv'd it from rotting. There stand in the garden two handsome stone pyramids, and the avenue planted with rows of faire elmes, but the rest of these goodly trees, both of this and of Worcester Park adjoining, were fell'd by those destructive and avaricious rebells in the late warr, which defac'd one of the stateliest Seates his Majesty had.

During the remainder of the sixteenth century, other master plasterers continued to come to England from Italy. There was De Rudolfi in 1550, Leonardo Ricciarelli, who had previously worked at the Palazzo Vecchio, at Florence, in 1570, and Luca Romano as late as 1586.[11] English craftsmen had ample opportunity to learn from these Italian masters and although they soon became adept at the craft of stucco work they do not seem to have contributed much towards its artistic development. One early example of English lime stucco work is to be seen at Old Hardwick Hall, built between 1590 and 1597. In 1630 Inigo Jones used stucco on the fronts of buildings round the Covent Garden Piazza.

The mixtures used in England were of lime with various organic additives many of which have been named in the literature of the subject, e.g. rye dough, barley water, hog's lard, bullock's blood, cow dung, wort and eggs, wort and beer, milk, gluten, buttermilk, cheese, curdled milk, saponified beeswax, fig and other fruit and vegetable juices, all intended to improve its adhesive qualities.

In the middle of the eighteenth century another group of stucco mixtures, now known as 'oil mastics' or 'oleaginous cements', were used. An early one dates from 1765 and was patented in that year by David Wark, of Haddington. In 1773 Liardet, a clergyman of Switzerland, produced another mixture (British Patent No. 1040—1773). The Adam brothers acquired both these patents and they called the mixture 'Adams new invented patent stucco', and it became known as 'Adams Cement'. They used it for the fronts of buildings in Portland Place and Hanover Square, and Thomas Leverton used it in Bedford Square.

Similar compositions were marketed by Christopher Dihl in 1815 and 1816 (British Patent No. 3872—1815 and No. 4033—1816) and by Hamelin in 1817 as 'Hamelin's cement' (British Patent No. 4144—1817). Dihl's mastic cement was made of linseed oil boiled with litharge and mixed with porcelain clay finely powdered and coloured with ground bricks or pottery, turpentine being used as a thinner. It was used by John Nash for the ornaments of the Regent's Park Terraces (1821–4), and for much of the external stucco and the ornamental work at Carlton House Terrace (1827–33).

Hamelin's cement contained powdered limestone, brickdust, and siliceous sand mixed with litharge and ground up with linseed oil. It was very similar to a mixture used by P. Loriot in the early eighteenth century and later by French engineers at La Rochelle in 1826[12] who used a mixture containing 14 parts (by volume) of siliceous sand, 14 parts (by volume) of pulverized calcareous stone, $\frac{1}{14}$ of the united weights of sand and stone, of litharge and $\frac{1}{7}$ of the total weight of linseed oil. Other engineers in Paris used a mixture containing 6 parts by weight of 'cement', sometimes natural cement, or sometimes burnt clay, 1 part of white lead, 1 part of litharge, 3 parts of linseed oil, and $\frac{1}{2}$ part of a richer oil (probably animal oil). Nash used Hamelin's cement for the front of the United Services Club, Pall Mall, in 1828, and D. Burton used it for the frieze of the Atheneum Club (1829–30).

The views expressed by Gwynne[13] in 1766 are very much in line with those held by others at the time. He said that 'no publick edifice ought to be built of brick unless it is afterwards stucco'd, for a mere brick face . . . makes a mean appearance'. By 1782, Nash, who received his training in the office of Sir Robert Taylor, was building houses in London the fronts of which were covered with a stucco of lime and sand. A group of these houses built in 1783 survives at the corner of Great Russell Street and Bloomsbury Square. From 1796 Nash used Roman cement until about 1820 when he changed to mastic cement (Hamelin's or Dihl's).

Reference has already been made to the so-called 'Roman cement' invented by Parker and which was sold by Charles Wyatt and Co., Bankside, London. It superseded the trass and pozzolana mortars that had previously been used for stucco work. James Wyatt (1747–1813), who was Surveyor-General, did much to popularize its use, and used it on many of his buildings, but it was Nash who used it for decorating the fronts of better known buildings in Park Crescent, London (1812–19).

According to Nicholson[14] writing in 1842 the usual stucco mixture consisted of equal parts of 'Roman cement' and clean gritty sand, and this was applied to the wall as quickly as possible after mixing, and incessantly trowelled until it set. As soon as this happened, it was frescoed with a colour wash, containing 5 ounces of copperas (sulphate of iron) to every gallon of water, and mixed up with as much 'Roman cement' and fresh lime as would produce the effect required. When the whole area had been covered and had assumed a uniform colour it was tinted in imitation of Bath, Portland, or other freestone and carefully ruled to represent well bonded masonry. The surfaces had to be redecorated after a few years.

'Roman' cements continued in use but during the latter part of the nineteenth century Portland cement tended to replace them for many purposes, as it was more reliable. Experience in this century has shown that renderings in modern Portland cement mortar are unnecessarily hard and tend to shrink and crack, and in order to reduce this trouble it is now customary to add hydrated lime to the mixture in an amount equal in volume to or up to twice the volume of the cement.

REFERENCES

(1) PARTINGTON, J. R., 1935, *Origins and Development of Applied Chemistry*, Longmans Green.

(2) HEATON, NOEL, 30 Sept. 1911, 'Minoan Lime and Plaster and Fresco Painting', *Journal* of the Royal Institute of British Architects, 3rd series, XVIII, 697.

(3) DINSMOOR, W. B., 1950, *The Architecture of Ancient Greece*, Batsford, 70.

(4) PLINY, *Secundi Naturalis Historiae*, Book XXXIV, XXIII, 55. (See Bailey, K. C., 1932, *The Elder Pliny's Chapters on Chemical Subjects*, Part II, Arnold.)

(5) VITRUVIUS, *De Architectura*, Book II and Book VII. Translated by Gwilt, 1880, London.

(6) O'NEIL, H. E., 1947, 'The Roman Villa at Park Street, near St. Albans, Hertfordshire: Report on the Excavations of 1943–45', *Archaeological Journal*, CII.

(7) HAMILTON, R. W., 1953, 'Carved Plaster in Umayyad Architecture', *Iraq*, XV, Part 1.

(8) VAN BERCHEM, MARGUERITE, 31 Jan. 1953, 'Uncovering a lost city of the Sahara: excavating Sedrata, the thousand year old capital of the Ibadites in S. Algeria,' *Illustrated London News*.

(9) Canonici MSS (No. 138) Bodleian Library, Oxford.

(10) VITRUVIUS, *De Architectura*, Book VII, 2–6.

(11) VASARI, G., *Lives of the Painters, Sculptors and Architects*, translated by A. B. Hinds, 1927, Dent, IV, 193.

(12) BURNELL, G. R., 1856, *Limes, Cements, Mortars and Concretes*, Weales' Rudimentary series, 2nd ed., Crosby Lockwood.

(13) GWYNNE, S., 1766, *London and Westminster Improved*.

(14) NICHOLSON, P., 1823, *New Practical Builder*, Thos. Kelly, London.

14

Mortar and Concrete

'MORTAR' IS A TERM loosely applied to material used for bedding, jointing, and rendering brickwork and stonework and it normally consists of cementitious or other binding material, with or without a suitable filler or fine aggregate.

The oldest mortar used for building was mud, and it still is used in many countries throughout the world. In ancient Egypt mud mortar was used with sun-dried bricks, but for bedding the stonework of monumental buildings, gypsum was used. In the latter case the large stone blocks were so carefully worked that the joints between them were often very thin, and the gypsum mortar acted not so much as a bonding material, but as a film of lubricant to allow the blocks to be accurately set in position by sliding if necessary.

The Babylonians and Assyrians used several kinds of mortar. Clay or mud, usually with chopped straw or reeds, but sometimes without, was used from the earliest times, and still survives all over the Middle East as the traditional type of mortar. Asphaltic mortars were used for bedding burnt bricks at least as early as the third millennium B.C., and continued in use for a long while. In later buildings at Babylon, of Nebuchadnezzar's time, asphaltic mixtures were to a large extent replaced by hydrated lime, to which clay, bitumen, ashes, or other materials were sometimes added. Lime-burning had apparently been practised in Mesopotamia at least as early as 2450 B.C. for the remains of a lime-kiln are recorded from Khafaje.[1] Gypsum mortar also has been used throughout the Middle East for four thousand years or more.

Cements have always been relatively expensive materials to produce, and in order to eke them out in building mortars, the tendency has usually been to dilute them with cheaper materials, such as natural sand, crushed stone, tile dust, and ashes. The kinds of sand that can be used vary widely. Some have a pozzolanic effect and contribute towards the strength of the mortar, others act merely as inert dilutants. If the sand is well-graded and the spaces between the larger grains are filled with smaller grains, a good mortar can be produced with a relatively small amount of cement or binder. If on the other hand the sand is badly graded, for example with a preponderance either of fine or of coarse grains, the mortar will be of inferior quality.

A good reason, no doubt discovered long ago, for adding a considerable amount of sand to lime and other cements was that the mortar so produced did not shrink so much when it dried as did the cements if used neat or when only a smaller amount of sand was added. These kinds of mixtures were always used as the undercoats for stucco renderings and frescoes in order to avoid shrinkage cracks, or 'crazing', as it is called.

Recent researches have shown that brickwork built with a relatively 'lean' mortar, that is one with a relatively low cement content, may be considerably stronger than that built with a much 'richer' mortar.[2]

It is apparent from the comments made by Vitruvius[3] that much was known in Roman times about the importance of proper selection of the sand for building mortars and some of his statements are worth repeating:

> . . . Now where there is no quarry sand we must use washed river or sea sand. . . .

which draws attention to the importance of washing sand to remove the impurities. The crushed stone of the quarry sand would be clean and generally need no washing.

> . . . Now in rubble structures we must first inquire about the sand, that it is suitable for mixing material into mortar, and without the admixture of earth—

the sand should not be deficient in fine material.

> . . . that [sand] which makes a noise when rubbed in the hand will be best; but that which is earthy will not have a like roughness—

in other words the sand should be what in modern terminology is called 'sharp'.

> . . . Also, if it is covered up in a white cloth, and afterwards shaken up or beaten, and does not foul it, and the earth does not settle therein, it will be suitable—

the sand must be clean and not contaminated with earth.

> . . . But if there are no sandpits whence it may be dug, then it must be sifted out from the river bed, or from gravel, not less also from the sea shore . . .

This suggests that sifting, or sieving, was resorted to on occasion to prepare a suitable sand. Vitruvius goes on to point out the disadvantages of sea sand in that it causes efflorescence on walls. He also says:

> . . . But sea sand has these faults in buildings; it dries with difficulty, nor does the wall allow itself to be loaded continuously without interruptions for rest, nor does it allow of vaulting—

pointing out quite correctly that the salt being hygroscopic, the mortar remains damp, and as would be the case with lime mortar its hardening may be delayed, thus slowing up the rate of building. The disadvantage of sand derived from stone quarries is that if it is left exposed to weather before use, it may disintegrate and become dusty:

> For if after being taken out [from the quarry] it lies too long, it is weathered by the sun and the moon and the hoar frost, and is dissolved and becomes earthy.

The term *concrete* is also very wide and includes almost any solid materials called *aggregates* bound together by cementitious materials such as hydraulic limes and Portland cement. The differentiation between mortar and concrete is a purely arbitrary one. In modern practice the aggregates for mortar normally pass through a sieve with $\frac{3}{16}$-inch square openings, whereas mixtures with aggregates coarser than this would be classed as concrete.

Possibly the earliest use to which concrete was put by the Romans was in foundations, as in the *podia* of the temples of Concord and of Castor, 121 and 117 B.C. Concrete, as we understand it, was probably already in use by the Romans by the end of the third century B.C.

The Romans also used concrete, or *opus caementicium*, to a very great extent as a filling or hearting to walls faced with stone blocks. It was composed of layers of broken stones and broken tiles which they called *caementa*, each layer being grouted with lime mortar so as to fill the interstices. In the first and second centuries B.C. the stone block facing was often replaced by a facing of small stone, and the work was called *opus incertum*. This usually necessitated the use of timber formwork. A development of this type of work was *opus reticulatum* like that shown in the breakwater, near Naples, in Plate XLIV. It consisted of squared pieces of stone, set with their sides at 45 degrees to the horizontal, to form a netlike, or reticulate, pattern; and was in use for about 150 years from the first century B.C. to the second century A.D.[4] Concrete walls faced with brick, called *opus testaceum*, were more popular and were commonly used from the first century B.C. until the end of the Western Empire. Sometimes, from the third century A.D. onwards, stone and bricks were mixed to produce work which the Romans called *opus mixtum*.

The more daring and important use to which the Romans put concrete was in the construction of vaults and domes, and as Middleton[4] pointed out it had a very important effect upon the general forms adopted by the Roman architects under the Empire. He comments that

> As the use of buttresses had not been systematised, it would have been impossible for the Romans to build and vault their enormous spans if they had used vaulting of brick or masonry, such as were built in medieval times. The Roman concrete vault was quite devoid of any lateral thrust, and covered its space with the rigidity of a metal lid. Such vaults as those over the chief halls of the great Thermae would at once have pushed out their supporting walls if a true arched construction had been used. But by using the form without the principle of the arch these apparently daring structures stood with perfect safety. It is true that in many cases, such as the Basilica of Constantine, and the Thermae of Caracalla and Diocletian, brick arches are embedded in the concrete vaults at various points, especially at the intersection of two vaults, but, just as in the brick facing of the walls, these arches are merely superficial, and only tail a few inches into the mass of concrete vault, which very frequently is as much as 6 feet thick.

Ward Perkins,[5] Director of the British School in Rome, has also more recently pointed out in an excellent summary of the subject that

> many an unsuspecting visitor leaves Rome under the impression that the Pantheon and the

Baths of Caracalla really are brick buildings. In actual fact the brick is a purely superficial skin, its principal purposes were to provide an even surface and to contain the concrete core while it dried out. Another common fallacy is due to the fact that the brickwork often incorporates what appear to be obviously structural devices, like relieving arches over doors and windows. This has led some scholars to talk about Roman vaulting in terms of the collection and transmission of thrust, just as if a Roman concrete building were a dynamic organism in the same sense as, let us say, a Gothic Cathedral. The truth is that, once it had dried out, Roman concrete was almost completely inert. Relieving arches and the like did have an important part to play during construction; but once the building was finished, it stood by virtue of the immensely tough monolithic qualities of the concrete itself. Walls and vaults might in theory be built to any shape the architect chose, so long as the resultant shell was strong enough to stand up under its own dead weight.

The coffered concrete vaults in the Roman buildings already mentioned are magnificent, but the example chosen to illustrate this type of construction is the apse of the ruined Temple of Venus and Roma, at the east end of the Forum in Rome (Figure 84). The temple was dedicated by Emperor Hadrian in A.D. 135 to Venus, mother of the Julian Gens, and to the Goddess Roma. It is thought that Apollodorus designed it. He was the architect of Trajan's Forum, the Pantheon, and the Villa near Tivoli.

Sometimes, in later work, as at Verulamium and elsewhere in Britain, flints or large stones were placed in layers in timber formwork, and mortar was spread on each layer before the next was placed. The mortar in this case was of stiffer consistence, and did not penetrate far into the interstices between the stones. By building in this way, rather than by grouting, as was done earlier, the pressures on the timber formwork during the building of the wall were greatly reduced, and work could proceed at a greater pace with less fear of collapse. It was usual, however, to carry up the concrete in 'lifts' about 3 feet in height, and then to lay on a bonding course of two or three thicknesses of tile. Apart from the fact that these string courses, or bonding courses, strengthened the work and helped to ensure its stability, they also provided a level base on which to place the next lift of concrete.

Neuberger[6] records that in the reign of Caligula (A.D. 37–41) a mole was built at Naples of concrete blocks which had been allowed to harden before use. If in fact this was so it is probably the earliest instance of the use of precast concrete.

Varieties of concrete and the uses to which it has been put, particularly during the last hundred years or so, have been infinite, and it has become one of the most important building materials.

The study of the composition of mortars and concretes has been very useful to archaeologists in helping to relate various parts of a building, when other dating evidence is absent. Mortar analysis by itself, however, cannot be used for dating purposes except possibly within very broad limits. It is quite a common experience, on a given site, to find that the composition of mortars used in building walls changes at different periods of construction, simply because the raw materials for making the mortar at one period were derived from a different source from that of an earlier period. The mortar from the later period may also include re-used material from the earlier period. In the absence of dating evidence it has often been possible to show that a particular length of wall was built with the same kind of mortar as that in another length of wall of predetermined date. The fact that the mortar is of the same composition in the two lengths of wall is, of course, no proof that the walls were built at the same time. It is, however, highly probable that they were. In some cases, the examination of the mortar spill in a 'robber trench' has made it possible to relate the removed wall to some other part of the structure which is still intact and of known date. Although some mortar compositions may be typical of certain periods it is not at present possible to date an isolated sample of mortar with any certainty.

Pioneering work in this field of investigation was undertaken in Rome by Miss Van Deman[7] working under the auspices of the American Academy of Archaeology. The type and composition of the materials of construction were found to vary at different periods, and this provided a means of establishing which buildings and monuments were of similar date.

The study of ancient building mortars and concretes has been rather neglected in England until recently, and it is clear that archaeologists should look at them rather more closely than they do. One of the best examples of this kind of study was made on the mortars of the Roman Villa at Park Street, near St Albans, excavated by Mrs O'Neil.[8] Here it was possible by a study of the mortar composition to relate various walls of the villa. The walls of the successive buildings were of coursed flints set in lime mortar, and with occasional courses and quoins of tile. Twenty-three samples of mortar were taken for analysis. The position from which these were taken is indicated by the numbers in Figure 64. The samples were treated with dilute acid to separate the carbonated lime from the aggregate, i.e. the sand and other ingredients. In this way it was possible not only to study the grading and other characteristics of the aggregate, but also to determine the approximate proportion of lime putty used in the original mixtures. A summary of these analyses, made at the Building Research Station, is given in the Table on page 126, in which the samples are grouped according to the respective periods determined by excavation. The analyses show that the character of the mortar varied considerably at successive periods. For example, in period A the lime content was low, and the sand was coarse pit sand with little clay and silt, and was perhaps acquired when the pit was dug for the construction of the cellar. In period B the lime content was increased and the sand, probably obtained from another local source possibly nearer the river, was of finer grading with rather more clay and silt, while in period C the mortar was very much richer in lime, and the sand still finer with more clay and silt than in periods A and B. The sand used in period A was uncrushed. Four of the eight samples of period B contained some crushed material. All the samples of period C contained crushed material making the sand sharp and angular.

A further important feature was noticed. In period A there was a complete absence of red tile dust from the mortar, while in period B, with one exception, traces of tile dust were present, but the addition was so small as to be considered accidental. In period C,

Plate XXXIX. Chinese pottery brick or block from a mortuary chamber of the Han Dynasty (206 B.C.–A.D. 220) (see page 89).

QVESTA·ORA·AFACTA·FARE·LACONPAGNIA·DICASTELSAGIO VANNI·PELANIMA·
DEBENEFATORI·EOPERATORI·DIDETTA·CONPANGNIA

Plate XL. Terracotta panel of the Madonna and Child in the Basilica of S. Croce, Firenze, by Luca della Robbia; fifteenth century (see page 89).

Plate XLI. Terracotta ornament in the gateway to Syon House, Brentford, built by Robert Adam; eighteenth century (see page 90).

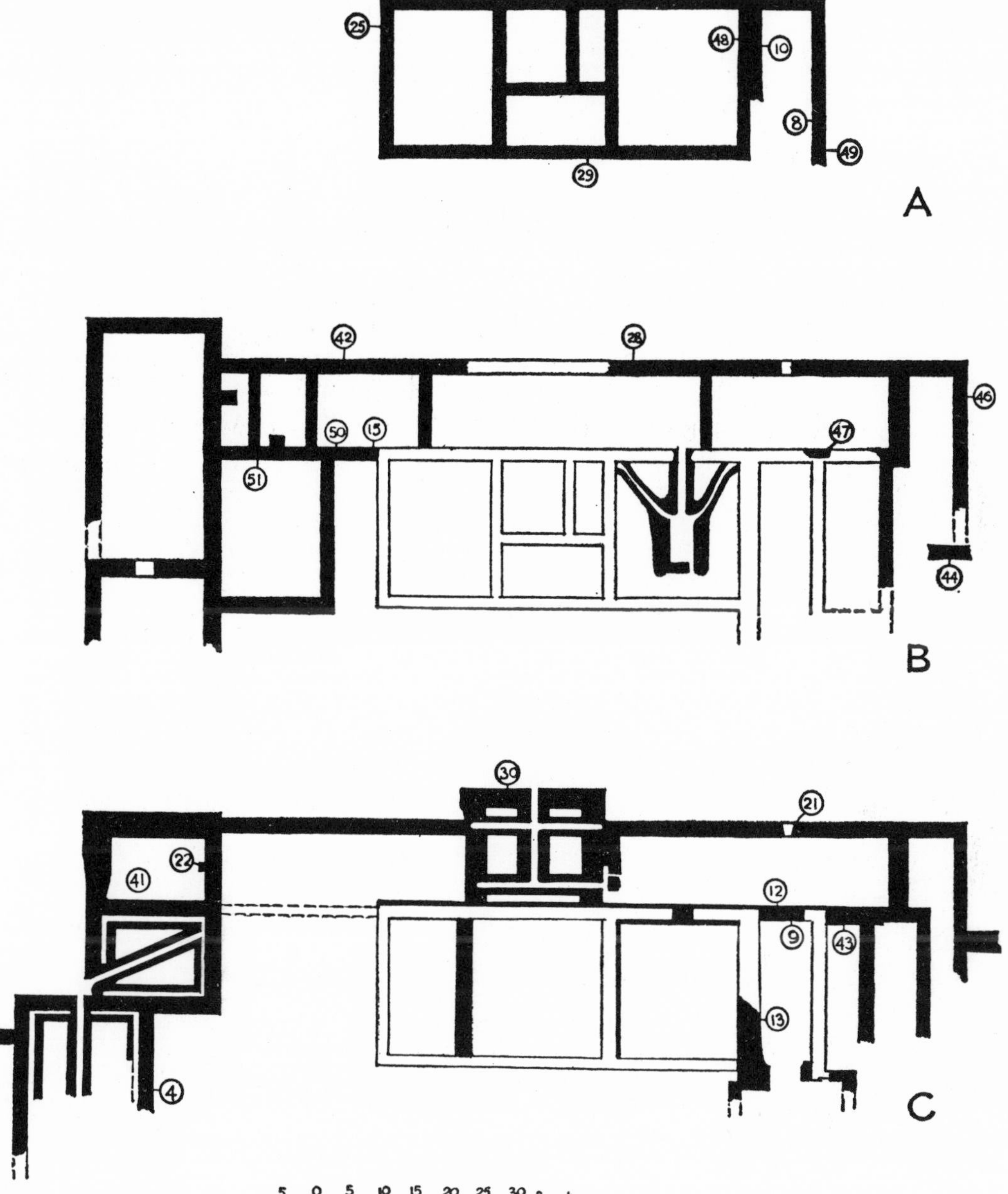

Fig. 64. Roman Villa at Park Street, near St Albans, showing walls of three successive periods of construction.

however, with only one exception, there was a deliberate inclusion in the mixture of crushed tile, and in three instances crushed rubble, while one mixture contained chopped straw. The colour of the mortar also varied from orange in period A to almost white in period C.

K

ANALYSIS OF MORTARS USED IN THE CONSTRUCTION OF THE WALLS OF THE ROMAN VILLA AT PARK STREET, NEAR ST ALBANS

		TYPE OF SAND			MORTAR	
Period	*Sample Nos.*	*Grading*	*Clay and silt content*	*Admixture*	*Approximate proportions of mixture: volumes of sand to one volume of lime putty*	*Colour*
(A) Late first to mid second century	8, 10, 25, 29, 48, 49	Coarse sand of natural grading Av. F.M.* = 4·6	Low Av. = 9%	Nil	Av. = 3·1 Range = 2·2–3·9	Orange
(B) Late second century	15, 28, 42, 44, 46, 47, 50, 51	Sand of variable grading, but finer than Period A Av. F.M. = 4·1	Medium Av. = 12·8%	Trace of tile; probably accidental inclusion	Av. = 2·3 Range = 1·3–3·5	Yellow
(C) Early fourth century / Middle fourth century	12, 13, 21, 22, 30, 41, 43 / 4, 9	Sand of finer grading than Periods A and B Av. F.M. = 3·0	High Av. = 16·3%	Deliberate additions of crushed tile and/or rubble	Av. = 1·2 Range = 0·5–1·9	White

* The Fineness Modulus (F.M.) is a convenient index for comparing the relative fineness of various sands. It is obtained by adding the percentages, by weight, of material retained on a range of nine selected sieves and dividing the result by 100. The British Standards sieves used are $1\frac{1}{2}$ in., $\frac{3}{4}$ in., $\frac{3}{8}$ in., $\frac{3}{16}$ in., Nos. 7, 14, 25, 52, and 100.

The average proportions of mixture used in period A—one volume of lime putty to approximately three volumes of sand—agree with those recommended by Vitruvius.[9] He stated that:

> ... When it [the lime] is slaked, let it be mingled with the sand in such a way that if it is pit sand three of sand and one of lime is poured in; but if the same is from the river or sea, two of sand and one of lime is thrown together. For in this way there will be the right proportion of the mixture and blending.

The interesting technical point here is that the use of river and sea sand which would in general be of finer grading, and consequently had a higher surface area than the pit sand, necessitated an increase in the proportion of lime. For the same reason, the lime content of the period B mortars from Park Street, in which the sand was of finer grading, was increased in the manner recommended by Vitruvius, i.e. one volume of lime putty to approximately two volumes of sand. The general agreement between the proportions of mix used in the Park Street Villa mortars, and those recommended by Vitruvius, who wrote somewhere about 27 B.C. or earlier, is not without significance.

An examination of some hundreds of samples of Roman mortars and concretes from many Roman buildings in England has indicated that the sand and coarse material was selected for size, and may have been specially screened for some work. For example, of 58 samples of wall renderings, 55 had sand that passed through a screen with slots ·48 inch (*semuncia*) wide; of 209 samples of masonry mortars 200 had sand and coarse material all passing through ·76 (*digitus*) slots; and of 95 samples of concrete for floors and foundations, the material of 90 of them passed through ·97 inch (*uncia*) slots. This points very strongly to some means of grading the aggregates for particular work. What precise form the screens took remains to be discovered.

REFERENCES

(1) FRANKFORT, H., JACOBSEN, T., and PREUSSER, C., 1932, 'Tell Asmar and Kafaje, the first season's work in Eshnunna, 1930–31', Chicago University Oriental Institute Communication No. 13.

(2) DAVEY, N., 1937, *Strength of Brickwork in relation to that of Brick and Mortar*, International Association for Testing Materials, London Symposium, 384.

(3) VITRUVIUS, *De Architectura*, Book I, II, and Book II, IV.

(4) MIDDLETON, J. H., 1888, 'On the Chief Methods of Construction used in Ancient Rome', *Archaeologia*, LI, Part 1, 41–60.

(5) WARD PERKINS, J. B., 1 and 8 Nov. 1956, 'Roman Concrete and Roman Palaces', *The Listener*.

(6) NEUBERGER, A., 1930, *The Technical Arts and Sciences of the Ancients*, translated by H. L. Brose, Methuen, 404.

(7) VAN DEMAN, ESTHER BOISE, 1912, 'Methods of Determining the date of Roman Concrete Monuments', *American Journal of Archaeology*, XVI, 230–387. For an account of Miss Deman's later work published after her death see BLAKE, MARION ELIZABETH, 1947, *Ancient Roman Construction in Italy from the Prehistoric Period to Augustus*, Carnegie Institution of Washington, Publication 570.

(8) O'NEIL, H. E., 1947, 'The Roman Villa at Park Street, near St. Albans, Hertfordshire: Report on the Excavations of 1943–45', *Archaeological Journal*, CII.

(9) VITRUVIUS, *De Architectura*, Book II, V. Frank Granger's translation 1931, Heinemann.

15

Asphaltic Bitumen

THERE ARE MANY varieties of bitumen, and many forms in which it has been used for building, particularly for waterproofing purposes. The term 'bitumen' is a generic one and is applied to a non-crystalline, semi-solid, or viscous mixture of complex hydrocarbons derived from petroleum deposits. It occurs either naturally in association with mineral matter, when it is known as 'asphaltic bitumen', or is obtained artificially by refinery processes from crude petroleum.

Bitumens occur in Natural Rock Asphalt, which is found in many parts of the world and which ranges from soft varieties of limestone bearing from 6 to 14 per cent of bitumen, to the more massive crystalline types of limestone bearing from 2 to 20 per cent. In this latter case the impregnation is often very uneven. Most of the rock asphalt used today comes from

- (i) the Cretaceous deposits in the Neuchâtel-Val de Travers region in Switzerland, and in the Pyrimont-Volent (Seyssel) region of Ain and Haute Savoie in France;
- (ii) the Oligocine deposits of the Department of Gard in France;
- (iii) the Tertiary deposits in the Ragusa region in the province of Syracuse in Sicily.

Bitumen also occurs naturally in Lake Asphalt, obtained mainly from Lake Trinidad in the British West Indies, and which is a fluid mixture containing 50 to 60 per cent of bitumen and the rest very fine siliceous silt and clay and some insoluble organic matter. The supply of Lake Asphalt from Trinidad seems almost inexhaustible, and great quantities are exported all over the world. The existence of this lake was first recorded by Sir Walter Raleigh, who notes in his journal that having left England in February 1595 he reached Trinidad on 22 March, where he visited a place called Parico, and in his *History of the Discovery of Guiana* he wrote:

> From thence I rowed to another part, called by the naturals 'Piche', and by the Spaniards 'Tierra de Brea . . .', there is that abundance of stone pitch that all the shippes of the world may be therewith loden from thence, and wee made trial of it in trimming our shippes to be most excellent good, and melteth not with the sunne as the pitch of Norway, and therefore for shippes trading the South parts very profitable.

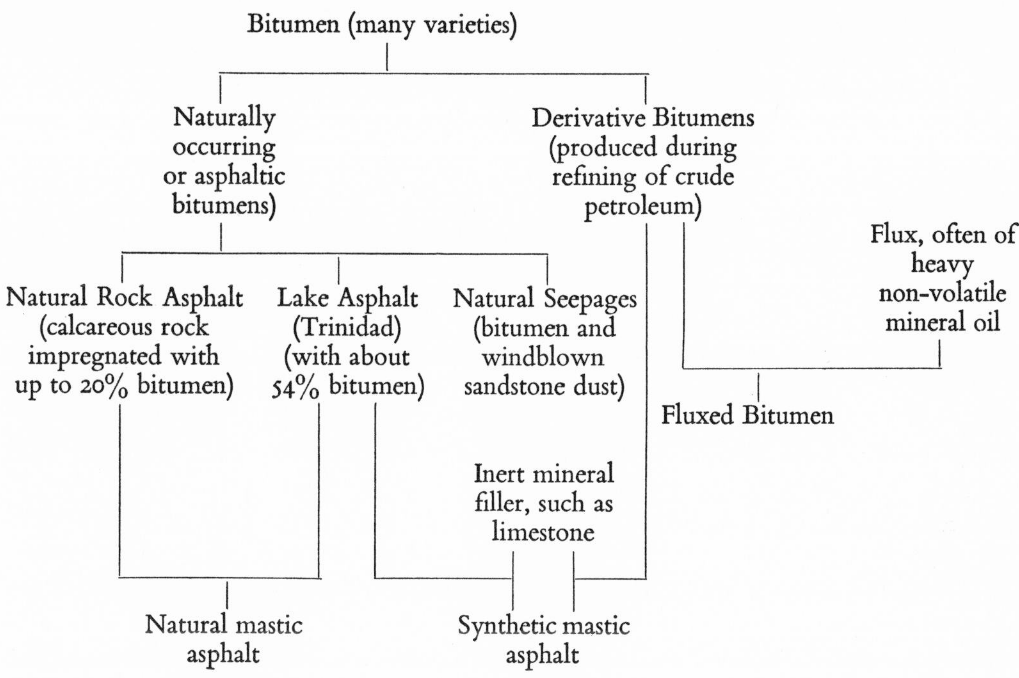

However, it was not till the beginning of the eighteenth century that the material was exploited commercially to any great extent. Other lake deposits exist in Bermuda, Venezuela, Cuba, and Texas.

Another source of supply comes from natural seepages of bitumen through veins in the earth, and which have absorbed wind-blown sand and other matter to form a kind of asphalt. Such seepages occur in many parts of the Middle East from Egypt to Pakistan, and it is generally considered that it was from such deposits as these that the early civilizations in the area obtained their supplies of material for bonding brickwork, for damp-proof-coursing, for lining drains, water basins, and baths, and for covering floors. The material is exceedingly tough and difficult to remove, and in consequence it has not much commercial value today, although it is collected in small pieces for local use. Plate L shows Arabs digging out the material, with odd tools, from a bitumen pool at Burgan in the Arabian desert not far from Kuwait. Other seepages occur at Quijarah, Ramadi and Abu Gir, west of Baghdad, and farther east at Bushire and Bundar Abbas in Iran, on the Persian Gulf. There are many more. When such seepages as these occur at the bottom of a lake or pool, or from the sea bed, as it does in the Dead Sea, the material rises and floats on the surface of the water, to be collected in lumps or skimmed off with matting. The Dead Sea was known to classical writers as 'Lacus Asphaltites' and the bitumen obtained from it as 'Bitumen Judaicum'.[1] The Sea overlies the ancient 'Vale of Siddom' which according to Genesis xiv. 10, was full of 'slime pits'. It is now generally accepted that this Biblical reference in the English texts to 'slime' alludes to asphalt. The word translated as 'slime' in the Bishops' Bible of 1568 appears as 'asphaltos' in the Greek

Septuagint version (third century B.C.), as 'bitumen' in the Latin Vulgate (fourth century A.D.) and as 'bitume' in the Douai translation (A.D. 1609–10) which was in fact based on the Vulgate version.

In spite of the presence of bitumen in the Dead Sea and in deposits on its shores, there is so far very little evidence of the extended use of bitumen in Palestine for building purposes, although Garstang[2] found brick walls at Jericho cemented with 'bituminous earth' dating from about 2500–2100 B.C. It is in Babylonia that the greatest use was made of bituminous mixtures even as far back as the middle of the fourth millennium B.C., and the most important sources of supply were at Hit and in the neighbourhood of Babylon. Herodotus[3] mentions the first site saying:

> There is another city called Is [Hit] eight days journey from Babylon, where a little river flows, also named Is, a tributary stream of the Euphrates, from the source of this river rise with the water many gouts of bitumen and from thence the bitumen was brought for the wall of Babylon.

Strabo[4] (63 B.C.–A.D. 24) wrote:

> Babylonia produces great quantities of asphalt, concerning which Eratosthenes [of Alexandria 276–194 B.C.] states that the liquid kind, called napha, is found in Susa [Iran] but the dry kind which can be solidified, in Babylonia. There is a fountain of this latter asphalt near the Euphrates [at Hit], and when this river is at its flood at the time of the melting of the snows, the fountain of asphalt is also filled and overflows into the river, and that these large clods of asphalt are formed which are suitable for buildings of baked bricks. Other writers say that the liquid kind also is found in Babylonia. Now writers state in particular the great usefulness of the dry kind in the construction of buildings, but they also say that boats woven with reeds and when plastered with asphalt, are impervious to water.

Abraham[5] records that samples from the deposits at Hit, from Ain el Maraj (near Kirkuk) and from Ain Ma'Moura (Ain Mamurah) contained between 64 and 79 per cent of asphalt and the remainder water.

Houses dating from about 3500 B.C. excavated near Al'Ubaid consisted of a simple frame of arched bundles of reeds to which rush matting coated with bitumen had been attached to form the walls. This appears to be the earliest use of bitumen in building so far discovered. Excavations in 1931[6] at Tell Asmar, fifty miles north-east of Baghdad on the east bank of the Diyala River, and at Khafaje in the same area, also revealed the skilled use of the material a little later for pavements, for bonding clay bricks in walls, for protecting exterior masonry surfaces, for trowelling over the surface of interior floors and stair treads, and for water-proofing baths and drains. The temple of Ur-Nina, King of Lagash (*c.* 2800 B.C.), in the City of Kish, had foundations of plano-convex bricks cemented with bituminous mortar, and buildings of the same period at Nippur about sixty miles south of Baghdad had walls of natural stone blocks jointed with it, and gutters built of brick laid in bituminous mortar. These early mortars contained from 25 to 35 per cent of bitumen, the rest of the mixture being loam and chopped straw or reeds. At this time the value of bitumen as a water-proofing material was also appreciated by the people in the Indus valley. At Mohenjo-Daro, twenty-five miles south of Larkana, in Sind, Pakistan, for example, in front of a temple dating from 3250 to 2750 B.C. was found in 1923 a water-tank measuring 39 feet by 23 feet by 8 feet deep. It is recorded[7] that on the outside of its 3 to 4 feet thick walls was a 1 inch layer of rock asphalt retained in position by further brickwork. The underside of its floor, and three large supply and drainage channels, had been water-proofed in a similar way.

Koldewey[8] has described the building of walls in Babylonia and Nineveh as first a course of bricks, then a layer of asphalt, then a layer of clay and then another course of bricks. Thus in each course there was asphalt and clay. In every fifth course the layer of clay was replaced by a matting of reeds. He records that in one locality (Temple of

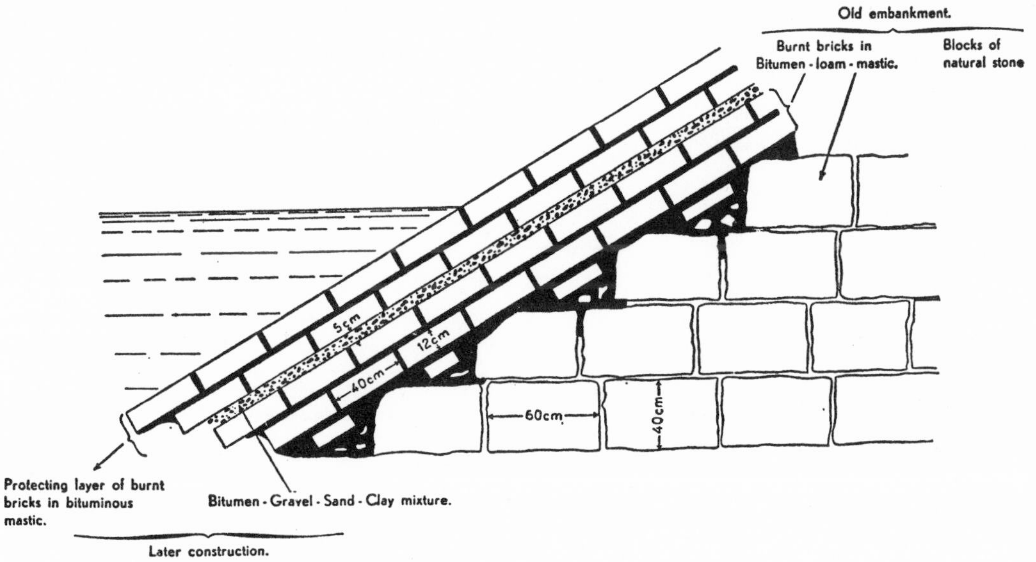

Fig. 65. Construction of Tigris Embankment at Assur; 1300 B.C.

Borsippa) the clay was omitted from the joints so that the asphalt was in direct contact with the bricks. Koldewey offers no suggestion as to why the clay was generally used, but it seems possible that whereas the asphalt mastic when trowelled on hot would make excellent contact with the bricks below, when it cooled and hardened the upper course of bricks would not adhere to it. The skimming coat of plastic clay would remedy this defect and give an even bed and ensure greater stability to the wall.

The use of bituminous mortar continued in Babylonia until the beginning of the Christian era, although in the city of Babylon itself it does not seem to have been used until the time of the great King Hammurabi (Amraphel of the Bible, *c.* 2000 B.C.). Later on, in the sixth and seventh centuries B.C., when walls of the more important buildings were covered with glazed bricks, the joints were only partly filled with bituminous mortar to avoid staining. This mortar had a much higher content of bitumen than that used by the Sumerians. Herodotus records that the walls of Babylon were built in Nebuchadnezzar's time (604–561) with burnt bricks cemented with hot bitumen from Hit (Is), with layers of wattled reeds between the courses. Towards the end of Nebuchadnezzar's reign, however, bituminous mortar was abandoned in Babylon—for what reason is obscure—in favour of a much less stable lime mortar to which varying quantities of bitumen were added. After the collapse of the New Babylonian Empire, the new rulers, the Persians and Seleucids, abandoned even the addition of bitumen to lime mortar and used the very inferior loam or mud mortar.

The construction of an embankment 5,000 feet long on the banks of the river Tigris, in the reign of King Adad-Nirari I in 1300 B.C., is interesting (Figure 65). A retaining wall was first built with limestone blocks. This masonry was protected by an outer wall of burnt bricks jointed in bituminous mortar consisting of bitumen and loam, or bitumen, sand, and gravel.

Bituminous mixtures were also used for flooring and road-making in ancient Babylon, more particularly for the Processional or Royal roads, connecting temples with royal palaces, like the road called Aibur-Shabu, a section of which is shown in Figure 66.

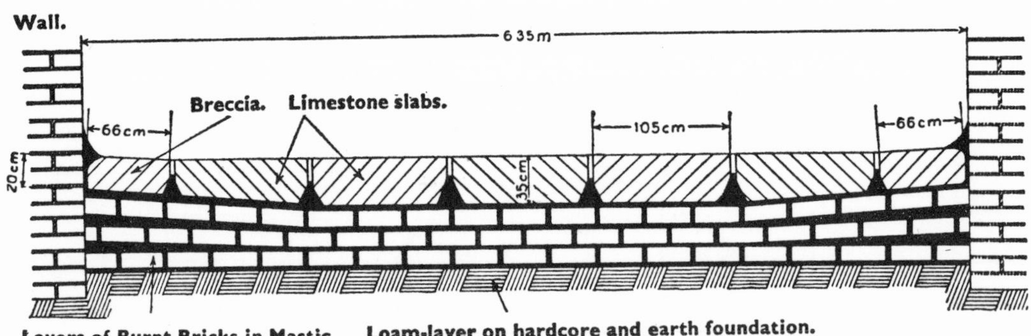

Fig. 66. Processional road 'Aibur-Shabu' at Babylon.

The roads were built with a foundation consisting of several courses of baked bricks jointed with mastic. A section through another road in the Temple of Ishtar at Assur is shown in Figure 67.

Over two thousand years were to pass before asphalt mastic was to be used again for road making and for waterproofing buildings. It was in 1712 that Eyrinus d'Eyrinus, a Greek, discovered deposits of rock asphalt in the Val de Travers near Neuchâtel. He found that by blending this rock, in powdered form, with hot pitch he obtained a material suitable for surfacing floors and stair treads—a material very like that used so extensively today. This success quickly led to the discovery of more deposits, for example in Alsace at Lobsann and Pechelbronn, in Hanover at Wietz, in Sweden at Osmundsberg, in Hungary, and Rumania. Perhaps the most important discovery was made in France at the close of the eighteenth century (1797) near Seyssel, when Count de Sassenay found that by mixing powdered rock asphalt from this site with bitumen, instead of with pitch as

Eyrinus had done, he obtained a mastic of much better quality. It was successfully used in France, Switzerland, and Germany for floors and pavements, a notable example being the surfacing of the Place de la Concorde in Paris in 1835. Two years later, in 1837, Claridge, an Englishman, visited France and, being impressed by the potentialities of asphalt mastic, returned and obtained a British Patent for 'a Mastic Cement or Composition applicable to Paving and Road making, covering buildings and the

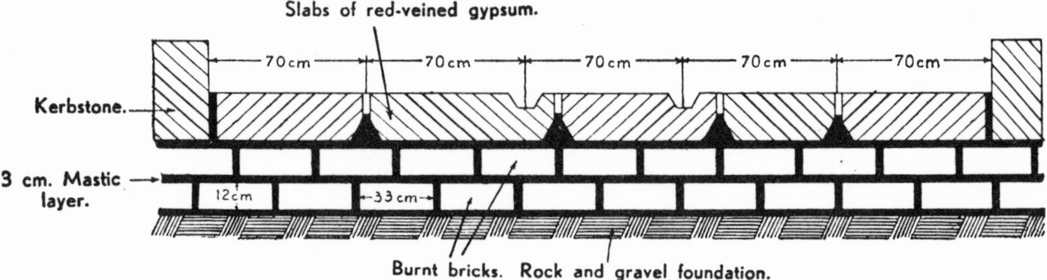

Fig. 67. Processional road in the Temple of Ishtar at Assur.

various purposes to which Cement, Mastic, Lead, Zinc or Composition are employed'. The great English engineer Brunel was quick to appreciate the value of the new material, and many distinguished architects and engineers followed his example and by 1860 it had become one of the indispensable materials used in building. In 1869 the first roadway in England, that of Threadneedle Street in London, was resurfaced with rock asphalt from Travers in France. From that time onwards the use of bituminous asphalt has boomed not only for road surfacing, but for roofing, tanking, damp-proof coursing, and flooring in building construction.

REFERENCES

(1) Forbes, R. J., 1936, *Bitumen and Petroleum in Antiquity*, E. J. Brill, Leiden, Holland.

(2) Garstang, J., 16 December 1932, 'The Fate of Jericho revealed by the Spade', *Illustrated London News*.

(3) Herodotus, I, 179, Everyman's Library edition, Dent.

(4) Strabo, *Geographica*, XVI, C 743, Loeb Classical Library, Heinemann, 1930, Vol. VII, 292.

(5) Abraham, Herbert, *Asphalts and Allied Substances*, D. Van Nostrand, New York.

(6) Frankfort, H., Jacobson, T., and Preusser, C., 1932, 'Tell Asmar and Khafaje—the first season's work in Eshnunna 1930–31', Chicago University Oriental Institute Communication No. 13; 1933, Second Preliminary Report of the Iraq Expedition, Chicago University Oriental Institute Communication No. 16; 1934; Third Preliminary Report, Communication No. 17.

(7) Marshall, J., 1923–4, 1925–6, *Indus Civilization*, Archaeological Survey of India, Annual Reports; and 1931, *Mohenjo-Daro and Indus Civilization*, A. Probsthain, London.

(8) Koldewey, R., 1914, *Excavations at Babylon*, Macmillan.

16

Arches

MANY FEATURES OF the stone buildings of Ancient Egypt were based on the pattern of earlier wooden structures, the most striking being the post and lintel construction. The spanning of openings with flat stone lintels and slabs, although heavy and cumbersome, remained popular throughout all the periods of Egyptian architecture, and was later copied by the Minoans and Hellenes; and by megalith builders in many lands.

The weight of single stone slabs to span distances even up to 10 feet was very great, and the task of placing them in position difficult. The slab which covers the portal of the Lion Gate at Mycenae (*c.* 1200 B.C.) shown in Figure I, weighs between 25 and 30 tons, although it spans as little as 10 feet. The enormous slab that roofs the entrance passage, 8 feet in width and 29 feet long, to the nearby Tomb of Agamemnon weighs over 100 tons. When one considers the great expenditure of effort and money in 1958 to raise a stone lintel at Stonehenge, weighing only about 15 tons, even with elaborate mechanical aids, it seems almost incredible that early man could have manhandled into position such enormous masses of stone.

By resting two inclined slabs against each other larger spans could be bridged, but the walls against which the stones abutted had to be rigid enough to resist the great outward thrust. The method was more suitable therefore, where the structure was excavated in solid rock, like the ancient shrine of Apollo on Mount Cynthus at Delos. Here ten large slabs, five on either side, span a distance of about 20 feet (Figure 68). But the principle of true arch construction was also known to the Egyptians, an example dating as far back as the 3rd Dynasty (*c.* 2700–2600 B.C.) is in the tomb of Bêt Khallâf.[1] Other examples of Egyptian brick arches occur in the Mastaba at Saqqara of 6th Dynasty date (*c.* 2350–2200 B.C.) and in the 12th Dynasty (*c.* 2000–1800 B.C.) Sepulchral Chamber of Amenemhat III's pyramid at Hawara.[2]

However, the small semicircular brick arch at E Dublal-Mah, Ur, is said by Woolley[3] to be very much the earliest example known of an arch employed as an architectural element in the façade of a building and it is the earliest arch known to be still surviving in a wall above ground. Built in the reign of Kuri-Galzu (1400 B.C.) it is only 32 inches wide, but is formed of kiln-burned voussoir bricks excellently made and fitted. The thickness of the wall where the arch is inserted is 64 inches.

Woolley states that the principle of the arch was known long before this and that there were found at Nippur a roughly formed brick arch which seems to date back to pre-Sargonic times, and at Tello an arch well built in brick but of doubtful date; but these are small underground structures, drains or conduits, and the Nippur arch is so crude that its builders seem to have had little experience of such methods of construction, whereas the arch of Kuri-Galzu is a finished piece of work perfectly regular in form and composed of true wedge-shaped voussoir bricks, showing long practice in arch building.

Fig. 68. Shrine on Mount Cynthus, Delos.

A later example, shown in Figure 69, of the thirteenth century B.C. excavated by Ghirshman[4] is the brick arch over the stairway in the Ziggurat of King Untash-huban, dedicated to the Elamite God, Inshushinak at Choga-Zembil, near Susa, Persia.

The Greeks seemed very slow to appreciate the advantage of a true arch, and like the Egyptians before them maintained a preference for the large flat stone lintel. The Etruscans, on the contrary, were very quick to appreciate its possibilities, and built arches with large specially cut stone voussoirs with close fitting joints needing no mortar for bedding. An example is the semicircular arch in the Etruscan walls at Perugia. The upper part of the gateway, above the frieze, was added by Augustus, and in consequence the arch later came to be known as the Arch of Augustus.

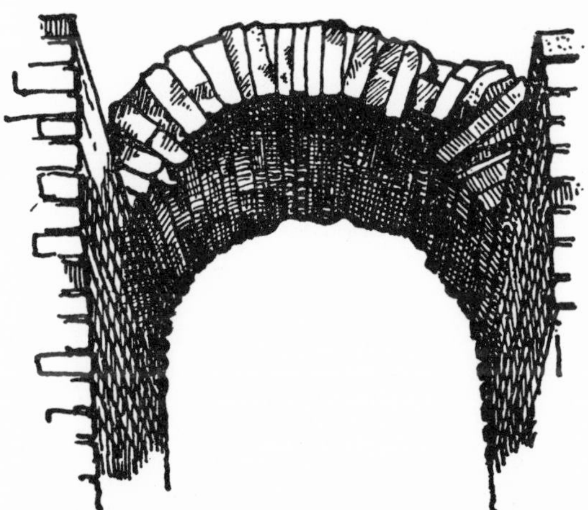

Fig. 69. Brick arch of a stairway in the Ziggurat of King Untash-huban at Choga-Zembil, near Susa.

The Romans adopted the semicircular arch from the Etruscans for spanning openings in walls, for relieving arches, and for vaulting. Plate LI shows the construction of stone masonry voussoir arches thought to be of Roman date

Fig. 70. Arches of the Via Nova, at the foot of the Palatine, Rome.

which supported the roof over the water cistern below the theatre at Delos. In contrast to these are the tile arches of the Via Nova at the foot of the Palatine in Rome (Figure 70). Many arches like these are built of mass concrete and are only faced with tile in the manner shown in Figure 71.

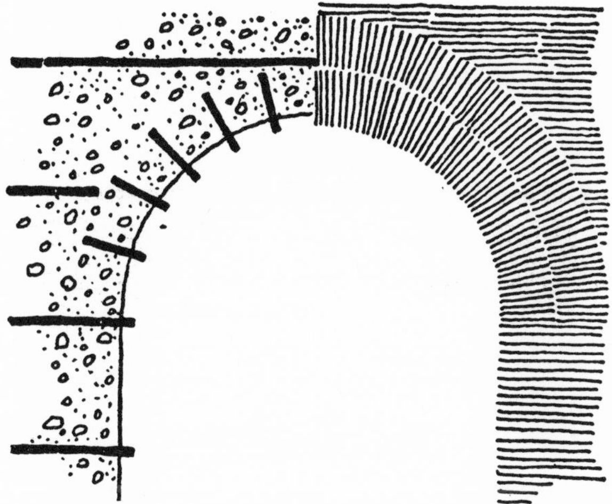

Fig. 71. Roman arch, showing the mass concrete interior.

The Romans, however, often made special tapered arch tiles, which were in effect like thin voussoirs. Such a tile was found during excavations[5] at the South Gate of Silchester. It was 17 inches by 6 inches and it tapered in thickness from $1\frac{3}{4}$ inches at one end to $1\frac{3}{8}$ inches at the other, and had evidently been used in the 10-foot-span archway. Another tapered tile was found at the West Gate, and it measured $2\frac{3}{8}$ inches at the thick end and tapered to about $1\frac{3}{4}$ inches at the lower.

By the first century B.C. the segmental vault and the intersecting barrel vault had been developed, some examples, among many, being found in the Temple of Hercules at Tivoli, and in the Tabularium in Rome (78 B.C.). Later on, vaults were built of brick rings, the compartments between being filled with concrete. A fine example of this technique is seen in the Basilica of Maxentius (A.D. 306–310) in Rome, later known as the Basilica of Constantine.

The semicircular arch continued to feature very prominently in the Byzantine architecture of the Eastern Roman Empire which developed after the time of Constantine (A.D. 323–337), and spread to Russia and throughout the Balkans. It also featured in the Romanesque architecture which developed in Western and Central Europe after the fall of Rome in A.D. 476. The Romans often used joggled voussoirs, to facilitate erection by preventing the voussoirs from sliding on each other, and locating them in position. Examples of the technique can be seen in the bridge over the Salado river near Villa del Rio between Cadiz and Madrid, and in that over the Pedroches near Cordova, where the joggled springer blocks of the arches remain; also in the theatre at Orange (*c.* 44 B.C.),

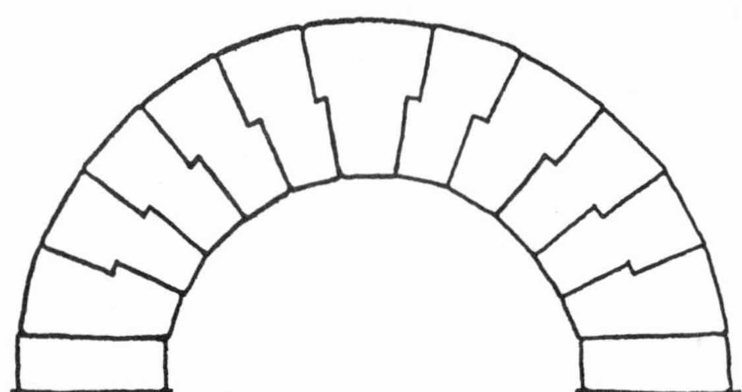

Fig. 72. Stone arch with joggled voussoirs in the Mausoleum of Theodoric, Ravenna.

in the Porta Aurea at Spalato, in the Porta Ferrea, of Diocletian's Palace (*c.* A.D. 303–305) and in the lower storey of the Mausoleum of Theodoric at Ravenna (*c.* A.D. 519) (Figure 72).

Sometimes the Romans used a flat stone voussoir arch, like that at the foot of the stairs of the Tabularium (78 B.C.) shown in Figure 73, or the flat tile arch near a doorway in the Temple of Divus Augustus on the west side of the Palatine, Rome, shown in Figure 74, but when this was done a semicircular relieving arch was invariably inserted into the walls immediately above to relieve the flat arch of load and to concentrate the thrust at its supported ends.

It is not yet certain when and where the pointed arch was first used, but it was well known in Romanesque styles, and was brought about simply by the interlacing of semicircular arches as in arcading, or by intersectioning of circular vaults. Butler[6] records the use of pointed arches in the Church at Qsar Ibn Wardan, fifty miles north-east of Homs in Syria in A.D. 561–564. Creswell[7] likewise gives many Islamic examples and has concluded that the existence of the two-centred pointed arch at Qusayr Amra (A.D. 712–715) and Hammam as-Sarakh (*c.* A.D. 725–730) in Syria, suggests that this type of arch may in fact have originated in Syria, particularly as no European examples are known until the end of the eleventh century or the beginning of the twelfth. Whether this was so or not there was certainly a natural and direct development of the two-centred pointed arch from the Romanesque semicircular arch during the latter half of the twelfth century, that became general in Europe, except in Italy, by the middle of the thirteenth century. This development could quite possibly have been independent of any Eastern influence. There are very sound structural reasons why the pointed arch was preferred to the semicircular one. An arch of the latter shape is not stable until its haunches are backed up with heavy masonry to counteract the outward thrust, and the supporting piers in their turn are also of heavy construction. The pointed arch, on the other hand, is much more stable and does not require this heavy haunching, and in consequence, taller and more graceful buildings could be erected, with thinner columns to support the lighter weights. Only slight external buttressing of the building, however, was required in the former case, but the stability of the structure with the

Fig. 73. Relieving arch at the foot of stairs of the Tabularium, Rome; 78 B.C.

pointed or 'Gothic' arches had to be assured by heavier external buttressing.

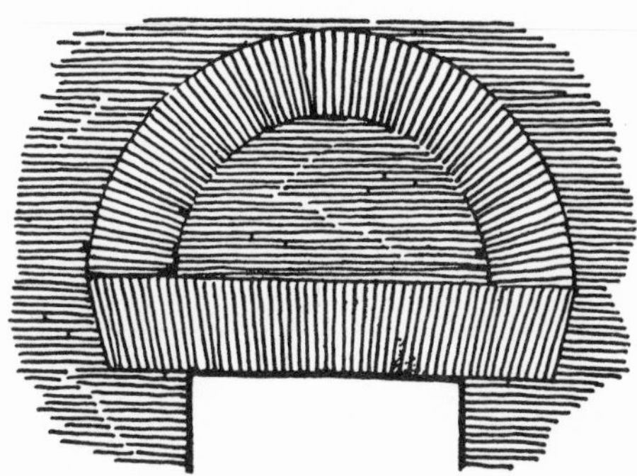

Fig. 74. Relieving arch at the Temple of Divus Augustus, on the west side of the Palatine, Rome.

Creswell considers that the round horseshoe arch is also of Syrian origin, and gives as the earliest examples those in the Baptistery of Mar Ya Gub at Nisibin, built according to a Greek inscription, by Volagesos the Bishop in A.D. 359. All the doorways have lintels with horseshoe relieving arches above. The culmination of this type of arch is seen in North Africa and Spain. A most striking example built at the end of the twelfth century A.D. is the Puerta del Sol, Gate of the Sun, which forms part of the ancient walls of the City of Toledo in Spain. It shows, in Plate LII, the blending of Islamic and Romanesque styles, the semicircular, the pointed, and the horseshoe arches all occurring together, and illustrates well how Spain was in fact a meeting point of East and West.

REFERENCES

(1) GARSTANG, J., 1902, *Mahasna and Bêt Khallâf*, 3–15, Quaritch.

(2) PETRIE, W. M. FLINDERS, 1890, *Hawara*, Egyptian Exploration Society, Quaritch.

(3) WOOLLEY, C. L., Oct. 1925, 'The Excavations at Ur, 1924–1925', *Antiquaries' Journal*, V, No. 4.

(4) GHIRSHMAN, R., 1954, *Iran*, Penguin Books.

(5) FOX, G. E., and ST JOHN HOPE, W. H., 1890, 'Excavations on the Site of the Roman City at Silchester, Hants', *Archaeologia*, LII, Part 2.

(6) BUTLER, H. C., 1904, *Ancient Architecture in Syria*, Section B, *Northern Syria*, 26–45, Heinemann.

(7) CRESWELL, K. A. C., 1958, *A Short Account of Early Muslim Architecture*, Penguin Books, 103.

17

Vaults and Domes

DOME CONSTRUCTION WAS practised as early as the sixth or fifth millennium B.C. Buildings, probably shrines, were excavated at Arpachiyah[1] about four miles east of Nineveh. They consisted of circular rooms made of pisé or clay, 12 feet or more in diameter. Only the springings of the vaulted roof remained, but they were sufficient to show that it had once been of domical shape. Mallowan points out that the tradition of circular building has survived in Northern Iraq and Northern Syria and in south-east Asia Minor to this day and can be seen in the 'beehive' village of Aleppo, and he also draws interesting parallels in the Mediterranean area to the circular buildings at Arpachiyah and the Neolithic site of Khirokitia in Cyprus. This form of construction influenced builders in the Mediterranean, for in about 2700 B.C. burial chambers with stone domical roofs called 'tholoi' appear in Crete.

The usual method of construction was to corbel successive courses of building material, and the dome tended to assume a conical shape, as illustrated so well, for example, in the Tomb of Agamemnon at Mycenae. This shape was dictated by the need to maintain structural stability. It is exceedingly difficult to close a true hemispherical dome by the corbelling technique.

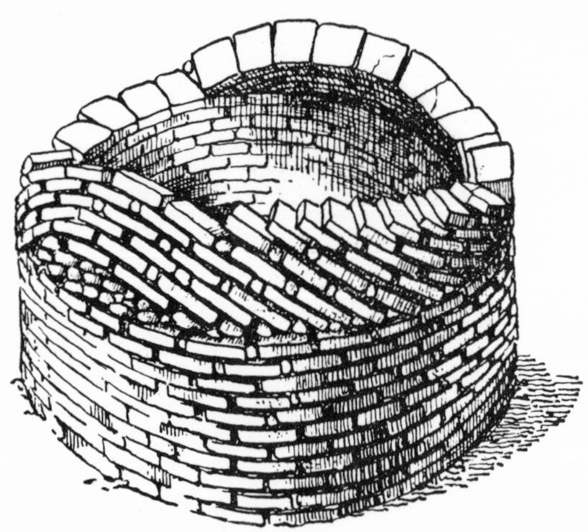

Fig. 75. Domed roof to a pit excavated at Khafaje, in Eshnunna; *c.* 2000 B.C.

An ingenious method of forming a small domed roof was revealed at Khafaje.[2] It covered a pit and was constructed about 2000 B.C. The first course of bricks was raised up on pieces of rubble at diametrically opposite sides of the pit as shown in Figure 75. As each successive course of bricks was added from each side, the dome took shape and was completed when the courses reached the crown.

Early examples of corbelled roofs,

Plate XLII. Burning gypsum in Persia (see page 92).

Plate XLIII. Base of a thirteenth-century lime-kiln at Cilgerran Castle, Pembrokeshire (see page 101).

Plate XLIV. A Roman breakwater near Naples, built with pozzolanic cement (see pages 103, 122).

shown in Figure 76, were found in the vaulted tombs at Ur by Woolley and these dated back to the third millennium B.C.

Fig. 76. Corbel-vaulted tomb at Ur; third millennium B.C.

A later Egyptian example is the roof of the Sanctuary in the Temple of Seti I at Abydos (1350 B.C.) completed by Rameses II. It was made by laying horizontal courses, each course projecting beyond the one immediately below it, and then rounding off the underside, by chiselling, to form a smooth surface to the vault. Both of these examples, however, were built with sun-baked brick and not stone. The method reached perfection in stone construction in the so-called beehive tombs of the Mycenaean period, the tomb of Agamemnon, or 'Treasury of Atreus', the tomb of Clytaemnestra, and the tomb of Genii, but a rather earlier and interesting example is the covered passageway, mostly subterranean, which gives protected access to a well outside the city wall of Mycenae (*c.* 1400 B.C.), shown in Plate LIII.

The best surviving examples of this technique are the 'trulli' buildings at Alberobello[3] in Southern Italy, shown in Figure 77. Many of them are modern, but their prototypes

Fig. 77. 'Trulli' buildings at Alberobello, in southern Italy.

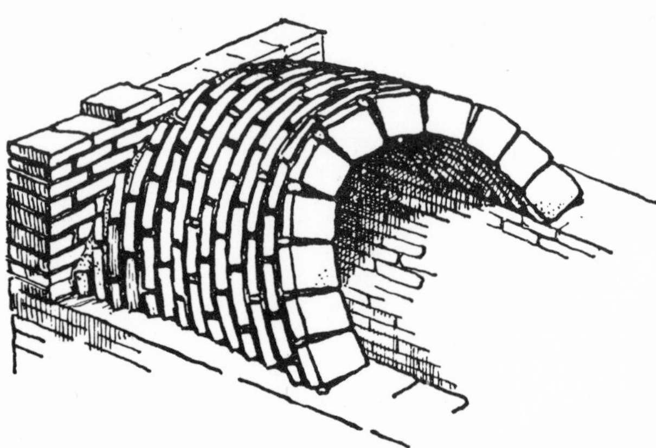

Fig. 78. Brick vault of the type excavated at Khorsabad, Assyria; 722 B.C.

are extremely ancient. Although ideally suited to a building of circular plan, the method of roofing has also been used for rectangular and other shapes of building. In more inclement climates, as in the Outer Isles of Scotland, the corbelled roof had to be made weather-tight by filling the gaps between the stones with clay or other suitable material, or by covering the whole structure with a mound of earth.

In timberless countries where the use of wooden centring for arch construction was almost impossible, another method was evolved which required no centring. The bricks forming the arch were laid so that each ring rested at an angle upon the previous one, and was maintained in position by the adhesive nature of the mortar, and by friction between the sloping bricks. The brick vault over a culvert in the great palace of Sargon at Khorsabad[4] in Assyria, illustrated in Figure 78, is an early example of this type of construction dating from the first quarter of the eighth century B.C. The method was used in Mesopotamia and Persia, and much later by Byzantine builders who thoroughly understood the principles of dome construction and built such masterpieces as Santa Sophia and SS. Sergius and Bacchus at Constantinople. Studies by Ward Perkins[5] have shown that in the fifth and sixth centuries the method of construction in practice at Constantinople was that proper to the eastern world where vaults were built *without* centring by laying the bricks at an angle, and not that in favour at Rome, where the bricks were set vertically and had to be supported on a wooden centring while construction was in progress. It seems that a mission sent by Empress Theodora in A.D. 540 to Nubia may have had a profound effect on the architecture in Egypt, for during the succeeding hundred years much similar vault and dome building was carried out up to the invasion of the Mohammedans in A.D. 640, when contact between Nubia and Byzantium virtually ceased.

Examples of vaults constructed in precisely the same manner as that at Khorsabad in Assyria are found in the Nubian Christian churches, and the method of construction has survived to modern times in Egypt. Mileham[6] has described the process of building the vaults. The side walls of the chamber to be roofed are built up to springing level of the vault. One end wall is then carried up to a height a little above the level necessary to cover the crown of the vault, and is often roughly shaped to the intended curve of the vault, the outline of which is marked out on the inner face of the wall, either by a sharp implement, or by means of a fillet of mortar. The actual vaulting is constructed by two men, each building one half of each ring of bricks independently, and meeting in the course of the work at the centre. The first two springers of half a brick each are set at an angle of about 75° to 80° to the horizontal, sloping towards the end wall. These are then covered with mud mortar consisting largely of cow dung, and whole bricks are then laid against them, their ends touching the end wall. The process is continued, each course of bricks starting alternately with a whole and a half-brick so as to break joint. The joints on the extrados of the vault are wedged with chips of stone or broken pottery to ensure greater stability.

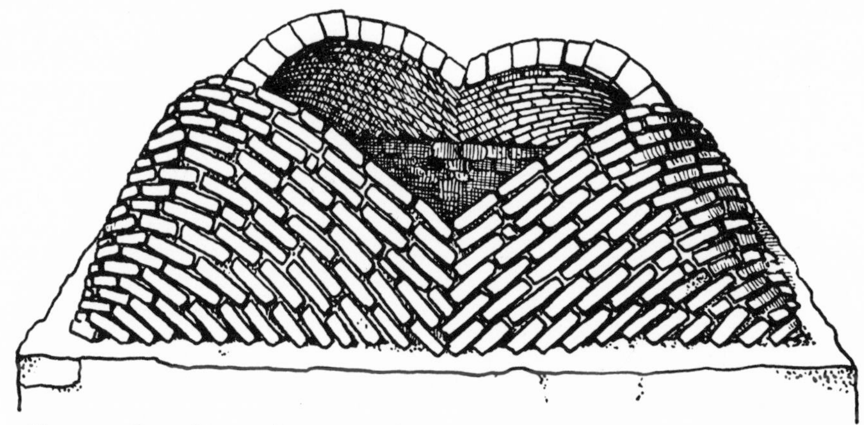

Fig. 79. Centreless vault to a modern rectangular building in southern Persia.

The drawing in Figure 79, which is based on a photograph taken by Eric Gordon, and published by Ward Perkins (1958), shows how the ingenious method of centreless arch construction is used to this day in southern Persia to roof a rectangular building.

The great arched vault at the Palace of Ctesiphon, near Baghdad, shown in Plate LIV, is possibly the most daring example of this technique. Built in A.D. 550, it is parabolic in shape and is about 83 feet in span and over 100 feet in height, the largest unreinforced brick vault in the world, and it is interesting that this masterpiece should have been produced by the techniques of construction that had been traditional in Iraq since Babylonian times. A much later development occurs in Persian work when arches and vaults were constructed with bricks on edge, as shown for example in a drawing (Figure 80) of part of the interior of Masjid-i-Jami, at Isfahan. A similar technique is apparent in the sixth-century vaulting of the narthex of St Eirene, in Constantinople.

Reference has already been made in Chapter 15 to the use by the Romans of concrete, or mortared rubble, for the construction of vaults and domes, and to the fact that these became, when hardened, rigid structures which did not behave in the same way as those built as true arches, as for example in the much later Gothic period. The Roman vaults and domes were cast on timber formwork, the impressions of which can still be seen on many of the surviving buildings in Rome and elsewhere. Sometimes, as in the construction of vaults at the Golden House of Nero, a layer of mortar was spread on the formwork and a ring of bricks was built at the exposed ends of the vault to give a fair finish to it, and also to contain the rubble concrete which was next poured in behind to complete the construction. In other cases a layer of tiles was first laid flat on the timber formwork, with occasional tiles laid on edge to provide a good key into the concrete when it was later poured into position. When the timber forms were struck a tiled soffit to the vault was exposed, and this could be rendered and decorated if desired. Examples of this type of construction occur in the Colosseum, at Hadrian's Villa near Tivoli, and in the Baths of Caracalla.

During construction, and until the concrete had thoroughly hardened, the weight on the timber formwork could be enormous, and to relieve the formwork of some of this load, brick ribs were often first built at intervals along the transverse lines of vaults (Figure 81b), as at Hadrian's Villa; along the diagonal lines of intersection of crossing vaults, as in the Baths of Diocletian; and along the meridians in cupolas and apses (Figure 81a), as in the Sibylline Temple at Tivoli, in the Temple of Minerva Medica, and in the Baths of Agrippa in Rome; or the ribs may be interlaced, as in the apses of the Temple of Venus and Roma. These brick ribs, built in pozzolanic mortar, formed arches capable of supporting a large proportion of the load of the concrete which was subsequently poured in the intervening spaces. When the concrete had appreciably hardened and became a monolithic structure capable of supporting its own weight, the functioning of the brick ribs became of quite secondary importance.

Fig. 80. Masjid-i-Jami, Isfahan. The arches and vaults on the south-east side of the Great Dome Chamber.

Various other devices were adopted to lighten the structures. One was to introduce a system of coffering seen so well illustrated in Rome in the recessed squares in the soffit of the dome of the Pantheon (Figure 82), in the recessed octagonal vaults of the Basilica of Constantine or Maxentius (Figure 83), and in the lozenge-shaped recesses in the roof of the apses of the Temple of Venus and Roma (Figure 84). The last, with its stucco ornament, is a particularly fine example of coffered work. Another device was to imbed hollow terracotta pots in the concrete or mortared rubble. Sometimes storage jars and amphorae were used, but more often terracotta tubes made for the purpose. The dimensions of the tubes varied, but were usually about 8 to 10 inches long and $2\frac{1}{2}$ to $3\frac{1}{2}$ inches in diameter. Sometimes they tapered along their length, but often they had parallel sides, as shown in Figure 85. One end of the tube was open and the other sealed and provided with a protruding conical stem which fitted into the open end of the next tube and so formed a continuous line of tubes. Examples occur in Rome from the tomb of Scipios on the Via Appia and from excavations in the Golden House of Nero.

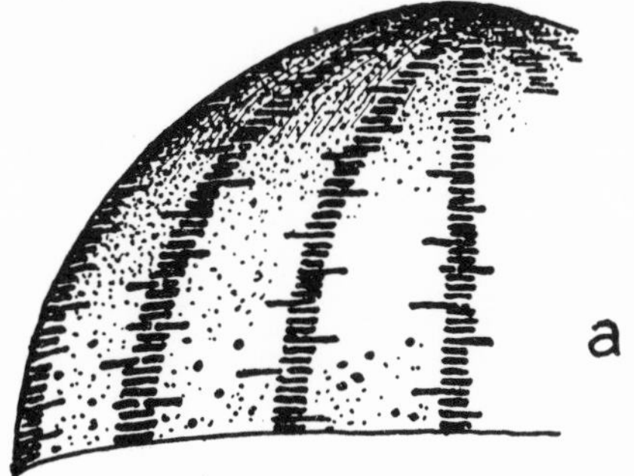

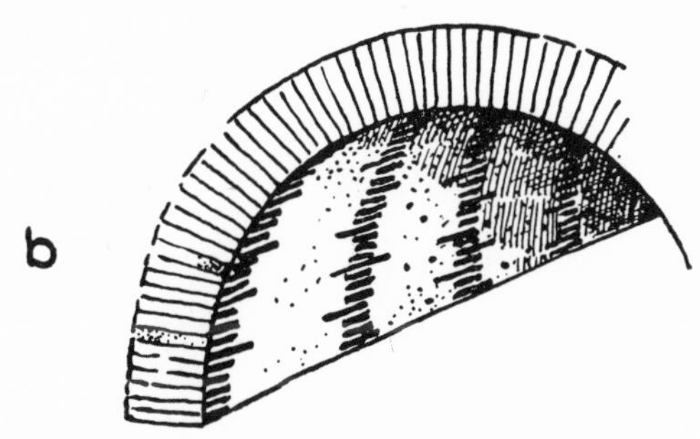

Fig. 81. Brick ribs in Roman vault construction.

In the Baptistery of Neone, at Ravenna (A.D. 449–452), sometimes known as the Battistero Ortodosso or San Giovanni in Fonte, the dome contains superimposed rings of these small terracotta tubes. The dome and the four barrel vaults of the Mausoleum of Galla Placidia in the same town, also built about the middle of the fifth century A.D., contain amphorae and terracotta wine jars of various sizes. Professor Verdozzi[7] records that they followed the slope of the roof so that, with a little mortar between, the roofing tiles could be laid on them. In the adjacent Roman Byzantine church of Santa Vitale, built by Giuliano Argentario by order of Bishop Ecclesius and consecrated in A.D. 547 by Archbishop Massimian, and renowned, as is the Mausoleum of Galla Placidia, for its magnificent mosaics, jars about 2 feet high and about $5\frac{1}{2}$ inches in diameter were built standing upright into the drum wall below the dome, and small tubes about 7 inches long laid base to neck in a continuous spiral were embodied in the concrete of the dome itself.[8] Cuming[9] records that the tubes were of red terracotta about $2\frac{3}{4}$ inches in diameter, slightly curved to give the arc of the cupola, with broad spiral grooves on the exterior of the tubes to provide a key to the mortar, and with the usual short conical stem or spike at the solid end.

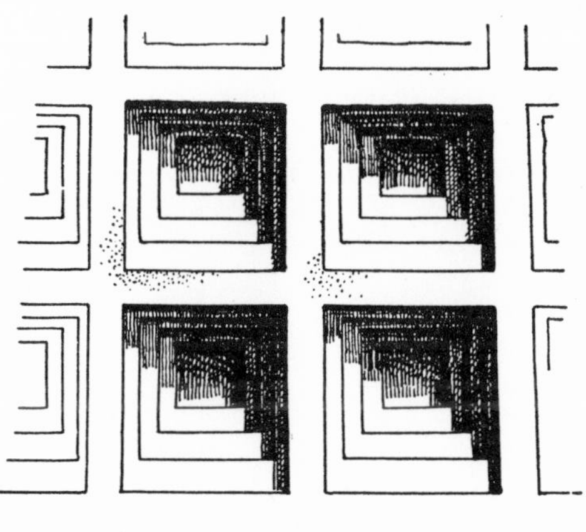

Fig. 82. Coffering on the dome of the Pantheon, Rome.

Pottery vessels inserted in walls and roofs in the manner described above must not be confused with the 'acoustic vases' or 'acoustic

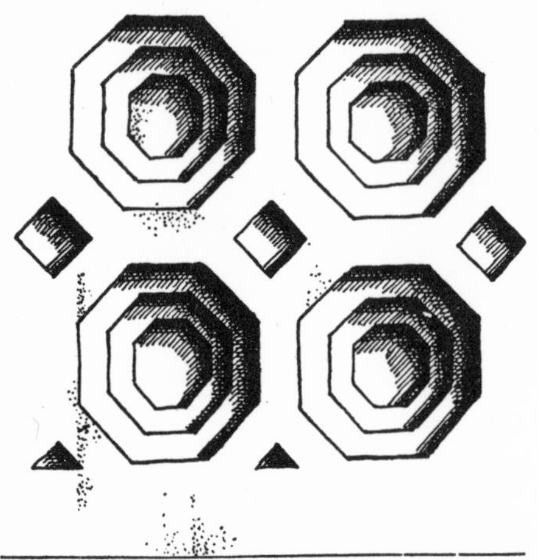

Fig. 83. Coffering on the vault of the Basilica of Constantine or Maxentius, Rome.

pottery' known to the Greeks as *echeia*, which were used from Classical times and throughout the Middle Ages for the purpose of improving the acoustics of the building. The vessels were laid in the walls of theatres and churches with their open end exposed on the inner surface of the wall of the building. The assumption that the pots were intended for acoustic purposes rests mainly on the text of Vitruvius,[10] and on a passage in the Chronicle of the Monastery of the Célestins of Séans at Metz,[11] which states that in A.D. 1432 an arrangement of urns or pots was introduced into the walls of the church of the Célestins of Séans to improve the acoustics of the building.

The Romans also constructed hollow vaults with special hollow terracotta blocks through which warm air could be circulated. Such vaults are described in Chapter 23, and were usually formed over baths, where the avoidance of condensation was important, or where the heating of the walls and ceiling of the *caldarium* or the *sudatorium* was necessary. Over a thousand years were to pass before

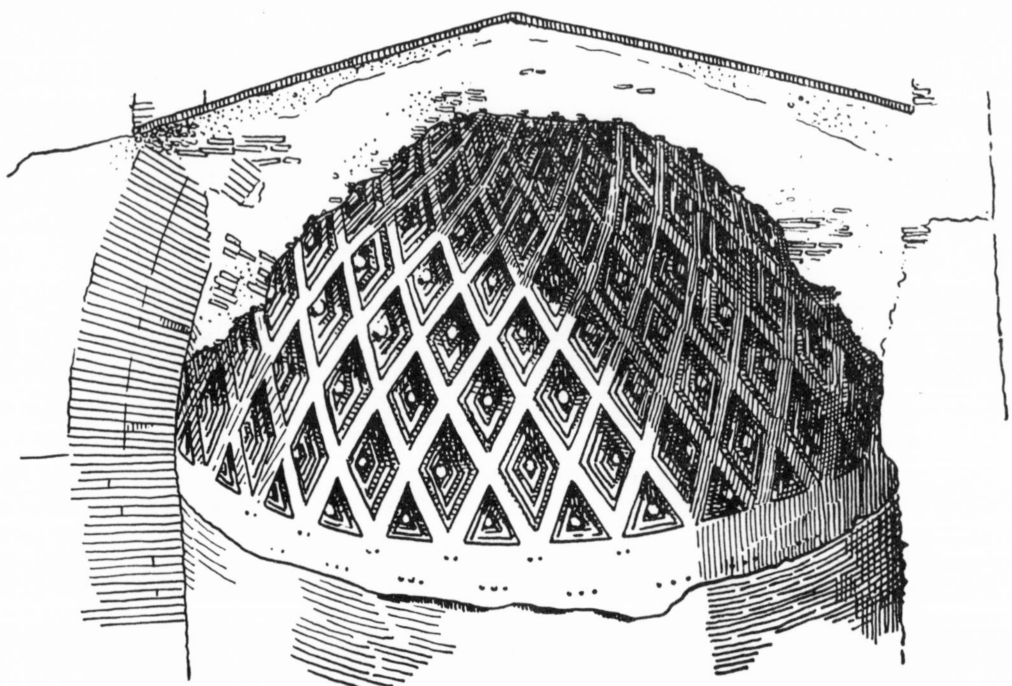

Fig. 84. Coffered apse of the Temple of Venus and Roma, Rome.

hollow vaults were again used. Hamilton[12] records that arches of hollow blocks were built in 1778 by J. D. Antoine at the Palais de Justice, Paris. In 1785 an architect named St Fart used special hollow pots much like flower pots, about 7 inches long and 4 inches wide, with both ends closed, the wider end being hexagonal, in the construction of floor panels, arches, and domes. The pots were usually set in plaster of Paris, as at the Palais Royal, the Bourse, the Madeleine, the Chambre des Deputies, the Archives de la Cour des Comptes, and elsewhere in Paris. Almost immediately the use of these 'bottle-bricks', or 'cones' as they came to be known, spread rapidly in England. They varied somewhat in shape and size. Henry Holland used pots square at one end, like those shown in Figure 86, in 1787 in the construction of the domed portico for Prince Frederick, Duke of York and Albany, at Dover House, Whitehall, formerly known successively as Featherstonhaugh House, York House, and Melbourne House. George Dance used them and so did Sir John Soane, who constructed the dome and arches of the Stock Office at the Bank of England in 1792 and 1793. William Strutt used cylindrical pots about $4\frac{1}{2}$ inches in diameter in 1803 and 1804 in arched floors and in the arches that carried the flat roof of a mill at Belper,[13] and much later still the

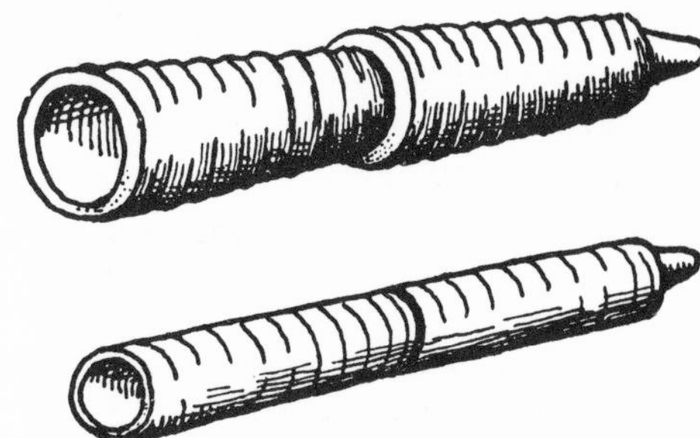

Fig. 85. Hollow tubes used in ancient domes and ceilings.

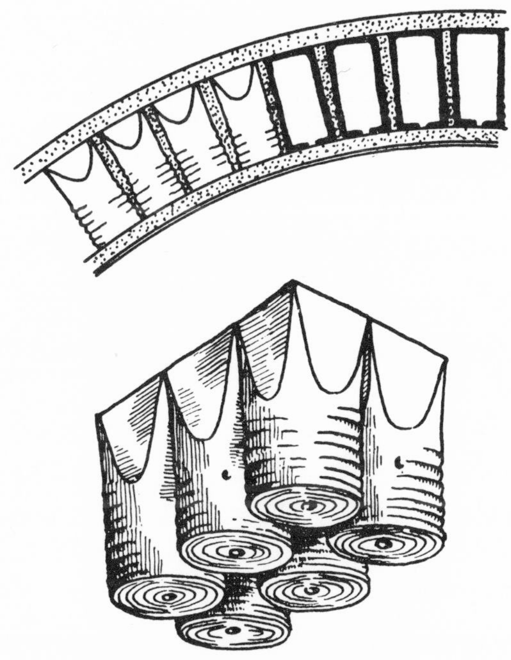

Fig. 86. 'Bottle-bricks'.

great ceiling of St George's Hall, Liverpool, completed in 1849, was constructed with about 140,000 hollow blocks each being 12 inches long and 4 inches square.[13] This type of construction is no longer used for the construction of vaults, which have to a great extent been superseded by floors of hollow flat construction. Hamilton[12] has given a good account of these later forms of construction.

REFERENCES

(1) MALLOWAN, M. E. L., 1956, *Twenty-five Years of Mesopotamian Discovery (1932–56)*, British School of Archaeology in Iraq.

(2) FRANKFORT, H., JACOBSEN, T., and PREUSSER, C., 1932, 'Tell Asmar and Khafaje—the first season's work in Eshnunna 1930–31', Chicago University Oriental Institute Communication No. 13.

(3) BARK, LANCELOT G., Dec. 1932, 'Beehive Dwellings of Apulia', *Antiquity*, VI, 407.

(4) PERROT, G. and CHIPIEZ, C., 1884, *Histoire de l'art dans l'antiquité*, Vol. 2, *Chaldee et Assyrie*, Hachette, Paris, Fig. 93.

(5) WARD PERKINS, J. B., 1958, *Second Report on Excavations carried out on behalf of the Walker Trust of St. Andrews in the Great Palace of the Byzantine Emperors at Constantinople*, Edinburgh.

(6) MILEHAM, GEOFFREY S., 1910, 'Churches in Lower Nubia', *Eckley B. Coxe Jnr. Expedition to Nubia*, II, University Museum of Philadelphia.

(7) American Face Brick Association, 1925, *Brickwork in Italy—a brief review from Ancient to Modern times*, Chicago, 51.

(8) ECK, C. L. G., 1841, *Traité de Construction en Poteries et Fer*, Paris, 2nd ed., II, Plate IV.

(9) CUMING, SYER, 1860, 'On the Use of Vessels and Hollow Bricks in Buildings', *Journal* of the British Archaeological Association.

(10) VITRUVIUS, *De Architectura*, Book I, I, and Book V, V,—'On Sounding Vases in Theatres'.

(11) DE BOUTEILLER, M. ERNEST, 1862, *Notice sur le Couvent des Célestins de Metz*, Metz, quoted by Viollet-le-Duc in *Dictionnaire raisonné de l'Architecture Française*, VII, 471.

(12) HAMILTON, S. B., Feb. 1959, 'The History of Hollow Bricks', *Transactions* of the British Ceramic Society, LVIII (2), 41–61.

(13) HAMILTON, S. B., 1958, *A Short History of the Structural Fire Protection of Buildings particularly in England*, H.M.S.O., London, 7, 11.

Plate XLV. Mixing trough depicted on Trajan's column in Rome (see page 113).

Plate XLVI. Mixing trough excavated at a Roman bath building in Chelmsford, Essex (see page 113).

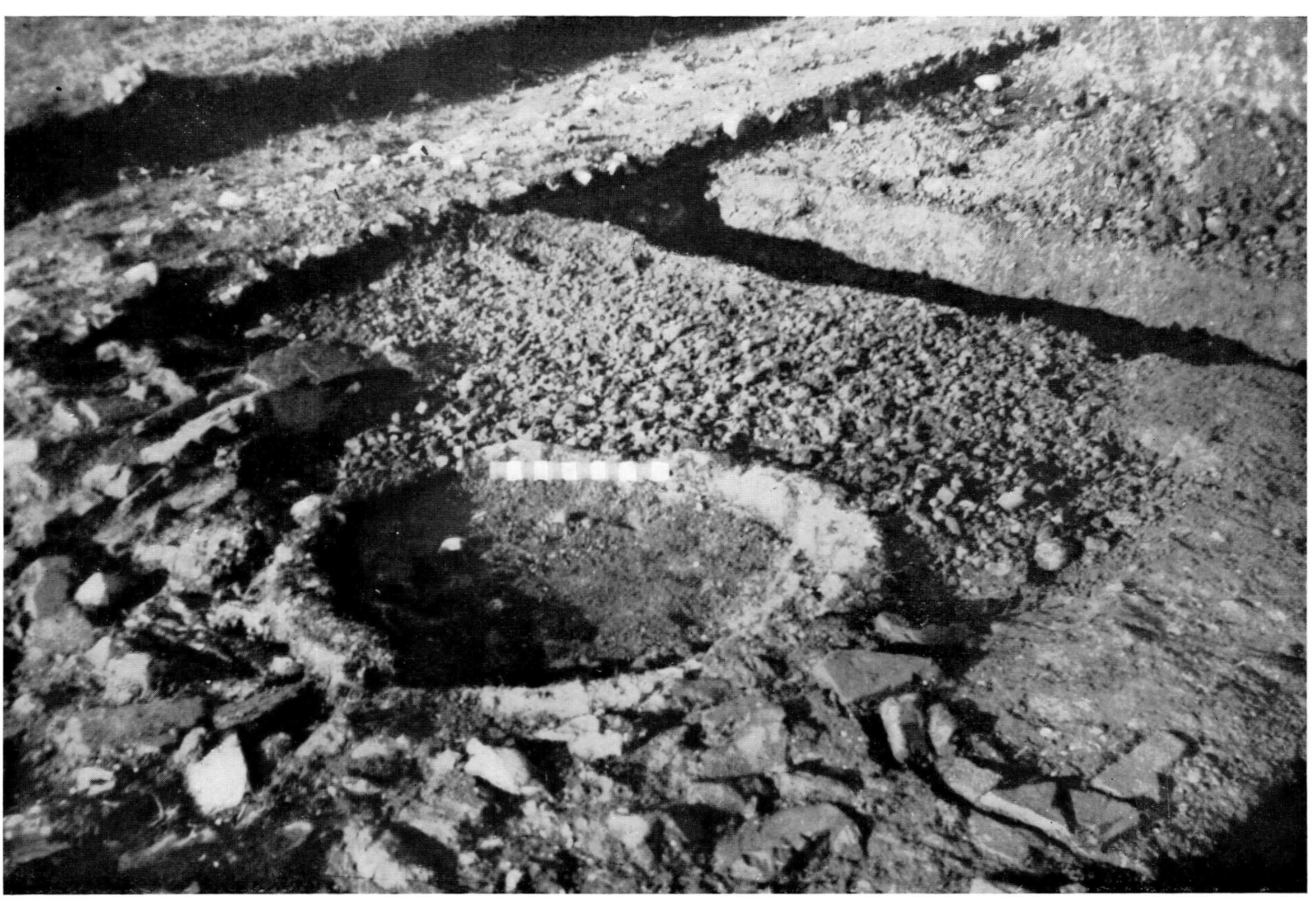

Plate XLVII. Mixing pit excavated in the grounds of a Roman villa at Park Street, near St Albans, Hertfordshire (see page 114).

Plate XLVIII. Stucco decoration in low relief, from a Roman building at the Villa Farnesina; now in Museo Nazionale, Rome (see page 114).

Plate XLIX. Modelled and carved stucco from Samarra; ninth century A.D. (see page 115).

Plate L. Arabs removing asphaltic material from a seepage deposit at Burgan, in the Arabian Desert (see page 129).

18

Roof Tiling

Stone Tiles

THE FLAT ROOF so common in ancient Egypt and the Middle East was a difficult one to keep weathertight in wetter climates. The pitched roof was better from this point of view, and in timber buildings had presented no great problem as the surfaces could be thatched or plastered to provide a good run-off for the rain. The provision of a suitable roof for the more permanent stone buildings was difficult, and although there is some rather indirect evidence that early Greek temples, for example, may have been thatched (Figure 38), something more durable was needed and interlocking terracotta tiles were devised in the seventh century B.C. or earlier, which could be fixed to low pitched roofs.

The Romans used many stone roofing tiles, some almost oval, others four-, five,- or six-sided, pointed or slightly rounded at their lower extremity, and hung by a single wooden peg upon the battens or nailed to them. When laid on the roof the exposed bottom edges of the tiles, which sloped upwards at 45°, formed a diagonal reticulate pattern like that shown in Figure 87. Various types of limestone and sandstone were used. At Chedworth in Gloucestershire, for example, not only was the local limestone used but also sandstone from the Forest of Dean. Ridge tiles and finials were carved from stone. The finial (*b*) from Bath is in the Museum there and measures 18 inches in height.

Tiles of polygonal shapes are depicted on the Anglo-Danish coped or gabled tombstones, often called 'hogback' tombstones in the North of England, and thought to represent the houses of the Vikings (Figure 88), probably of late tenth or early eleventh century date. Of what material the tiles were made is not known. They could have been wood shingles which towards or just after the end of the Roman occupation probably replaced stone and clay tiles to a large extent. The building appears to represent a long house with steeply sloping roof and slightly cambered plaited ridge, terminating at each end with the forequarters of a bear who holds the ridge in its jaws. The use of a beast's head to decorate the ends of the ridge was not unusual in Viking architecture. A low wall is shown on which the timber framework rests, the spaces between the posts or studs being filled with wattle represented conventionally here, as in other hogback tombstones, by an interlacing pattern. By the thirteenth century, stone tiles or 'thak-stones' were again being used for important buildings. The fact that a church of this period in Lincoln had a stone roof was considered at the time to be of such importance that it was called St Peter Steintheked (stone-roofed). Unfortunately the church no longer exists.

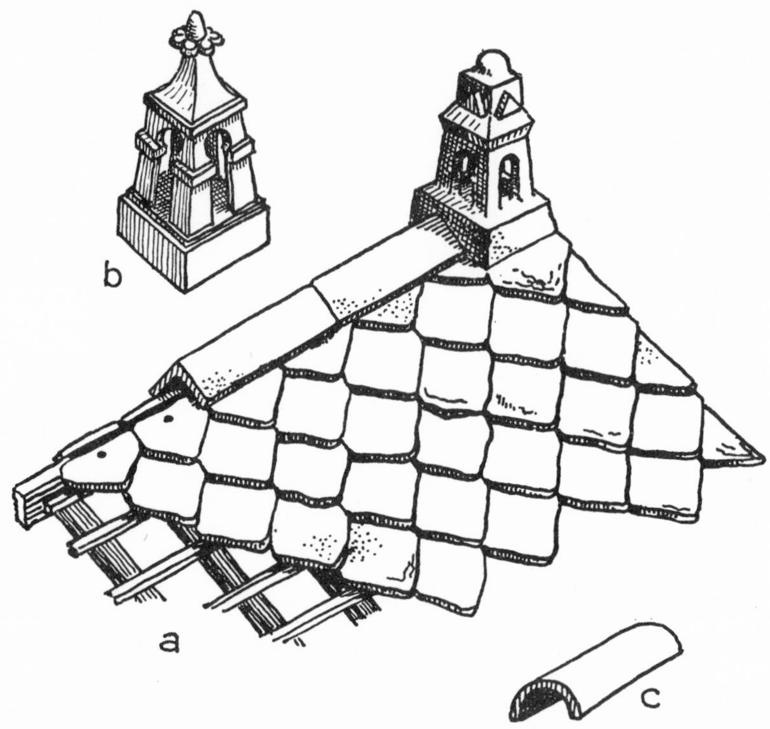

Fig. 87. Romano-British stone roof.

Stone roofing tiles have continued in use in Britain since Roman times. They have been made from various sedimentary rocks, limestones and sandstones which split naturally into thin slabs, $\frac{1}{2}$ inch to 1 inch thick, which can be trimmed to rectangular shapes and sizes, suitable for use as roofing tiles. Suitable rocks occur in the following geological strata:

(*a*) Cambrian and Silurian, with its highly micaceous sandstone of the Upper Silurian (Ludlow group), quarried to the north of Ammanford in South Wales, and the slate stone, known as 'Green Slate' rock, quarried at Honister Crag, near Keswick.

(*b*) Devonian, producing the fissile sandstone of the Old Red Sandstone in South Wales, and at Caithness in the North of Scotland.

(*c*) Carboniferous, producing thin flaggy sandstone, from Wales, Derbyshire, Lancashire, Yorkshire, and the Scottish coal fields, sometimes called 'grey slate'.

(*d*) Jurassic, rocks from the Lias formation in Somerset and Shropshire; from marl-stone in Wiltshire; from calcareous sandstone (Duston slate) from Duston in Northamptonshire; from sandy limestone at Colleyweston, south of Stamford in Northamptonshire; from the calcareous sandstone at the base of the Great Oolite at Stonesfield, between Charlbury and Woodstock in Oxfordshire, Eyford and Kyneton Thorns in Gloucestershire, and other parts of the Cotswold area; from thin limestone of the Forest Marble which occurs in several small quarries in Gloucestershire; from hard siliceous limestone at Brandsby, Yorkshire, and from the Lower Purbeck Beds in Dorset.

(*e*) Cretaceous, producing Horsham Stone of the Wealden Beds in Sussex.

Fig. 88. Hogback tombstone of the late tenth or early eleventh century, Brompton, Yorkshire.

The industry at Stonesfield, which unfortunately died out at the end of last century, was probably in its heyday the most extensive in Britain, the stone slates having been worked over an area of about two square miles. The earliest workings, which were certainly in use in the thirteenth century, followed the outcrops of stone in the steep-sided dry valleys of Stockley Bottom and Bagg's Bottom. Later on, workings were driven into the valley sides, and vertical shafts were sunk in and around the village of Stonesfield to a depth of 60 or 70 feet to reach the Stonesfield Slate Beds at the base of the Great Oolite formation. Thirty feet or more in thickness, they consisted of a variable series of sandy flags, oolitic freestones, limestones, and 'slate', or tile-stones. The particular bed from which the slates were obtained, known locally as 'Pendle', consists of fissile calcareous sandstone rarely more than a foot in thickness, and this accounts for the great area that had to be worked in order to recover the 'pendles', as the slabs of stone were called. The 'pendles' were laid flat on the ground and left there until the winter frosts commenced to split them horizontally. Sometimes they had to be left throughout the whole winter for this to happen and they had to be wetted in order to encourage splitting. The slatemaker completed the splitting by means of a special hammer with a sharp curved edge. Then he rested the pieces of stone upon a horizontal iron blade mounted in a heavy block, trimmed them to the required shape, and pierced a hole in them with a pick, at a suitable point near the top so that they could be hung to the roof battens by oak pegs or clouts. Slater's tools are illustrated in Figure 134.

Very few stone-slates are now produced in the Cotswold area, and a recent observer[1] found only one practising stone slatemaker, and that was at Naunton, where he was producing slates mainly for repairing the roofs of Naunton village.

The stone slates range in length from 23 inches down to 5 inches and in thickness from 1 inch to ½ inch, the smallest size being used at the crest of the roof and the largest at the bottom, or eaves. There is thus gradation of sizes up the roof resulting not only in a reduction in weight towards the crest or ridge, but imparting to it an aesthetically more pleasing appearance. The slater referred to the different sizes not by dimensions but by picturesque names that have come down through history: for example, long sixteen (23 inches); short sixteen, long fifteen (21½ inches) short fifteen, long fourteen (20 inches); short fourteen, long thirteen (18½ inches); short thirteen, long twelve (17 inches); short twelve, long eleven (15½ inches); short eleven, long wivett, wippett, or wibbut (14 inches); short wivett, long nine (12½ inches); short nine, long bachelor (11 inches); short bachelor, long beck or back (9¾ inches); middle beck, short beck (8½ inches); muffity or movity, long cutting (7½ inches); short cutting, long prick, cock, or tant (6 inches); middle prick, short prick (5 inches). The slater had his own peculiar rule or measure engraved with these various sizes.

Slate Tiles

Slate is a sedimentary argillaceous stone produced by metamorphism of primary or igneous rocks. The original material in the form of fine clay, sometimes with sand or volcanic dust, was deposited under water and consolidated by vertical pressure into mudstone and shale. In this condition the sedimentary particles were cemented by carbonates of lime and magnesia, by kaolin, or by various iron compounds. Intense heat and great lateral pressure subsequently converted the product into slate, the kaolin and felspar of the original sediment being transformed into sericite, a potash-bearing mica which had a crystalline form of minute overlapping flakes and fibres oriented in planes running at right-angles to the direction of pressure. This structure imparted great strength and elasticity to the material. The cleavage planes formed in the material do not necessarily coincide with, and may in fact be quite oblique to, the sedimentation beds formed during the deposition of the original material.

A block of slate can easily be split with hammer and chisel along the cleavage planes, into a number of laminae, and generally the thinner they are the better is the quality and durability of the tile. The principal minerals present in slate are various compounds of silica and alumina such as chlorites, felspars, muscovite, and quartz, but there may be, in lesser quantities, others such as magnetite, pyrites, sulphide of iron, marcasite, and calcite (calcium carbonate), this last being detrimental if the tiles are to be used in an urban atmosphere, as sulphur fumes may attack the calcite to form calcium sulphate, and in doing so may scale or split the tiles. There is documentary evidence to show that

English slates have been used since the twelfth century A.D.[2] There was a considerable trade in Cornish and Devonian roofing slates along the south coast as far as Kent. They have been found at more than twenty-five medieval sites along the south coast of England and its hinterland. Some of the oldest quarries are in Devon and Cornwall, particularly along the north coast region, notably at Delabole, but many quarries have long since been abandoned.

The other main area for English slates is in Cumberland, Westmorland, and North Lancashire, particularly in the Lake District, at Broughton Moor near Coniston, Buttermere and Burlington near Kirby-in-Furness. Welsh slates were quarried until recently in the Prescelly mountains close to the Pembrokeshire-Carmarthen border; the main supply now comes from North Wales from the Bangor and Caernarvon veins, in the Nantle Valley at Dinorwic, Penrhyn, and Vronlog, from the Festiniog or Portmadoc veins, and from the Corris or Aberdovey veins, particularly at Machynlleth. Scottish slates come from Argyllshire, notably from Ballachulish, Perthshire, the Oban district, and the Isle of Easdale. Irish slates are quarried in the counties of Cork, Kerry, Limerick, and Tipperary.

The colour of the slates varies considerably in the different areas and in the individual quarries. For example, the Westmorland slates vary in colour from light green to dark olive green, those from Cornwall are bluish-grey or greenish-grey, while those from North Wales have a much wider colour range including green and blue, purple and red, grey and blue. There was a very great increase in the use of slates in all parts of Britain in the nineteenth century, and for a time they practically replaced clay tiles. A tax was imposed by Pitt in 1831 on both slates and clay tiles, but the tax on slates was removed to the detriment of clay tiles, although soon this tax also was removed. In the meantime, however, a great impetus had been given to the slate industry. In the twentieth century there has been a great increase in the use of concrete roofing tiles.

The various sizes of slate are known by quaint names in very much the same way as are stone tiles. The largest, called Empresses, measure 26 inches by 16 inches; Small Empresses, 26 inches by 14 inches; Princesses, 24 inches by 14 inches; Duchesses, 24 inches by 12 inches; Small Duchesses, 22 inches by 12 inches; Marchionesses, 22 inches by 11 inches; Wide Countesses, 20 inches by 12 inches; Countesses, 20 inches by 10 inches; Wide Viscountesses, 18 inches by 10 inches; Viscountesses, 18 inches by 9 inches; Wide Ladies, 16 inches by 10 inches; Broad Ladies, 16 inches by 9 inches; Ladies, 16 inches by 8 inches; Wide Headers, 14 inches by 12 inches; Headers, 14 inches by 10 inches; Small Ladies, 14 inches by 8 inches; Narrow Ladies, 14 inches by 7 inches; Small Headers, 13 inches by 10 inches; Doubles, 13 inches by 7 inches; Wide Doubles, 12 inches by 8 inches; Small Doubles, 12 inches by 6 inches; Singles, 10 inches by 8 inches; and Units, 10 inches by 6 inches.

Terracotta and Clay Tiles

Some years ago Morse[3] made a valuable study of the older forms of terracotta roofing tiles. The earliest form, found in the ruins of the Temple of Hera, at Olympia (*c.* 640 B.C.), consisted of two elements, a wide tile (*tegula*) either square or rectangular, more or less curved in section, and a narrow semi-cylindrical tile (*imbrex*) usually slightly tapering at one end, to fit into the wider opening of the one adjoining. The *tegula* was placed on the roof concave face upward, and the *imbrex* placed concave face downward, covering the joint between two adjacent *tegulae*. The open end of the *imbrex* where it bordered the eaves was closed by a circular disc, ornamented in rosette pattern.

Morse concluded that the older roofing tiles of the world grouped themselves into three distinct types, which he called the normal, Figure 89 type A, or Asiatic tile; the

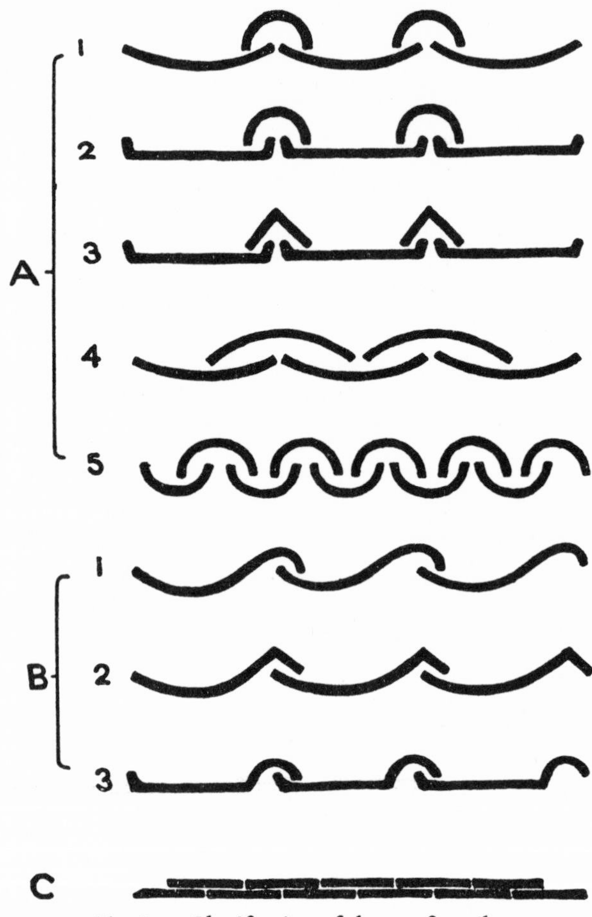

Fig. 89. Classification of clay roofing tiles.

pan, or Belgic tile, type B, which is an outgrowth of the normal tile; and the flat or Germanic tile, type C, which is an independent form. The normal tile, the earliest known form, covers by far the greater number of roofs, and with few exceptions appeared to be, at the time of Morse's survey, the principal form of tile used in Asia, Asia Minor, Greece, Italy, Sicily, Spain, the countries bordering the southern shores of the Mediterranean, and all the Spanish and Portuguese colonies. The treatment of the roof covered with this tile in the Orient and in the Occident differs widely. In China, Korea, Japan, and countries to the South of China the ridges are, as Morse points out, usually conspicuous for their elaborate structure. The tiles are aligned with great care, the eaves tiles have turned margins of graceful outline with ornamental designs upon them in relief. The roofs of the more important buildings have their ridges, hips, and eaves in strongly curved lines and with this treatment the curved *tegula* is in harmony. In the Occident, there is little attempt at architectural treatment of the tile, the ridge is rarely more than a single course of semi-cylindrical tiles, though some Swiss and English glazed ridge tiles have had finials moulded upon them. The eaves tiles also differ in no respect from those of the roof and the only attempt at decoration has been the introduction of stucco or white mortar between the courses, as occasionally seen in modern Greek houses and medieval Spanish ones. In ancient Greece the ridge and eaves tiles, the huge discs terminating the ridges, the antifix, etc., decorated in polychrome, added greatly to the beauty of the roofs. Morse also pointed out that the fully developed tiling with curved *tegula* and disc-closed *imbrex*, found at Hera in Ancient Greece, was identical with that of eastern Asia, and led him to the belief that the Far East may have been the original source of this type of tiling. The model of the Chinese house shown in Plate LV, dating from A.D. 58, and the earlier one of the Han Dynasty (206 B.C. to A.D. 23) (Plate XXII) both have roofs evidently intended to represent this type.

The curved *tegula* gave way to the broad flat *tegula*, which became the dominant form for the monumental buildings of Ancient Greece, Italy, Sicily, and Etruria, and the form survives in Italy to this day.

Figure 89 shows the outlines of various terracotta roofing tiles based mainly on Morse's observations. Group A are the oldest and what he calls normal (Asiatic). Group B the pan (Belgic), and C the flat (Germanic). Type A1 with the curved *tegula* and the semicircular *imbrices* is probably the oldest and occurs in the Orient, in Ancient Greece, and Italy and is called the Laconian type by Dinsmoor. Type A2, with flat *tegulae* and semicircular *imbrices*—the Sicilian type— occurs in Greece and Italy, both Ancient and Modern. Type A3, the Corinthian type, with flat *tegulae* and *imbrices* of triangular cross-section, occurs mainly in Ancient Greece. Type A4, with curved *tegulae* and similarly shaped tiles as *imbrices*, is common throughout China and India; while type A5, with semicircular *imbrices* and similarly shaped tiles as *tegulae*, occurs in the Orient and in Mediterranean countries roughly south of latitude 44°.

Type B1 is the common pantile of England and Scandinavia, and Type B2 is that common in Belgium, Holland, Scandinavia, and as far away as Japan and Java. Type B3 is comparatively modern and is now used in many countries. Type C, the flat tile, is common in Germany, Austria, Hungary, Poland, Switzerland, France, England, all countries in which wood shingles were originally or still are used, and for which the flat or 'plain' tile is the fireproof substitute.

Dinsmoor[4] groups Greek terracotta roof tiles into three general categories; the Laconian (Spartan) type, probably the earliest, like that described by Morse, which had concave pantiles with the joints protected by convex cover tiles semicircular in section; the Corinthian type, flat pantiles with raised rims and inverted Vee-shaped or saddle-shaped cover tiles; and the Sicilian type, flat tiles and semicircular cover tiles, which was the form adopted subsequently by the Romans. To accompany these were various special forms of eaves tiles, antefixes, *simas*, ridge tiles, ridge cover tiles, and *acroteria*. The Corinthian type tiles were directly copied in marble in the fifth and fourth centuries B.C.

No original examples of these early tiled roofs survive above ground but an impression can be obtained from the tiled roof of the underground shrine of Hera, at Paestum, dating from the latter part of the sixth century B.C., and excavated by Professor P. Claudio Sestieri.[5] It consisted of a series of limestone slabs, covered with flanged roofing tiles as shown in Figure 90. The outward thrust of the inclined slabs at the ends of the roof was

Fig. 90. Tiled roof of the underground shrine of Hera at Paestum; sixth century B.C.

resisted, not entirely successfully, by housing them in a stone tie beam, clearly simulating a simple timber truss as it might have appeared in a temple above ground. The flanged roofing tiles seem also to have been used for the same reason, but unfortunately the cover tiles are missing.

For a great many of their buildings the Romans used the flat *tegula* usually about 17 inches long by 10 to 11 inches wide with a semi-circular *imbrex* or cover tile; but sometimes the size was much larger. The *tegulae* were tapered in width, being narrower at the bottom, and so shaped as to fit into the one immediately below. This is shown in Figure 91. The *imbrices* were also tapered so that they overlapped, and were mortared, or torched, to the *tegulae* to form a weathertight seal. The roofs were very heavy and were consequently of low pitch and constructed with very substantial timber. Wheeler[6] found at Verulamium that some of the first and early second century A.D. *tegulae* were lighter and more sharply angled than those normal at later periods, although he did find in one reconstructed building of the late third century A.D. an exceptionally thin type of tile, only $\frac{5}{8}$ inch thick.

A stamp on a tile probably from the roof of the Baths of Silchester, and now in the

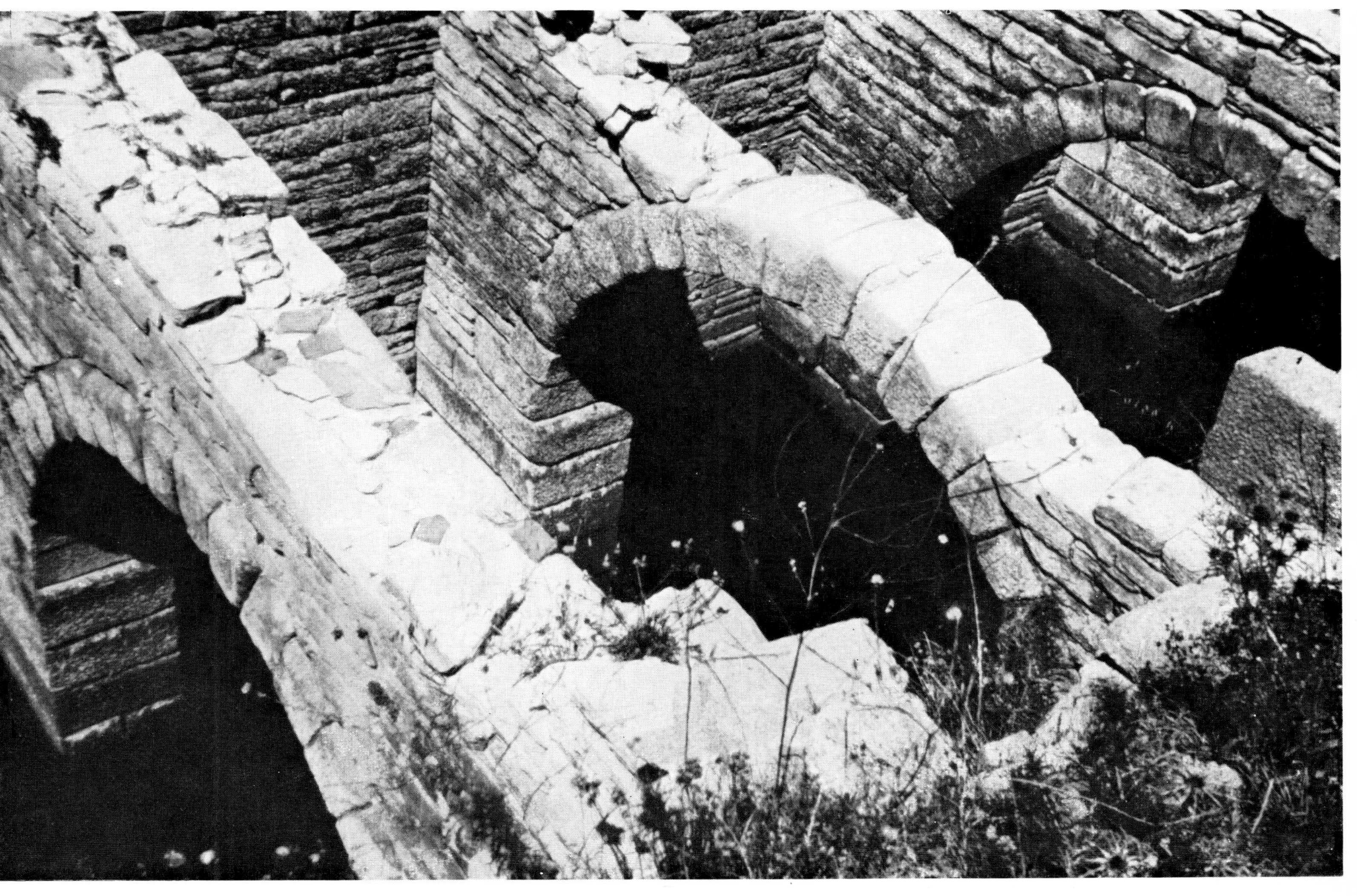

Plate LI. Arches of a cistern below the theatre at Delos, built to collect its water; possibly of Roman date (see page 135).

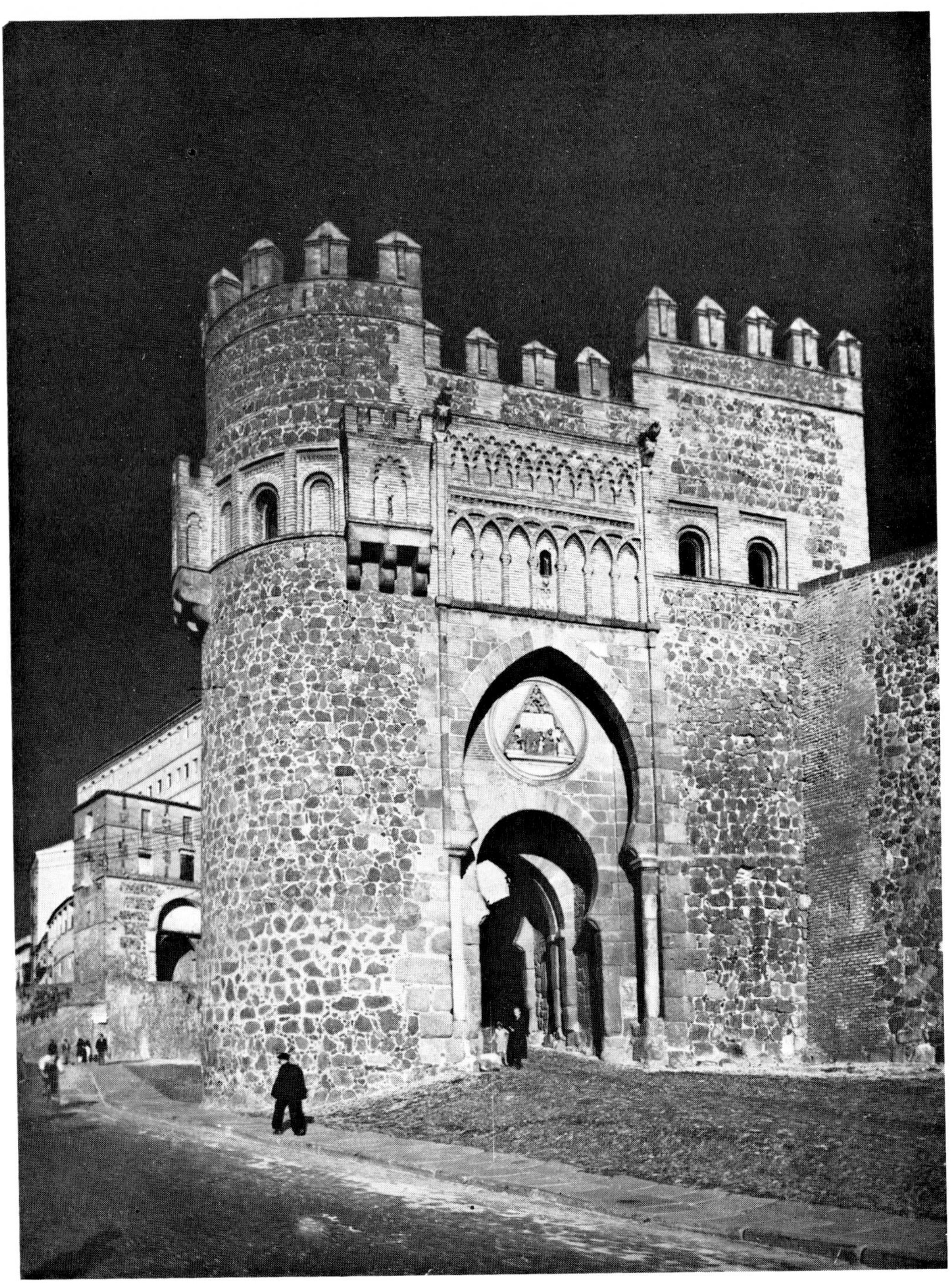

Plate LII. The Puerta del Sol (Gate of the Sun), Toledo, Spain; end of the twelfth century A.D. (see page 139).

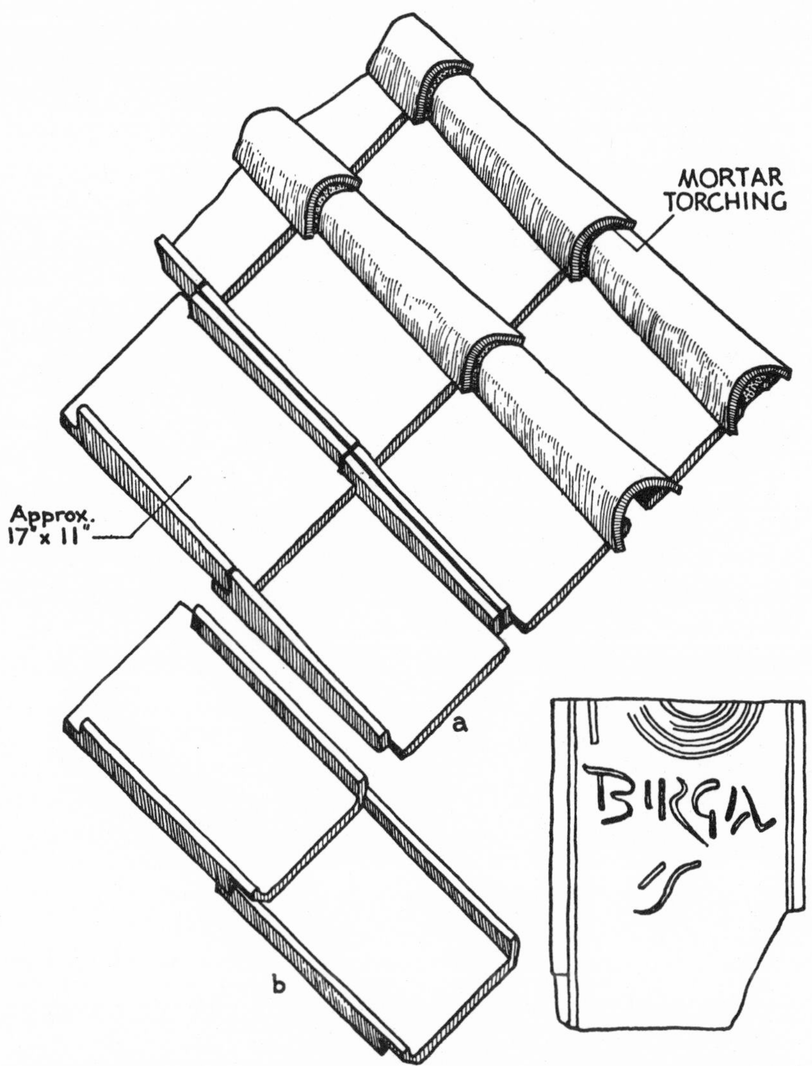

Fig. 91. Roman roofing tiles: flat, tapered *tegulae* showing different methods of shaping to fit one tile into the next (a, b). Inset. Roman *tegula* with the maker's name BIRGINVS scratched on it; from the roof of the Basilica at Silchester (Reading Museum).

Reading Museum, reads N [E] R C L C Æ AV G G ER — N [E] R(O) CL(audius) CÆ(sar) AVG(ustus) GER(manicus), and the tile is evidently from a state-owned tile factory of the time of Nero (A.D. 54–68). This stamp, which is one of the earliest in Britain, is circular in form. It was impressed by a die, perhaps of wood or of baked clay, over the surface of which cloth was tightly stretched to prevent the moist clay from clogging the engraved letters. The impression of the cloth can be seen on the tile. Occasionally the roofing tiles, like other kiln products, bear the mark of the maker. One such tile (Figure 91) from the

Fig. 92. Pear-shaped clay roofing tiles of Romano-British period from Wykehurst Farm, near Ewhurst, Surrey.

roof of the Basilica at Silchester, and now in the Reading Museum, is a *tegula* upon the surface of which is scratched the name BIRGINVS.

Some pear-shaped clay roofing tiles, evidently made in imitation of stone slates or of wood shingles, were found in 1936 on the site of a Roman kiln of the usual rectangular updraught type, at Wykehurst Farm near Ewhurst, Surrey.[7] The tiles were 15 inches from the top to bottom, 10 inches across at their widest, and 3 inches wide at the top edge. They were pierced about 3 inches from the top with nail holes (Figure 92).

The ridge of the Roman roof was capped with semicircular tiles cemented in position. Some apparently unique ridge tiles were found in a Roman kiln at Canterbury.[8] They had slots cut into their lower edges, as shown in Figure 93, two a side, to fit snugly over the two flanges of adjacent *tegulae*. All the tiles had a lattice pattern incised on their upper surface, and it seems that the intention must have been to render them with mortar to seal the joints between the tiles, to make them weather-tight. Alternatively, it may have been intended to cement a second layer of ridge tiles upon the first layer to cover the joints.

In better work antefixes were often placed to cover the ends of the *imbrices* at the eaves, and a ridge terminal feature might be placed at the gable ends. A number of antefix tiles were found on the site of a pottery at Castle Lyons, Holt, Denbighshire, and as seen in Figure 94 show in relief a boar, which was the emblem of the 20th Roman Legion, long stationed at Chester. The terminals often had a saddle piece like that shown in Figure 87, and are a direct link with the *acroteria* of Greek architecture.

The development and use of clay roofing tiles in post-Roman times is somewhat obscure, but the Sicilian and Laconian forms have survived with minor and local variations in size and shape in the countries bordering the Mediterranean. Throughout north-western Europe a smaller type of flat tile was developed, almost identical in size and shape with our present day clay plain tile. It is in fact a fireproof substitute for the timber shingle. When and where this type was first developed is in doubt, but it had certainly reached this country from Flanders by the

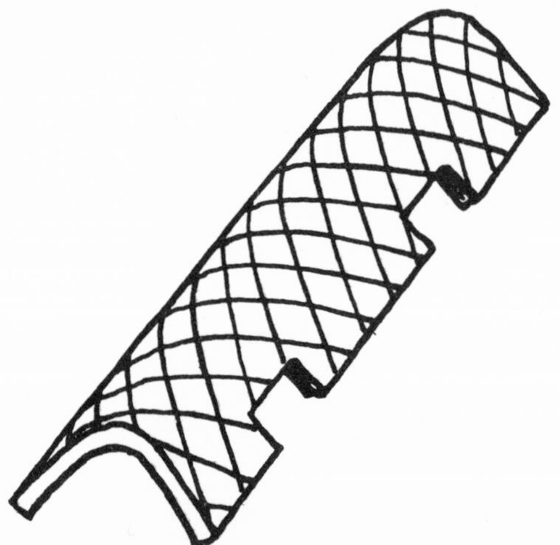

Fig. 93. Roman clay ridge tile fired in a kiln at Canterbury (Durovernum).

beginning of the thirteenth century, when in 1212 the use of tiling was enforced in the City of London to reduce the risk of fire.

Following many complaints about the bad quality of roofing tiles, an Act of Parliament was passed in 1477 (Stat. 17 Edw. IV)[9] to regulate their manufacture. It stated:

Fig. 94. Antefix tile of the 20th Legion from Holt, Denbighshire (British Museum).

> Whereas in divers parts of this realm great damage hath been and daily is, and by likelihood in time to come will much increase, for default of true seasonable and sufficient making, whiting and annealing of tile, called plain tile; otherwise called thak tile, roof tile or crest tile, corner tile and gutter tile, made and to be made within this realm; Our Lord the king . . . hath ordained . . . the Earth . . . shall be digged and cast up before the first day of November next before that they shall be made and that the same Earth be stirred and turned before the first day of February then next following the same digging and casting up and not wrought before the first day of March next following: and that the same Earth . . . be truly wrought and tried from stones: and also that the veins called Malm or Marle, and Chalk, lying commonly in the ground . . . shall be . . . severed and cast from the said Earth . . . Every such plain tile . . . shall contain in length ten inches and half, and in breadth six inches and a quarter of an inch, and in thickness half an inch and half a quarter.

Ridge tiles or crests were to be 13½ inches by 6¼ inches and gutter tiles 10½ inches long. The generally accepted size for roofing tiles has remained practically the same in England for five hundred years, the size of a British Standard roofing tile in 1959 being 10½ inches long by 6½ inches wide, and in thickness not less than ½ inch.

Pantiles appear in England in the seventeenth century, particularly in the eastern and northern counties where they were imported from the Low Countries. They are of double curvature and are in effect an adaptation of the normal tile in combining the two elements, the *tegula* and the *imbrex*, in one piece. Manufacture of them in England was established in the eighteenth century in East Anglia. They were mostly red in colour and unglazed, but some were given a black vitreous finish, and more recently blue and green vitreous finishes have also been produced.

Wooden Tiles, or Shingles

Wooden tiles, or shingles, are naturally more closely associated with timber buildings the heavily forested areas like Scandinavia, Germany, Russia, and parts of North

Fig. 95. Wooden church at Larchenhag, in the forest area of Gleiwitz, Poland.

America. Although in many other countries, as in Britain, it was quite common practice in medieval times to use wood shingles, the denudation of the forests quickly led to a decline in their use. In spite of this, however, there are still many ancient buildings with roofs and spires covered with shingles. They had in fact been used since the Roman occupation. Pliny[10] writing in A.D. 77 says that:

> The most suitable roof-shingles are got from the hard-oak, and the next best from the other acorn bearing trees, and from the beech; those most easily obtained are cut from all trees that produce resin, but these are the least good to last with the exception of those from the pine. Cornelius Nepos informs us that Rome was roofed with shingles right down to the war with Pyrrhus. . . .

The war with Pyrrhus began in 281 B.C., so it would appear that wood shingles had already been in use in Rome, when Pliny was writing, for over 350 years.

The shingles used in Britain in early times were of cleft straight-grain oak, but now cedarwood shingles are imported from Canada, where, as in other parts of North America, this timber and oak, cypress, and redwood (Scots pine) are used. Ancient wood shingles were often little more than 8 inches in length and 4 to 5 inches wide, and were fixed by wooden pegs at a gauge of 4 inches. The greater part of the roof therefore had the protection of only two thicknesses of tile. The modern method is to use shingles at least 12 inches long and to lay them to a rather closer gauge, fixing them by copper nails towards the centre. The nail of each shingle overlaps by at least 1½ inches the top of the shingle in the third course below, and in this way there are at least three thicknesses of tile over most of the roof, giving much better weather protection.

Wood shingles last longer if they are laid on roofs with a steep pitch—at least 40°. The roof of the wooden church at Larchenhag, in the forest area of Gleiwitz, in Poland, shown in Figure 95, illustrates this point well. The roofs, which are typical, are of steep pitch and covered with wood shingles, carried downwards and outwards as aprons spreading well beyond the walls of the building so that the snow and rain can be discharged easily.

REFERENCES

(1) SLEE, JOHN, 6 Nov. 1958, 'A Disappearing Craft —Slate-making in the Cotswolds', *Country Life*.

(2) JOPE, E. M., and DUNNING, G. E., 'The Use of Blue Slate for Roofing in Medieval England', *Antiquaries' Journal*, XXXIV, 209, Fig. 1, and Pl. XXII.

(3) MORSE, E. S., Jan., Feb., Mar. 1892, 'On the Older Forms of Terracotta Roofing Tiles', *Bulletin of the Essex Institute*, Salem, XXIV, Parts 1, 2 and 3.

(4) DINSMOOR, W. B., 1953, *The Architecture of Ancient Greece*, Batsford, 43.

(5) SESTIERI, P. CLAUDIO, 23 Oct. 1954, 'The Magnificent Intact Vases of a truly Unique Discovery—The Underground Shrine of Paestum', *Illustrated London News*.

(6) WHEELER, R. E. M., and T. V., 1936, *Verulamium*, Research Report of the Society of Antiquaries of London.

(7) 'Roman Britain in 1936,' 1937, *Journal of Roman Studies*, XXVII, Part 2, 244; WINBOLT, S. E., *Surrey Archaeological Collections*, XIV, and *Antiquaries' Journal*, XVI, 463f.

(8) JENKINS, F., 1956, 'A Roman Tilery and Two Pottery Kilns at Durovernum (Canterbury)', *Antiquaries' Journal*, XXXVI, 40.

(9) Statutes of the Realm, II, 463–5.

(10) PLINY, *Natural History*, Book XVI, XV, translated by H. Rackham, Loeb Classical Library, Heinemann.

19

Decorative Tiles

THE WORD TILE, derived from the French *tuile*, means strictly a baked clay roofing tile or *tegula*, as it would be called in Latin. In the English language the term tile has been given a wider meaning, to include also tiles of a decorative character for walls and floors. In Egypt for example, as far back as the 3rd Dynasty small glazed tiles, bright blue, green, and almost black, were used in the step pyramid at Saqqara.[1] There are others with the name of Pepi I (6th Dynasty), yellow and green in colour;[2] while Rameses III had a Temple at Tel-el-Yehudiyeh in the Delta the walls of which were decorated with small glazed tiles set in cement like mosaic. Some were decorated with processions of captives, ornamental work, and the names and titles of the monarch.

From the ninth century B.C. onwards the Assyrians and the Babylonians made both glazed wall tiles and earthenware bricks with designs painted on their surface with coloured glazes. After the collapse of these nations, the Persians carried on the art and produced very beautiful tilework, a notable example shown in the frontispiece being the Frieze of the Archers, or royal bodyguard, from the walls of the Palace of Darius I at Susa, in Persia (521–485 B.C.). It was excavated by M. Dieulafoy and is now in the Louvre, Paris. In this case bricks, decorated in relief and coated with tin glazes, very much resemble the glazed bricks on the walls of Nineveh and Babylon (1200 B.C.), in appearance at least. The colours used were ochre, dull red, white, various tones of green, and a brilliant turquoise. This technique of decoration appears to have died out after the conquest of Alexander the Great in the fourth century B.C. and neither the Greeks nor the Romans used glazed tiles for decorative purposes.

Another type of Roman pavement (*opus sectile*) is shown in Figure 96, in which pieces of coloured marbles are cut to various shapes and laid in mortar to form a geometric pattern. The example is a floor in the house of Cupid and Psyche at Ostia. The simple pavement at Silchester shown in Figure 97 is made with square, octagonal, and a few hexagonal hypocaust tiles with mosaic infillings.

The Persians revived the art and strove for many centuries to perfect their work. By the Sassanian period (A.D. 221–641), however, there was a preference for decorative stucco work, which in great palaces like Ctesiphon and Kish took the form of panels

Fig. 96. *Opus sectile* floor; the House of Cupid and Psyche, Ostia.

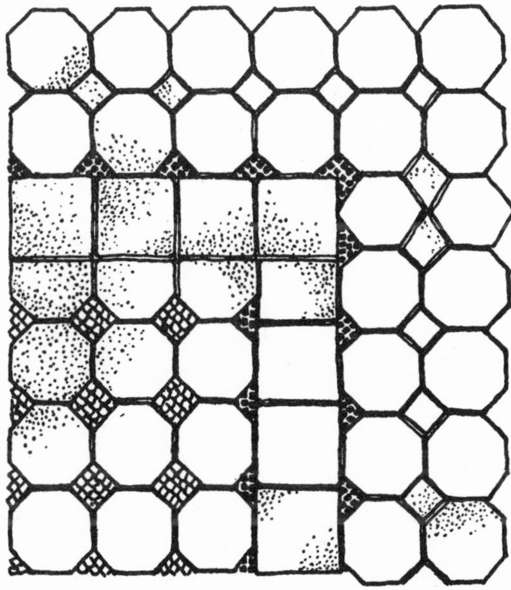

Fig. 97. Roman pavement from Silchester, laid with square, octagonal, and a few hexagonal hypocaust tiles with mosaic infillings (Reading Museum).

moulded and carved in gypsum plaster with figures and stylized plant ornament. This type of stucco decoration was adopted by the Islamic people who succeeded the Sassanians in A.D. 641, and it reached perfection in Mesopotamia during the Abbasid Dynasty between about A.D. 750 and the end of the following century. During this time great use was made of mural decoration, particularly in the palace of Samarra on the Tigris, to which reference is made in Chapter 13.

It was the Islamic peoples who revived the use of glazed tiles and who laid the foundations for a great ceramic industry, that was subsequently to have such a great influence on the techniques of the Western World. It was stimulated by direct contact with China and by the importation of wares from that country. The subsequent Mongol invasion of Persia in the thirteenth century also did much to link Persia and China both in commerce and in culture. Some of the Persian tiles of this period are hexagonal, others star-shaped with tiles of cruciform shape to fill the intervening spaces, and are decorated with lustre. They are coated with creamy white enamel upon which are painted most delicate designs in metallic lustre slips. Many were found on the site of the City of Rhè or Rhey (Rhages) south of the Caspian Sea, which was destroyed in the fourteenth century. The peak of development was, however, reached in Persia about A.D. 1600 and was mainly centred on the city of Tabriz.

Lane[3] records that Abbasid tiles, from Kairawan and Samarra, had a ground of opaque white glaze and were painted in yellow, brown, and sometimes red 'lustre' colours produced from a compound of silver and copper and applied with a medium of ochre slip. The metallic sheen was precipitated on the surface of the already fired glaze by a second firing in a smoky kiln, and the accretions of ochre were afterwards removed by polishing. He states that this technique, apparently first used on pottery in Mesopotamia, must have been a secret jealously guarded by a sort of guild, most of whose members migrated to Egypt in the Fatimid period (A.D. 969–1171), for there is no evidence definitely proving the continued manufacture of lustre ware in Asia at that time. In addition to these lustre tiles, the Persians made a mosaic tile from the thirteenth century onwards. Large monochrome tiles were cut up into small pieces which were assembled into rich and complex designs; at first the shapes were mainly straight-edged and geometrical, but later included curvilinear motifs and stylized plant forms. By the fifteenth century the method was fully developed and some of the most beautiful polychrome decorations were made. Good examples exist at Isfahan, in Persia, in the great portal of Masjid-i-Shah, and in the Mausoleum at Samarkand in Uzbekistan (A.D. 1404). The same process was followed in Egypt, North Africa, and Spain, but in Persia itself and the rest of the East the mosaic tiles were slowly abandoned in favour of painted faience.

The Persian influence extended also to Turkey and Syria and ultimately spread through the countries under Mohammedan rule in Asia and Africa, and finally to Spain. Centres of manufacture were set up in Turkey at Iznik (Nicaea) in Northern Anatolia, and at Kutahia, and in Northern Syria at Rakka, and later at Damascus, from which source it is thought the tiles for the Cairo mosques were supplied. The first examples in Europe of the Persian influence are the well-known *azulejos* wall tiles of Spain, first made at Seville in the twelfth century A.D. and seen at their best in the fortress palace of the Alhambra at Granada built chiefly between 1248 and 1354, and the Alcazar at Seville, built in the middle of the fourteenth century, by the Moors after their conquest of Spain. The term *azulejos* was derived from the Arabic word *zuleija* which meant literally burnt stone. The tiles were used in dadoes of geometric design, as shown in Figure 98, often surrounded by bands of inscriptions, and having above them contrasting arabesque patterns in stucco relief. Originally the tiles were small and of separate colours and were set into the walls in mosaic fashion to form geometric designs, very like the Persian wall mosaics already

Fig. 98. Detail of *azulejos*, Paço de Sintra, Portugal.

described. Later larger tiles were made with the design marked out by lines or furrows with the edges in slight relief, and the intervening spaces were filled with enamel of brilliant colours. The effect of this combination of light and shade was most striking. Patterns remained geometrical in design until about the middle of the sixteenth century, when under Italian influence, both Renaissance and Rococo, they became more pictorial, embodying not only classical motifs, volutes, and scrolls, but flowers, fruits, and figures both animal and human. Excellent examples of this type of work, ranging in date up to the present day, can be seen at many places in Spain and Portugal, and particularly fine examples can be seen at the seventeenth-century Palace of Fronteira to the north-east of Lisbon. In Europe, architectural tilework has never equalled in importance that of the Eastern countries.

In Turkey in the sixteenth century many fine buildings were erected, often with the inner walls decorated with dadoes of tile, and examples in the Victoria and Albert

Museum, London, of the painted tiles of the latter half of that century, particularly those from the Mosque of Eyub Erisari, in Constantinople, represent the finest ever made in that country.

Until the latter part of the twelfth century few decorated tiles were used in Europe, outside Spain, and then usually only for floors. These floors were of a mosaic type consisting of small tiles of red or brown clay cut into various geometric shapes such as squares, polygons, quatrefoils, circles, etc., while still soft, and fitted together after firing on a cement bed. The colours were varied by coating some of the tiles with a slip of white pipeclay, or by staining the lead glaze. The floor in the Abbey of St Denis, dating from

Fig. 99. Thirteenth-century mosaic pavement at Byland Abbey, Yorkshire.

the latter half of the twelfth century, is one of the earliest examples remaining. Floors of this type were derived from the so-called *opus Alexandrinum* floors—a term which in Roman times was applied to floors of green and purple porphyry but which by the twelfth and thirteenth centuries had come to include mosaic floors made with marbles of other colours. In Italy marbles in large discs cut from ancient columns were set amid geometric patterns formed with smaller pieces of various colours. It was as a substitute for these expensive marbles and coloured stones that the ceramic tiles were produced in Northern France and it was not long before both tile-mosaics and inlaid tiles were adopted in Holland and Britain. A good example of this tile-mosaic work is to be seen in the twelfth- or early thirteenth-century floor in the south transept of the Cistercian Abbey of Byland in Yorkshire. It is the largest Cistercian church in England and was commenced in A.D. 1177. Part of the similar floor from the north transept is in the British Museum,

London. The earthenware tiles were cut to various shapes to form the geometric pattern shown in Figure 99. The tiles have a pink body, lightly glazed in various shades, pale to deep yellow and pale to dark grey. Similar tiles have been found at Rievaulx Abbey, Yorkshire, and on the site of Meaux Abbey in the same county.

The glazed surface of these tiles did not stand up at all well to abrasion, and tiles with an inlaid pattern produced about the same time were a great improvement. They were made by first shaping the tile in a mould, drying it, and then impressing upon its surface a design which had been carved in relief on a wooden block. The impressions were then filled, or inlaid, with white pipeclay and finally glazed and fired. Sometimes the inlaid pattern was of darker clay and the background whitened. The inset patterns did not suffer from wear in the way the earlier tiles had done. Very many designs were produced to satisfy individual and local needs. Often the design on a tile was complete in itself, but it was not uncommon, as in the tile floor in the Chapter House at Westminster Abbey, for four tiles to form a pattern unit. This magnificent pavement, laid down in 1255, is in a

Fig. 109. Inlaid tiles in the Chapter House at Westminster, from the pavement laid down in 1255.

wonderful state of preservation, and is the finest of its kind now existing. The patterns include portraits of Henry III, Queen Eleanor, Archbishop Richard of Crokesley, the Royal Arms, hunting scenes, minstrels, animals, and fishes (Figure 100).

Tiles described as relief tiles, in which the pattern was formed either in relief or impressed, were developed in the fourteenth century in Northern Europe, mainly in

Fig. 101. Types of decorative tile: (a) Inlaid; Keynsham Abbey, Somerset, thirteenth–fifteenth centuries. (b) Raised relief; St Albans Abbey, thirteenth century. (c) Impressed; Marienhaus, near Neuwied, Germany, fifteenth century.

Germany. There were two types: one of unglazed tiles, about 8 to 9 inches square, called 'St Urban' tiles after the Monastery of St Urban near Zofingen where the main factory was situated, had the pattern applied to the surface by countersunk stamps of wood, earthenware, or stone, so that the pattern stood out in bold relief; the other type was smaller, measuring only about 5 inches square, and the soft clay was pressed into a wooden mould and impressed with a stamp bearing the pattern in raised relief. In this case of course the resulting pattern on the finished tile was countersunk. The various types of tile are illustrated in Figure 101.

Some tiles of the same period were made by the so-called 'Sgraffito' process in which the designs were engraved by hand through a coat of white clay which was in parts completely scraped away to show figures standing out against a brown background. Each tile was individualistic and a picture in itself, and was not a type for mass production, but rather one that was produced to special order.

The Cistercian Order of monks did much to establish the craft of tilemaking in Britain in the thirteenth century. Several abbeys, such as Chertsey, Great Malvern, St Mary Witton near Droitwich, and Repton, had their own kilns. Like their continental prototypes, the tiles were of local red earthenware with the pattern slightly sunk by means of a wooden die, or incised by hand, the hollows so formed being filled with white clay of creamy consistence. Other tiles were made by a process which gave a pattern in raised relief as in the German tiles, while others were just slip-painted. When this clay had hardened it was scraped down to the level of the original red body, leaving the pattern distinct and clear, and producing the so-called 'encaustic' tile. An alternative and slovenly method which became general in the Thames Basin in the middle of the fourteenth century involved only a single operation, which was in effect a printing process. The white clay was spread on to the raised portions of the wooden stamp and then impressed directly on to the clay tile. Whereas by the inlaid process the white clay was sometimes over $\frac{1}{4}$ inch deep and so allowed for considerable wearing down before obliteration of the design, and the edges of the design were clear cut, the outline of the design on the printed tiles was rarely clear cut and often smudged, or if too much white clay were put on the wooden stamp it spread untidily beyond the intended outline. Whichever method of patterning was used the tiles were coated with powdered lead ore which produced a transparent yellow glaze when fired in the kiln. The red colour of the body combined with the yellow of the glaze to produce a rich reddish-brown surface. The designs were multitudinous, consisting of geometrical devices, floral designs, heraldic devices, and religious symbols. Some pictorial scenes are particularly beautiful, among the finest examples being those in Ely Cathedral, depicting the miracles of Christ; and the Chertsey tiles, which in one series show episodes from the legendary history of Richard I, Cœur de Lion, and hunting and combat scenes, and in another show scenes from the romance of Tristram and Iseult, which was composed by the Anglo-Norman Thomas of Erceldoune about 1170. A huntsman on horseback fighting a lion is particularly fine (see Figure 102). The artist seems to have based his design on an earlier and possibly classical model. The tiles had a red body with white clay inlay and were coated with a gold-coloured glaze.

After the Dissolution of the Monasteries tilemaking virtually ceased in England for fifty years or so, and supplies had to be imported from the Continent, mainly from Holland, France, Germany, Italy, and Spain.

Although some tin-glazed floor tiles had been produced in Holland as early as the fourteenth century, it was not until the latter part of the sixteenth century that decorated wall tiles became popular when potters left Antwerp and started factories at Rotterdam, Utrecht, Harlingen, and Leeuwarden.

An Italian majolica painter named Guido di Savino had previously settled in Antwerp in about 1512 and commenced manufacture of majolica tiles there. The soft clay for the tiles was first pressed into moulds of uniform size, usually just over 5 inches square, and then coated with a white tin enamel. They were then set on a board with a nail at each corner to hold them and left to dry face downwards. The designs were then painted on the dried enamel, being first marked in outline by the method of 'pouncing'. A paper cartoon was prepared with the design pricked in outline, and this was laid on the tile,

Fig. 102. Inlaid floor tiles from Chertsey Abbey, founded in 666 and rebuilt in 1110.

powdered charcoal being sprinkled through the holes to leave a faint pattern on the tile for the painter a fill in, in the desired colours. The colours and glaze were fired together and this blended them into a very smooth surface. In the earlier methods of 'pouncing' used for transferring designs, particularly in Italy for frescoes, pumice powder, or 'pounce', was used. The late sixteenth-century designs were mainly geometrical with arabesque motives, and painted in blue, yellow, brown, and sometimes green. Some Dutch tiles were decorated with a metallic lustre pigment which, being susceptible to and adversely affected by high temperatures, had to be painted on to the previously fired enamel, the tile then being given a second firing at a lower temperature. For the same reason some of the eighteenth-century Delft tiles were twice fired in a muffle furnace.

In England majolica ware was already being produced in the sixteenth century by potters from Antwerp who settled in Norwich and later in London, in Aldgate, Southwark, and Lambeth. There appears to have been a constant interchange of craftsmen between England and Holland, and many Dutch potters from Delft settled in Lambeth, and English tin-glazed wares eventually became known as Delft ware. The craft, however, had declined considerably by the end of the century.

REFERENCES

(1) Petrie, W. M. Flinders, 1933, *Arts and Crafts of Ancient Egypt*, Davies, chapter VII.

(2) Maspero, G., 1902, *Manual of Egyptian Archaeology*, translated by Amelia B. Edwards, H. Grevel, London, 5th edition, 276.

(3) Lane, Arthur, 1939, *A Guide to the Collection of Tiles*, Victoria and Albert Museum, London.

20

Fresco, Secco, and Tempera

THE TERM *fresco* is derived from the Italian word meaning fresh, and is applied to the process of applying mineral and earthy pigments to the damp surface of lime stucco before it dries and hardens. The pigments penetrate the surface and become an integral part of the work and are encased eventually in calcium carbonate. True frescoes have remained in good condition after hundreds of years. The term fresco has also been rather loosely applied to some examples of Egyptian work where the painting was applied directly to a gypsum plaster base. In some instances a skimming coat of lime was applied over the gypsum plaster base to provide the ground for the painting and in these cases it may be that the work simulated more closely that of true fresco. However, most of the applied decoration in Egyptian work appears to have been done in water colour, the pigments being mixed with a water-soluble organic substance such as gum.

Professor Emery,[1] a few years back, revealed by excavation some very early Egyptian paintings on the walls of the mastaba of the tomb of Saqqara, south-west of Cairo, thought to be that of Pharaoh Ka-a, last king of the 1st Dynasty (*c.* 2900 B.C.). The walls were covered with brilliant white plaster on which were painted elaborate geometric patterns in imitation of mat-work in colours of red, white, black, blue, green, and yellow.

The walls of a tomb of the reign of Uadji,[2] the successor of Zer, who, according to Professor Emery, ruled Egypt about 3100 B.C., were faced with mud plaster $\frac{3}{4}$ inch thick, and over this was a gypsum stucco covered with a white lime wash, which formed the background for elaborate decorations in red, green, yellow, and other colours.

Dr Flinders Petrie found some fine but later examples on the walls and pavement of a building at Tel-el-Amarna, of the reign of King Amenhotep IV (*c.* 1800 B.C.). He records[3] that 'the colours were laid on while the plaster was wet and even while it could still be moved by the brush' thus suggesting the fresco technique. Lucas[4] made an analysis of the stucco and found that it was of gypsum plaster containing a large amount of calcium carbonate and particles of unburnt fuel.

Plate LIII. Entrance to a covered passageway, mostly subterranean, giving protected access to a well outside the city walls, Mycenae; *c.* 1400 B.C. (see page 141).

Plate LIV. The great arched vault at the Palace of Ctesiphon, near Baghdad; A.D. 550 (see pages 77 and 143).

Plate LV. Model of a Chinese house with an inscription which reads: 'Made in the first year of Yung Ping'—A.D. 58 (see page 155).

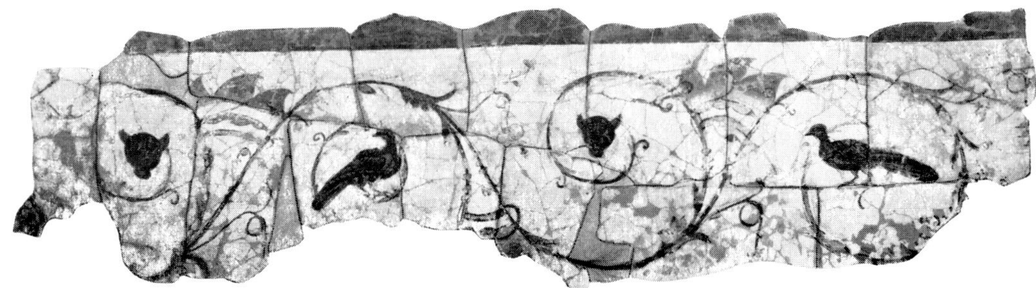

Plate LVI. A Roman mural recovered from the debris of a building excavated at Verulamium in 1956 (see page 174).

Plate LVII. Roman relief in Sens Museum, France, showing workmen painting a wall (see page 175).

According to Toch,[5] Egyptian pigments from the tomb of Per-neb (2650 B.C.) in the Metropolitan Museum of New York included red haematite, yellow ochre or ferruginous clay, blue frit, pale blue azurite, green malachite, black charcoal or bone black.

The colouring of lime stucco to a uniform red by a true fresco technique was carried out in the Early Minoan Period in Crete,[6] and seems to have been the only colour used at that time. The pigment was made by burning red and yellow ferruginous clay or earths. By the end of the Middle Minoan Period I (*c.* 2000 B.C.) white and black were also used, the white probably being hydrated lime, and the black a carbonaceous shale or slate, or charcoal. In Middle Minoan Period III other pigments were added to the list, a deep blue, thought to be powdered glass, prepared by fusing sand with soda and colouring with copper silicate,[7] and probably imported from Egypt; deep red possibly from haematite; and green, which was a mixture of the blue and yellow ochre, the latter derived from a suitable yellow clay in its natural state. Ground malachite, a natural carbonate of copper, was used later in Crete, but it had been used previously in Egypt.

The use of frescoes in Mesopotamia appears to have been a rather later development. In the Royal Assyrian Palace—built by King Adad-Ninari III (810–782 B.C.) at Nimrud, the ancient Assyrian Calah, Professor Mallowan[8] found walls covered with brilliantly coloured frescoes. The designs consisted of pomegranate, floral, and geometric patterns in continuous broad bands 6 feet above the level of the floor. Concentric circles and cushion-like lozenges surmounted by tiered battlements added to the variety; cobalt blue, red, black, and white pigments were used to render the building alive with colour.

A broad recess in the King's bathroom carried one of the most brilliantly executed frescoes in the building, a spirited design of a pair of bulls with their heads turned back, standing in heraldic fashion on either side of a great sun-disc. A similar scheme of design was also seen on a number of delicately carved ivories.

The Greeks and Romans made great use of fresco, but often used it in combination with other processes of decoration. Many of the Roman murals, for example, had a true fresco ground, but the applied decoration was tempera. In fact, recent research by Augusti[9] on the Pompeian paintings has led him to the conclusion that they were carried out with a distemper consisting of lime, soap, water, wax, and pigment. The soap was probably tallow (goat) saponified with vegetable ashes which would contain potash. The wax was probably beeswax. When mixed together the lime and soap would combine to form an insoluble calcium soap.

Augusti deduced that the procedure in preparing the base was first of all to apply one or two coats of well slaked lime and sand; if there were two coats the first coat was allowed to dry thoroughly before the second was applied. Each coat was thoroughly compacted with wooden tampers, and when the second coat had dried, a coat of lime and calcium carbonate (which could be powdered marble or other suitable limestone) was applied, thoroughly compacted and allowed to dry. Occasionally this coat consisted of lime and crushed tile. The next coat to be applied was the base on which the painting was to be done, and it consisted of lime, chalk, soap, and wax (beeswax). This was applied in a thin layer, allowed to dry out thoroughly and then smoothed with an iron trowel, and polished with marble, glass, or stone, and finally rubbed over with a cloth. The painting medium, consisting of a soapy solution of lime with wax and colour added, was then applied.

It is of interest to compare this technique with that followed in the Roman-British murals discovered at Verulamium.[10] Here in 1956 three extensive areas of fallen plaster were found in a second-century building. Two of the murals were found in a corridor. They had fallen face downwards, one on top of the other. The first one to fall, evidently from a ceiling (and if so it is unique in Britain), had a purple-red ground with yellow bearded wheat stalks enclosing panels supported by diagonal extensions. These panels contained doves in various poses, but in two of them there were feline heads. Between the panels were bluish-grey circles and ovals outlined in white, perhaps formalized flowers. This plaster is now restored and exhibited at the Verulamium Museum. The second mural, found lying above it, had a red ground and bore very slender candelabra surmounted by conventional wheels with projecting torches, reminiscent of Pompeian candelabra, from which floral swags in yellow or blue depended. There were also doves on perches. The third mural had fallen from the north-west wall of the courtyard, and presumably when it was in position on the wall it was protected by a verandah. The ground is bright yellow, and has an 'inhabited scroll' containing leopards' heads and pheasants painted upon it in green. The scale of the scroll, unusual details, such as the inclusion of flambeaux or torch-like motifs in the forks of the scroll, the long area of plaster recovered, and its fine state of preservation, made this discovery unique in Britain. In fact, a painted scroll of this scale, 12 feet in length and up to 5 feet in height, is quite exceptional in Classical art as a whole. It has been partially restored as shown in Plate LVI and exhibited at the British Museum.

The stucco for these murals was applied in two coats. The sand used throughout was clean siliceous pit sand, of rather coarser size in the undercoat (*arriccio*) than in the second or finishing coat (*intonaco*). For the latter practically all the sand passed through a sieve of $\frac{3}{16}$ inch square mesh. The undercoat of the 'purple' painting also contained fragments of earlier stucco decorated in white, black, and salmon pink with black flecks. There was chopped straw or grass in the undercoats.

The proportions of the mixtures used were, in the case of the 'purple' painting, for the undercoat, one volume of lime (assumed to have been run to a putty) and two volumes of sand, and for the second coat equal volumes of lime and sand. For the 'red' mural painting the corresponding mixtures were 1 : $2\frac{1}{2}$ and 1 : $1\frac{1}{2}$, while for the 'yellow' mural with the scroll they were 1 : $2\frac{3}{4}$ and 1 : 2 respectively. The amount of lime used in the finishing coats was therefore appreciably greater than that in the undercoats. The thickness of the coats varied. In the 'purple' and the 'yellow' murals the undercoats were $\frac{3}{4}$ inch thick and the second coats $\frac{3}{8}$ inch thick; in the 'red' mural the corresponding thicknesses were $1\frac{1}{4}$ inches and $\frac{1}{2}$ inch.

In each case the second coat had been applied after the first coat had dried, and the surface brought to a very smooth and compact finish. While it was still soft the ground colour coat was applied in fresco fashion with a broad brush or cloth in long horizontal sweeps. When this was dry, the decorative design was applied in tempera.

Two other significant features were revealed. The 'red' mural had fallen from a clay pisé wall, the surface of which had been impressed in herringbone fashion while the pisé was still soft, to provide a key for the stucco undercoat which in this case was much thicker than in the other two examples. This thick undercoat with the damp clay behind it must have required a considerable time to dry out sufficiently before the application of the second coat. During this period its surface was splashed with white and purple distemper, probably quite accidentally, while the 'purple' mural on the ceiling above was being painted.

A rather mutilated relief, illustrated in Plate LVII, in Sens Museum, France,[11] shows workmen engaged in painting a wall. A man is apparently engaged in mixing the mortar and two men, on a scaffold supported on trestles and reached by a ladder, are painting the wall. There are several receptacles containing the various mixtures.

Another method of decoration was introduced in the late Greek or early Roman epoch. The pigments were mixed with melted beeswax, the paint being applied with brushes or with a heated spatula (*cauterium*). The method was used in the Ptolemaic Period in Egypt for painting on wood. Petrie[12] describes decoration of this type at Hawara.

The finest frescoes were carried out during the period from the thirteenth to sixteenth centuries A.D. by numerous Italian artists from Giotto (1267–1337) to Raphael (1483–1520) and Michelangelo (1475–1564). Many beautiful examples of their work exist. Well-known frescoes by Giotto, a great exponent of the art of fresco painting, can be seen in the Basilica of S. Francesco at Assisi and by Raphael and Michelangelo in the Vatican, perhaps the most outstanding example being that by Michelangelo on the ceiling of the Sistine Chapel, which took 4 years from 1508 onwards to complete, and measures 133 by 43 feet.

Vasari[13] records that Giotto found that by adding brickdust to the finishing coat (*intonaco*) he obtained rendering which withstood more successfully the penetration of moisture, so that his work endured better. By doing so he was following the practice of the Romans when applying stucco in damp places.

In modern Italian work stucco is usually applied in two renderings, the first the *arriccio*, or roughcoat, and the *intonaco* or *scialbo*, the finishing coat. The usual mixture for the *arriccio* is one part of hydrated lime and two parts of sand, applied in two or three coats following in quick succession and building up to a thickness of about $\frac{1}{2}$ inch. Its surface is roughened to give a good key to the *intonaco*, and when it has dried thoroughly it is ready to receive the latter. Before this is applied, however, the *arriccio* is moistened with water, and the *intonaco* applied in two thin coats giving a thickness of about $\frac{1}{10}$ inch Sometimes marble dust is added to the stucco for the *intonaco*, but occasionally colour may be added to reduce the whiteness and provide a softer background for the fresco.

The procedure usually followed is for the painter to indicate to the plasterer the extent of the surface he wishes to cover, and the plasterer proceeds to apply the *intonaco*. The artist then transfers his design to the fresh surface by tracing the pattern with a stylus or by pouncing, the latter being preferred for more delicate work. When the day's work is finished any unpainted *intonaco* is cut away with a sharp instrument and the edge of the work is bevelled. The next day the plasterer applies fresh intonaco, and so on until the fresco is finished.

Secco

If the painting is done after the stucco has dried out, it is called *secco*, or dry work, and the durability generally is not so good. The colouring tends to be opaque. It is unfortunate that many of the sixteenth-century Italian artists, against Vasari's better judgment, abandoned the old method of true fresco work for an easier and what has proved to be the less durable secco technique. In this latter method the colour coats were not united with the moist plaster backing to become integral with it, in the manner of fresco, and many mural paintings executed by the secco method have deteriorated greatly; many in Tuscany and elsewhere are almost beyond reparation. It is encouraging, however, that Dr Ugo Procacci, the Director of the Florentine Soprintendenza, and his colleagues are rescuing many mural paintings, removing them, and after remounting on waterproof backing, returning them to the walls of the buildings where they belong.

Fresco-secco

There is a method, another poor substitute for true fresco (*buono fresco*), called 'fresco-secco' which at first sight appears to be a contradiction in terms. It is in fact a combination of the two techniques fresco and secco, and is carried out as follows. When the finishing coat (*intonaco*) is perfectly dry it is rubbed lightly with pumice stone to obtain a smooth surface. The day before the decoration is to be commenced, the surface is carefully washed with water to which a small amount of hydrated lime has been added. The next day this washing is repeated and the decoration commenced while the surface is still damp. The colours used are the same as for fresco. They are naturally absorbed into the surface of the *intonaco* where it has been moistened with lime-water and eventually, as this carbonates, the pigments receive some protection, but clearly not so effectively as if the pigments had been applied to the *intonaco* while that was still soft, as in true fresco work.

Tempera

The term 'tempera' is derived from the Latin *temperare*—to mix in due proportion. It is a water-colour process in which the water and pigment are mixed with organic binding substances such as the yolk or the white of an egg, gum tragacanth, glue, honey, gum arabic or mucilage, or milk and milk products, and applied to a dry surface; and in this respect it is like secco. Cennino Cennini writing in the fourteenth century mentions specifically the use of egg and the juice of the fig tree in tempera work.

The Egyptians used tempera very freely for interior and external decoration of their buildings. The Greeks and Romans also used it for interior decoration, often, as already noted, in association with other processes. For example, the ground of a mural or ceiling painting was often a true fresco, and the applied decorative design was in tempera. The process has been much used throughout all periods. The modern water-bound distempers are a direct survival of the early tempera mixtures.

The most widely used process in early medieval European wall painting was one involving both fresco and tempera, the broadly painted areas being done in fresco and finer detail being added later in tempera. In England in recent years there has been very grave concern about the condition of some of the finest primitive wall paintings. As long as the paintings lay hidden beneath the post-Reformation limewash applied to the church walls they were preserved, but during the last hundred years more and more have been exposed by the removal of the limewash, and have suffered badly on account of the deleterious effects of various varnishes, and more recently waxes, applied as preservatives. Far from preserving the painting, these relatively impervious skins have impeded the rate of evaporation of moisture from the damp walls behind the painted surface, and this has caused the disintegration of the surface.

The problem became so acute that in 1953 a Committee sponsored by the Central Council for the Care of Churches and the Society for the Protection of Ancient Buildings was formed to study the methods of conserving wall paintings. All those who have the care and maintenance of old wall paintings should study most carefully the report of that Committee.[14]

Wall paintings are liable to deteriorate if excessive damp has access to the walls on which they are painted and all possible measures should be taken to exclude damp from churches in which they exist, particularly when they are on outside walls, and the Committee recommend that there should be ample ventilation inside the building, and that most careful attention be given to the layout and installation of any heating system. The products of combustion from some types of stove may do irreparable damage to paintings.

One of the early (mid-twelfth-century date) English paintings still in good condition is the panel in St Anselm's Chapel in Canterbury Cathedral, representing St Paul and the viper. Other twelfth-century wall paintings of note are those at Barfreston (Kent) (*c.* 1180), Copford (Essex), Hardham (Sussex), which may be a few years earlier than the Canterbury painting, Kempley (Glos.), and Durham (*c.* 1180).

It is sad to see wall paintings which are losing or changing colour as a result of the use of faulty pigments or by overpainting by would-be restorers. The paintings by Cimabue (*c.* 1302) in the Basilica of S. Francesco at Assisi have faded and lost their colour, and attempts to restore them have met with little success. The colours in the almost contemporary paintings by Giotto (1267–1337) in the same church are, in striking contrast, still in brilliant condition.

Pigments for Wall Paintings

The types of pigment used in wall painting from the earliest times have been much the same the world over, being composed essentially of inert mineral compounds. They were necessarily those which would not be chemically altered by contact with the alkaline lime in the plaster. Some of the more important ones that have been used in fresco work are listed below.

WHITE

(i) hydrated or water-slaked lime ($Ca(OH)_2$), sometimes called 'lime white', formed by 'running' quicklime to a putty, and known to early Italian fresco painters as 'bianco sangiovanni';
(ii) white marble dust, chalk, and whiting (calcium carbonate);
(iii) mollusc shells (oysters and cockles for example) and egg-shells, calcined and ground.

BLACK

(i) carbon black, or charcoal black, well ground and washed to remove any potash. Produced by heating wood, preferably close-grained types, willow, beech, maple, etc.;
(ii) vine black, from carbonized vine twigs and vine wood, gives a slightly bluish-black colour;
(iii) burnt nut shells (peach stones, coconut shell, etc.), cork bark.

PURPLE

(i) calcined iron oxide (the anhydrous iron oxide Fe_2O_3) which occurs naturally as haematite, and gives a dark purple or maroon pigment.

BLUE

(i) lapis lazuli, or natural ultramarine blue, is a mixture of lazurite (blue mineral), calcspar and pyrites. Known to early painters as 'azurrum ultramarinum' or 'azurro ultromarino';
(ii) azurite, or mountain blue, a basic copper carbonate ($2\ CuCO_3.Ca(OH)_2$), called 'azurro della magna';
(iii) artificial copper blues, blue verditer, or blue bice, an artificial basic copper carbonate similar in composition to azurite.
(iv) Egyptian blue, blue frit or Pompeian blue ($CaO.CuO.4SiO_2$), an artificial compound of copper, calcium, and silica, made by heating a mixture containing silica, a copper compound (e.g. malachite), calcium carbonate, and natron (natural sodium sesqui carbonate).

GREEN

(i) terre verte, or green earth (Fe, Mg, Al, K, hydrosilicate), mostly originating as marine clay containing glauconite and celadonite (essentially hydrous iron, magnesium, and aluminium potassium silicates);
(ii) malachite, or mountain green ($CuCO_3.Ca(OH)_2$), a natural basic copper carbonate, similar to azurite but with more combined water, sometimes called 'verde azzurro'.

YELLOW

(i) yellow ochre, golden ochre, etc. (geothite, $Fe_2O_3H_2O$, clay, etc.), are natural earths consisting essentially of clay and silica. The shades of colour vary according to the quantity of hydrated iron oxide in them;

(ii) raw sienna, a special kind of yellow ochre from Sienna, in Italy, is hydrated ferric oxide with silica and alumina.

RED

(i) burnt sienna (Fe_2O_3, clay, etc.), obtained by calcining raw sienna and thus changing the hydrated ferric oxide to ferric oxide, giving a reddish-brown colour;

(ii) iron oxide (ferric oxide, Fe_2O_3); Indian red, 'rouge', or 'caput mortuum', is natural iron oxide from India; light red obtained by calcining yellow ochre; Tuscan red is red iron oxide with an organic pigment to brighten it, like alizarin red from the madder root; Venetian red, a natural oxide, partially hydrated, obtained by calcining a mixture of copperas (ferrous sulphate) and whiting (calcium carbonate);

(iii) vermilion, English vermilion, cinnabar, Chinese vermilion, etc., is red mercuric sulphide (HgS) occurring naturally as cinnabar, the principal ore of the metal mercury. Known to the ancients as 'minium', a term which later came to be applied to 'red lead'.

BROWN

(i) raw umber ($Fe_2O_3+MnO_2+H_2O$, clay, etc.), brown earth pigment, similar to ochres and siennas, but contains manganese dioxide as well as hydrous ferric oxide, giving a reddish-brown colour;

(ii) burnt umber ($Fe_2O_3+MnO_2$, clay, etc.), made by heating raw umber, thus changing hydrous ferric oxide to ferric oxide, giving a redder and warmer brown than raw umber.

REFERENCES

(1) EMERY, W. B., 15 May, 1954, 'Excavating the prototype of the Pyramids: the discovery of an immense Egyptian tomb of 5,000 years ago which may be that of the Pharaoh Ka-a', *Illustrated London News.*

(2) EMERY, W. B., 23 May, 1953, 'An Egyptian Royal Tomb 1,500 years before Tutankhamen: a major discovery in the Archaic cemetery of North Saqqara', *Illustrated London News.*

(3) PETRIE, W. M. FLINDERS, *Tell el Amarna*, p. 12.

(4) LUCAS, A., 1934, *Ancient Egyptian Materials and Industries*, 2nd ed., Arnold, 298.

(5) TOCH, M., 1918, 'The Pigments from the Tomb of Per-neb, *Journal Industrial and Engineering Chemistry*, 118.

(6) HEATON, NOEL, 30 Sept. 1911, 'Minoan Lime and Plaster and Fresco Painting', *Journal* of the Royal Institute of British Architects.

(7) PARTINGTON, J. R., 1935, *Origins and Development of Applied Chemistry*, Longmans Green.

(8) MALLOWAN, M. E. L., 15 Aug. 1953, 'A newly-found Assyrian Royal Palace of 2,750 years ago', *Illustrated London News.*

(9) AUGUSTI, SELIM, 1957, *La Technique de la Peinture*

Pompeienne, Edizioni Technique, Napoli.

(10) FRERE, S. S., Jan.–Apr. 1957, 'Verulamium Excavation Committee, Second Interim Report —1956', *The Antiquaries' Journal*, XXXVII, Nos. 1, 2.

(11) ESPÉRANDIEU, E., 1911, *Recueil général des bas-reliefs, et statues, de la Gaule romaine*, IV, No. 2767.

(12) PETRIE, W. M. FLINDERS, 1889, *Ten Years Digging*.

(13) VASARI, G., *The Lives of the Painters, Sculptors and Architects*, translated by A. B. Hinds, 1927, Dent, 71.

(14) *The Conservation of English Wallpaintings*, 1959, report published by the Central Council for the Care of Churches.

21

Mosaic

MOSAIC CONSISTS OF small pieces of coloured materials, set closely together in a matrix of cement, to form a smooth and patterned surface. Possibly the most primitive type of mosaic for decorating walls and floors, and still used in Africa and elsewhere, consisted of stones pressed into the surface of mud plaster and so arranged to form a simple pattern. In Sumeria, in the fourth millennium B.C., a similar though more elaborate method was practised for decorating the mud brick walls of important buildings. In addition to pieces of stone, fired clay cones of varying sizes up to 5 inches long were pressed into the walls, so that their flat bases just protruded from the mud plaster. These exposed ends of the clay cones, usually about ¾ inch in diameter, were sometimes coloured with red ochre or bitumen and were so arranged to produce attractive patterns (Figure 103a, b). A good example of the technique was revealed during excavations of a building at Warka (Uruk) in which the courtyard was enclosed by a wall with half columns as indicated in Figure 103c, and steps at one end led up to a platform on which stood a columned hall. The columns in this hall, the façade of the platform, and the walls and half columns of the courtyard were all decorated with cone mosaic. Woolley[1] has described this work and records that on every half column the pattern is different, and that the panels on the façade of the platform were framed by pilasters in relief, and filled with mosaics of delicate designs—zigzags, triangles, and lozenges—combined to produce an intricate scheme of decoration. These mosaics served to protect the mud plaster of the walls as well as providing a decorative finish.

The cones used for the mosaic varied in size according to the magnitude of the building. For example, the upper part of the walls of the massive stepped platform of the Ziggurat tower at Warka were decorated in panels with a mosaic of large clay cones like hollow vases and sunk in mud plaster. Cones up to 12 inches long and made of gypsum plaster, with the ends encased in thin sheet copper cemented on with bitumen, were also excavated in Eridu, while at Tell Al'Ubaid Woolley[2] found cones of baked clay with heads of white, black, and pink stone and other materials arranged to imitate flowers about 5 inches in diameter (Figure 103d), and these were used to decorate the walls of the small Temple of Ninkhursag of the 1st Dynasty at Ur (*c.* 3000 B.C.). In time silhouetted figures and geometric shapes of burnt clay were inset in panels and friezes against a background of cone mosaic, but the final step was to extend the technique of the figures to the background also, and instead of using the cones embedded in the plaster, a mosaic of flat pieces of stone was secured by copper wire and bitumen to a wood backing. This technique was revealed also at the Temple of Ninkhursag at Al'Ubeid, Ur, where the palm-wood columns, 7 feet 6 inches in height and 12 inches in diameter, at the main

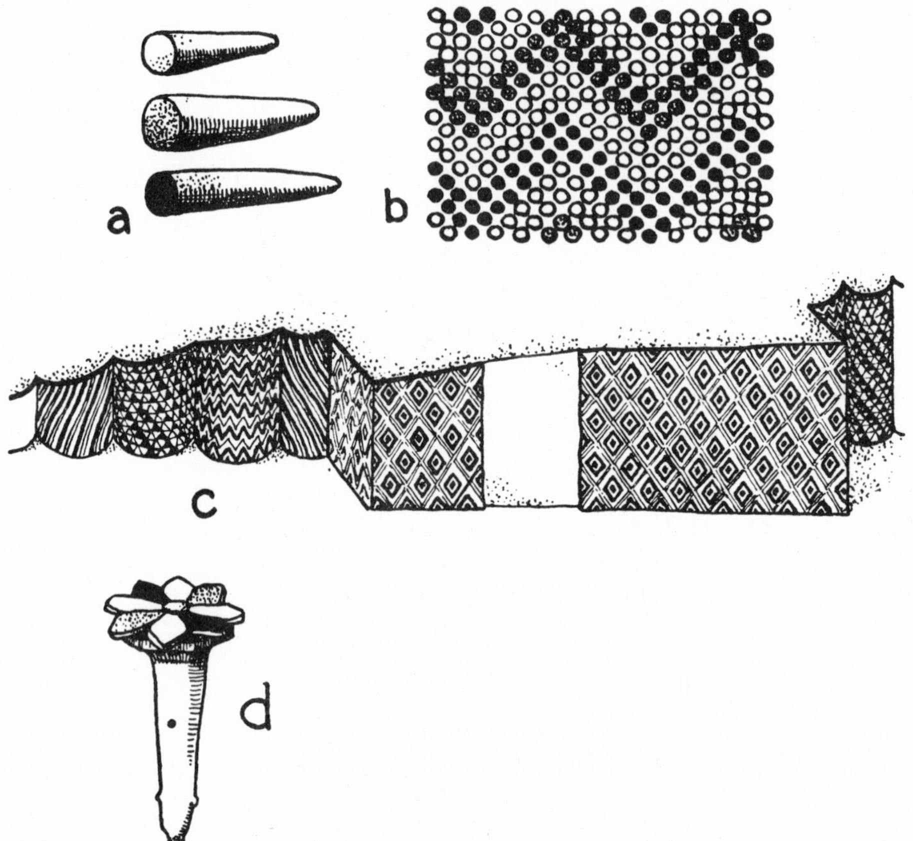

Fig. 103. (a, b) Small clay cones of different colours, red, white, buff, grey, etc., about $\frac{3}{4}$ inch diameter, 3 to 4 inches long, driven into the surface of mud plaster so that the heads formed mosaic patterns of various designs. (c) Cone mosaic decoration on walls and columns, Warka. (d) Cone with head formed of different coloured stones.

door of the shrine were covered with a thick coating of bitumen and encrusted all over, as shown in Figure 104, with square and triangular tesserae of light red sandstone, black bituminous stone, and mother of pearl, each tessera having a loop of copper wire at the back to secure it to the bitumen. The walls of the temple had friezes decorated with figures of cattle and birds, cut in limestone or shell and set against a mosaic background of black stone, in general character very like some of the later *opus sectile* work of the

Roman period. At this period also the mosaics were sometimes inlaid in solid stone slabs.

The Egyptians also followed a somewhat similar technique. Column capitals and wall tiles at Tel-el-Yehudia in Lower Egypt, for example, were decorated with pieces of coloured glass and earthenware inset in tile or stone to form lotus and other devices, and in a temple of Rameses II near Heliopolis (19th Dynasty, 1350–1200 B.C.) some wall reliefs are inlaid with glass paste.

Fig. 104. Mosaic column from the Temple of Ninkhursag at Al'Ubaid, Ur; 1st Dynasty of Ur, *c.* 3000 B.C.

A method of great antiquity which became highly developed in Hellenistic times was to embed small pebbles and pieces of stone in a matrix of mortar to form a decorative pattern. An interesting series of mosaic pavements of this type dating from the fifth and fourth centuries B.C. was excavated at Olynthos[3] in Macedonia. They were composed of red, white, blue, green, and purple pebbles. More recently most beautiful examples of this technique have been found. They are the pebble mosaics in a Hellenistic building at Pella, the birthplace of Alexander the Great, in Northern Greece,[4] dating from about the middle of the fourth century B.C. A portion of one of the pavements is shown in Plate LVIII. It depicts the head of Dionysos and the head of the panther on whose back he is sitting, and the design is made up of tiny natural pebbles in varying shades of black and white to render light effects, while in order to emphasize the profile of the face the artist has used strips of lead, and thin strips of baked clay to outline the hair curls.

Perhaps the earliest pebble mosaic, however, yet found is that excavated by Professor Young during his expedition from the University Museum of Pennsylvania which started in 1957. It is a floor patterned in coloured pebbles, in one of the megaron type buildings of the city of Gordion, capital of the Phrygian Kingdom in Asia Minor and destroyed by the Cimmerians in the seventh century B.C.

The transition from the use of pebbles to the use of cubes of stone was gradual, and seems to have been introduced after Alexander's conquests, but it is not uncommon to find pebbles incorporated in later mosaics. Great development in the use of mosaics for the decoration of pavements in Egypt and in particular in Alexandria took place in the Ptolemaic period from the fourth century B.C. onwards, and the art seems to have spread quickly throughout the rest of the Near East, Syria, Asia Minor, the Roman provinces, and to Constantinople. The Alexandrian influence persisted not only in design but in technique as well. An illustration of this is provided in what is possibly the earliest—certainly one of the very early—Roman picture mosaics, the celebrated pavement in the Palazzo Barberini at Palestrina showing an extensive view of the Nile and its surroundings. It is thought to date from the second half of the first century B.C. Many other Roman pavements incorporate design motifs which appear to be of Egyptian origin.

There are several conventional types of Roman mosaic. One is the so-called *opus tessellatum* composed of small cubes of stone or ceramic materials placed in regular manner to produce simple geometric patterns. In another type called *opus vermiculatum* the pieces of coloured materials were bedded in a more irregular fashion to produce pictorial effects. When used for the decoration of the surface of walls and vaults the type was known as *opus musivum*, and it is this which figured so prominently in Early Christian work. A technique closely related to mosaic is *opus sectile*, a marquetry, with pieces of marble and other coloured materials cut carefully to shape to fit the contours of the design. An example is shown in Figure 96 of part of the floor in the House of Cupid and Psyche at Ostia. Another well-known example is the floor of the Pantheon still in service. These two examples have geometric designs, but the process was also used for more pictorial subjects. A famous example, in Plate LX, dated to about A.D. 33, is that from the basilica of the Consul Junius Bassus on the Esquiline, Rome, which shows the Consul riding into the circus surrounded by mounted attendants. The technique was revived in the sixteenth and seventeenth centuries in principle at least—in the well-known Florentine *intarsia*, or marquetry work, for which many different woods were used.

There are very many Roman mosaics to be seen throughout the Roman Provinces and particularly fine ones in North Africa. The normal method of laying these floors in Britain was to apply a rendering of lime and crushed tile mortar to the concrete base of the floor. A slurry coat of hydrated lime and water, with or without an addition of brick dust, was then applied and the tesserae pressed down into it. A section cut through a piece of pavement from Verulamium of A.D. 300 shows this technique quite clearly, but it also reveals the fact that the floor has been re-surfaced (Plate LIX).

Marbles and stones of many kinds were used for the tesserae and in Rome itself marbles were imported from Greece and elsewhere, and occasionally cubes of glass enamel and even gilded tesserae were employed, as in the wall decorations and fountain niches at Pompeii. Often in Rome the tesserae were over an inch in depth, the exposed end being about half an inch square, but those in many pavements throughout the Roman provinces are of much shallower depth.

After Christianity was accepted as the official religion of the Roman Empire, mosaics were used mainly for the decoration of walls, depicting divine persons and religious scenes. Constantinople became the centre of activity in this field. The floor mosaics—in design at least—assumed a secondary importance, and, where used, tended to follow the older traditions, for example *opus Alexandrinum*, a refined form of *opus sectile*. The wall mosaics, however, were almost entirely composed of tesserae of glass, generally coloured by metallic oxides, and great use was made of gilded tesserae. To make these, gold foil was applied to the concave surface of a piece of glass and heated. Fused enamel, usually dark red or green in colour, was then poured on to the concave surface. The whole assembly was then flattened, fired again and allowed to cool, after which it was cut into pieces of the required size. Many of these early Christian wall mosaics remain, among them the world famous examples in Ravenna in the Basilica of S. Vitale, in the mausoleum of Galla Placidia, both of the fifth century, and in the Basilica of S. Apollinare Nuovo dating from the beginning of the sixth century A.D., where the wonderful mosaics form one of the largest areas of such work surviving from antiquity. They are essentially pictorial mosaics with Biblical scenes 'painted' with coloured tesserae, brilliant in colour. The less frequently occurring geometrical designs, like that chosen by way of illustration in Plate LXI, are of equal technical interest. The example is from the ceiling of one of the vaults in the Mausoleum of Galla Placidia at Ravenna. After a visit to Ravenna, Raphael was so impressed by the superb colour of the interior of the mausoleum that he adopted the same scheme for his loggia in the Vatican; so also did Pinturicchio in the library at Siena.[5]

The use of mosaic declined in Italy towards the tenth century A.D., but in the twelfth century a new phase of the art appeared in Rome, and under Byzantine influence many fine pavements were laid, such as those in Sta Maria Maggiore, San Clemente, and Sta Maria Trastevere. They were wrought with morsels of porphyry and precious marbles, mostly obtained from ancient buildings, and arranged in patterns usually in the form of meandering bands surrounding discs, sliced from marble columns in the *opus Alexandrinum* style. Schools were also formed in Venice, Southern Italy, and in Sicily, while eastwards in Greece a similar development took place. A characteristic example of Venetian work is shown in Plate III, in the floor of the Cathedral (L'Assunta) at Torcello.

A closely related type of floor but with an 'all-over' pattern of striking beauty is that shown in Plate LXII, of inlaid black and white marble at S. Miniato, Florence, dating from

A.D. 1207. It has the meandering bands of *opus Alexandrinum* but the intervening discs and odd spaces are filled with birds and animals and patterns based on vegetable forms. There are a number of such panels of varying designs in the church.

A refined type of mosaic *opus Romanum* with much smaller tesserae, often of glass, was developed in the early twelfth century. The pioneers were Paulus (1110–30), Ranuccius (*c.* 1135–1209) and Vassallettus (1220–76). Laurentius (Lorenzo) (*c.* 1150–1232) was founder of the famous Cosmati family and his son (Jacobus) Jacopo carried out decorations in S. Saba in Rome in A.D. 1205. Cosimo, son of Jacopo, and his family, Luca, Jacopo, Adeodata, and Giovanni, greatly developed the technique which became generally known as 'cosmati' work. The mosaic decoration was applied to pavements, and particularly to the furnishings in churches, pulpits, thrones, tabernacles, altars, and tombs.

Another famous marbleworker of the Cosmati school was Odoricus, who in 1268 came from Rome to lay the floor in the Sanctuary at Westminster Abbey with materials brought from there by Abbot Richard de Ware. The floor is of red and green porphyry and glass mosaic, inlaid in Purbeck marble, and has an inscription to this effect: '. . . the year of Christ 1268, King Henry the Third, the City [Rome] Odoricus [the marbleworker] and the Abbot [Richard de Ware] assembled these porphyry stones together'. The pavement of the Confessor's Chapel was apparently also laid by Odoricus, but very little remains of it.

Petrus, one of the sons of Odoricus, an equally famous craftsman, followed his father to London after he had finished the decoration of the tomb of Pope Clement IV at Viterbo, and carried out the 'cosmati' work on the pedestal of the Shrine of Edward the Confessor and on the tomb for Henry III. Both these monuments have in the course of time, particularly in 1538, been sadly mutilated, and little of the 'cosmati' work, carried out in red, black, gold, and white tesserae, remains, that on the north side of Henry's tomb being the best preserved. Peter signed his name on the base of the Confessor's Shrine . . . 'Petrus . . . Romanus Civis'. Originally the whole of the Shrine was encrusted with mosaic ('cosmati' work) generally on a gold background. There were squares and discs of rich coloured stones such as verde antique and porphyry. Around these were woven geometrical designs in precious stones, porphyry, cipollino, alabaster, yellow antique, and malachite.[5]

In Rome itself the most beautiful examples of 'cosmati' work are to be seen in the Cloisters of S. Giovanni in Laterano where in 1234 Vassallettus (Vassalletto) inlaid the delicate twisted Romanesque columns with patterns of glass mosaic; very similar work can be seen in the cloisters of S. Paulo Fuori le Mura.

Another type of marble floor embodying a 'graffito' technique was developed at Siena, in Italy, in the latter half of the fourteenth century and practised during the next two hundred years. Almost the entire floor of the Cathedral there is laid with it. Essentially the method was to fit together large pieces of white marble, to form a silhouette against a background of black marble. The details were then incised on the white marble with a graving tool and deepened where necessary to enhance the effect, by drilling out along these lines with rows of holes of large or small size and of varying depth, depending on the importance of the particular lines in the general design. The incised lines were then filled with a compound of pitch, resin, and clay. An example of this type of work is shown in Figure 105. It is a detail from the frieze of lions, designed by Bastiano di Francesco, which surrounds the pavement showing the Expulsion of Herod, designed in 1484–5 by Benvenuto di Giovanni del Guasta. Both the frieze and the pavement, like many of the others, have been heavily restored, as this type of work did not wear well.

The borders surrounding other pictures often contained marbles of various colours, and a later tendency was to introduce these colours also into the picture itself. The artist Bernardino Betti, called Pinturicchio, used many contrasting colours in the pictorial scenes he executed in the first few years of the sixteenth century, but a subsequent artist,

Fig. 105. Fragment of the frieze of lions surrounding a pavement in Siena Cathedral, laid by 'graffito' technique.

Domenico Beccafumi, called Mecherino, discarded these vivid contrasts and used only low colour tones, which shaded one into the other.[6]

The most striking pavements, however, were the earlier ones in which there was the least use of colour, and the artist relied for his effect almost entirely on simple black lines engraved on the white marble, which in turn was contrasted against the black marble surround.

The Muslims inherited great traditions in the ceramic art from Mesopotamia and Persia and even further East, but were much more interested in developing wall tiles than in imitating the Roman and Byzantine type of mosaic.

Anthony[7] has pointed out that mosaics played an important role in Mexican work in the early Mayan civilization and that the tesserae were of roughly square or rectangular pieces like those used in Roman and Christian mosaics. He mentions that jadeite, malachite, quartz, beryl, garnet, obsidian, marcasite, gold, bits of coloured shell, and mother of pearl were used, and cemented to the background of wood or stone, with a vegetable pitch or gum, or some other form of cement. The art was still flourishing under the Aztecs at the time of the Spanish Conquest.

REFERENCES

(1) Woolley, C. L., 1935, *The Development of Sumerian Art*, Faber.

(2) Woolley, C. L., Oct. 1924, 'Excavations at Tell el Obeid', *Antiquaries' Journal*, IV (4).

(3) Robinson, D. M., 1929–46, *Excavations at Olynthus*, 12 Vols., Baltimore.

(4) 'Discoveries at Birthplace of Alexander the Great', *The Times*, 13 September 1957, London.

(5) Formilli, C. C., 1911, 'Monumental work of the Cosmati at Westminster Abbey', *Journal* of the Royal Institute of British Architects, XVIII (3rd series), 69.

(6) Cust, R. H. Hobart, 1901, *The Pavement Masters of Siena 1369–1562*, Bell.

(7) Anthony, E. W., 1935, *A History of Mosaic*, Porter Sargent, Boston.

22

Glazes and Glass

GLAZES ARE MADE essentially from the same substances as glass. Silica, soda (sodium carbonate) or potash (nitre or saltpetre), and chalk, possibly with some magnesia occurring as impurities, are finely ground together, then fused, and reground to a fine powder. This is mixed into a paste with water and applied to the clay body and then fused in a kiln. Lucas[1] records that vitreous glaze was used in small amounts during the Badarian and predynastic periods in Egypt for coating stone. In this latter period objects were moulded of powdered quartz, heated with a small proportion of natron to make the quartz grains adhere, and these objects were then glazed. The product is called Egyptian faience. These alkaline glazes were also used in Assyria and Babylonia, but although they adhered well to highly siliceous clay bodies they did not adhere at all well to ordinary clay ones. The introduction of lead into the mixture produced a glaze that would adhere to almost any clay. It also had the advantage of lowering the fusing temperature of the glaze.

The earliest Babylonian recipe for glazes recorded on a clay tablet at least as early as 1700 B.C., contains potash, lime, copper, and lead.[2] The same substances appear again with the addition of another alkali (in the form of ash from the plant salicornia), antimony, and arsenic, on Assyrian tablets from the Royal Library at Nineveh set up by Assur-bani-pal (668–631 B.C.). Professor Turner,[3] who records these recipes, has found by analyses that ancient glazes were predominantly of the alkali-lime-magnesia-silica type, and that only about 10 per cent of those analyses contained lead.

Lead is added in various forms, as oxide (litharge, red lead, or minium), as carbonate (white lead), or as sulphide (galena). These lead compounds alone do not form a glaze, but have to be mixed with silica, usually in the form of sand, flint, or quartz, and various clays, particularly China clay and kaolin, and other materials rich in alumina such as felspar. Fusion with the silica renders them non-poisonous. Turner records that examples of lead glass, mainly opaque and coloured, have been found from 1400 B.C. onwards. Various metallic colouring materials have been used. Iron, cobalt, manganese, and copper are mentioned in Babylonian texts of 1700 B.C. and in the Nineveh tablets of the seventh century B.C. The metals are usually in oxidized form. Iron oxides produce varying shades of green, brown, and even red according to the conditions of firing; cobalt oxide gives

Plate LVIII. Pebble mosaic pavement from Pella; about the middle of the fourth century B.C. (see page 185).

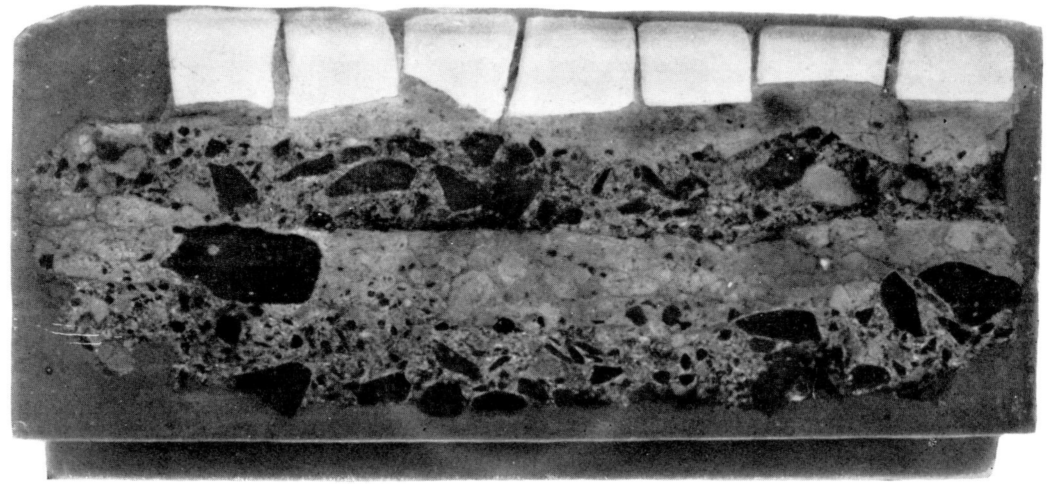

Plate LIX. A section cut through a Roman mosaic pavement from Verulamium (see page 185).

Plate LX. *Opus sectile* pavement in the basilica of the Consul Junius Bassus, Rome; *c.* A.D. 33 (see page 184).

blue colour; manganese dioxide and nickel oxide give purple to brown; cupric oxide gives blue and cuprous oxide under strong reducing conditions gives red; chromium oxide gives a yellowish green; and tin oxides (used in glazes for majolica ware), 'tin' ashes (which is a mixture of three parts of lead and one of tin heated together until fully oxidized), and zirconia produce a white glaze. Bone ash (calcium phosphate), fluorspar and cryolite are now commonly used to produce white glaze.

Many other oxides and substances have been used as colouring agents, some special ones being cadmium sulphide, silver salts, and sulphur, each giving shades of yellow; selenium giving a brilliant red and finely divided gold a rich ruby colour. The recipes for glazes are infinite in variety.

Window Glass

Various translucent materials have been used for filling window openings—thin slabs of marble as in the Roman Byzantine church of S. Vitale at Ravenna and in the church of S. Miniato in Florence (A.D. 1013) where slabs of Pavonazzetto marble with red purple markings are used, alabaster, mica, shell, horn, oiled fabrics, and parchment—but none so effectively as glass. Glassmaking was well established in Egypt at the beginning of the 18th Dynasty (*c.* 1580–1350 B.C.) for Newberry[4] records the remains of glassworks of that period, and until the early part of the Christian era Egypt was an important centre for glassmaking, the industry being centred on Alexandria. In the Ptolemaic period (*c.* 332–30 B.C.) the craft spread to other parts of the Near East—Palestine, Syria, Greece, and Italy. The skill of glass manufacture had also been known in Mesopotamia from very early times for Frankfort[5] found a cylinder of light blue glass at Tell Asmar, north-east of Baghdad, which he considered was probably of the Akkad dynasty about 2700–2600 B.C. It was not until the Imperial period of Roman times that glass was used at all extensively for window panes. The panes were generally made from mould-blown glass, the development of which resulted from the invention of the blow pipe. It seems probable that its use for this purpose was an innovation of the Christian era. Harden[6] considers that one of the Syrian glassworkers, who 'were undoubtedly among the very first makers of mould-blown glasses', probably invented the method of producing free blown glass. Its use was certainly well established before the destruction of Pompeii in A.D. 79, for in the ruins of this town have been found parts of bronze window frames which appear to have held sheets of glass measuring about 21 inches by 28 inches. An even larger pane of glass which presumably must have been cast, and which measured 40 inches by 28 inches by nearly ½ inch in thickness, with one surface slightly frosted, was found there in a bathhouse.

About this time also glass was in use in conservatories. Martial,[7] who published his Epigrams towards the end of A.D. 93, made frequent mention of this use of glass.

> . . . your vineyard blooms shut in transparent glass, and the fortunate grape is roofed and yet unhid [Book VIII, lxviii]. That your orchard trees from Cilicia may not grow wan and dread the winter, nor too keen an air nip the tender boughs, glass casements facing the wintry south winds admit the clear suns and daylight undefiled. But to me is assigned a

> garret, shut in by an illfitting window, in which even Boreas himself would not care to abide. Is it in such a lodging you cruelly bid your old friend dwell? Then as the guest of one of your trees I shall be more protected [Book VIII, xiv].

It seems from this and the following quotation that windows in dwelling houses were a source of trouble, and that they were at this time far from perfect.

> Gellius is always building; now he lays down thresholds, now he fits keys to doors and buys bolts, now these, now those windows he repairs and alters; provided only he be building, Gellius does anything whatsoever, that to a friend who asks for money he may be able to say that one word, 'Building' [Book IX, xlvi].

Glass manufacture expanded rapidly throughout the Roman Empire, but after the decline of the latter, it was continued by Byzantine workers, who became particularly skilled in the production of coloured glass, which they used to great effect in their mosaics.

The primary materials from which glass has been made through the ages, as we have already seen in the case of glazes, are silica usually in the form of sand, but sometimes powdered quartz, and an alkaline base such as soda (sodium carbonate) or potash (nitre or saltpetre), usually with the addition of a second alkaline base like chalk. These are fused together at a temperature varying from 1000° to 1300° C., and as it cools from its molten state, and becomes solid, it forms an amorphous or non-crystalline but transparent material. Various metallic oxides already described under Glazes are added to control the colour and quality of the glass. Lead oxide is used, for example, to give brilliance and clarity in crystal or flint glass.

Window glass has been made in four different forms, slab, sheet (or cylinder), crown, and plate. It seems likely that the production of window glass by the cylinder method continued in use in those parts of Europe evacuated by the Romans, for as early as A.D. 675 craftsmen came from France to Monkwearmouth to glaze the windows of the Church.[8] Bede records that 'they not only did the work required, but taught the English how to do it for themselves', yet in spite of this in A.D. 758 glaziers from the Rhineland had to be sent for by the Abbot of Jarrow.

Theophilus[9] described the use of wood-ash (potash) with sand, but soda or natron was also used by the medieval glassmakers. It was not always possible to obtain white iron-free sand and in consequence much of their glass has a greenish or even brownish tint, but later on it was found that manganese dioxide, or 'glass-maker's soap' as it was called, added to the mixture counteracted this defect.

Harden[10] observes that centrifugal or crown glass discs appear in the Middle East from the fourth to the seventh centuries A.D. The windows of St Sophia at Constantinople, begun in 532, contained small panes of glass cut to about 7 inches square and cemented in a marble lattice. It is rather thick and not very clear and has the appearance of slab glass.

The art of staining glass, of Near Eastern, Syrian, or Byzantine origin, spread to Italy, and Venice became an important centre for the craft. It reached France by the end of the sixth century for it is recorded that both Gregory of Tours (A.D. 593) and the Bishop of Protus (A.D. 609) used coloured glass for glazing.[11] The art was fostered by the Benedictine monks in Western Europe and was well established by them by the ninth century A.D.[12] It is recorded that Adalberon, Bishop of Rheims from 969–988, rebuilt the Cathedral and redecorated it with windows representing various stories. Emeric-David[13] records that the historian of the monastery of St Benig, at Dijon, who wrote about A.D. 1052, stated that there existed in his lifetime a very ancient glass window in the church of the monastery, representing the martyrdom of St Paschasie, and that this painting had been taken from the old church restored by Charles the Bold. In England stained glass was being extensively used by the end of the twelfth century, the small pieces of glass being leaded in mosaic-like patterns, like that in the windows formerly in the Choir at Canterbury (*c.* 1184), but now distributed throughout the church.

Morey (1938) suggests that as an indirect result of the Crusades and of the fall of the Eastern Empire, glass manufacture entered a period of expansion in Venice about the beginning of the eleventh century, which soon made that city the centre of the glass industry, and that it maintained this dominant position for several hundred years. In 1291 the glass works were moved to the island of Murano, a suburb of Venice. John Evelyn[14] made an interesting entry in his diary for the year 1645, about this place, which reads

> . . . Three days after, I returned to Venice, and passed over to Murano, famous for the best glass in the world, where, having viewed their furnaces, and seen their work, I made a collection of divers curiosities and glasses, which I sent to England by long sea. It is the white flints from Pavia, which they pound, and sift exceedingly small and mix with ashes made of a seaweed brought out of Syria, and a white sand, that causes this manufacture to excell.

Slab glass is probably the earliest type used by the Romans for windows. To produce slab glass a blowing iron was inserted into the molten glass, or 'metal', in the melting pot and the glass so gathered was blown into the form of a bottle inside a square mould. When cool the four sides of the glass bottle were cut along the corner edges to give four clear panes of glass. Although the glass could be cut by diamond it was also cut by tracing a line with a hot iron dividing-rod and then wetting the glass, or by laying a string of hot glass along the line of the desired cut. The sheets were laid flat in an oven and re-heated to soften the edges, if need be, and then allowed to cool very slowly.

Sheet glass, or 'cylinder' glass, became the more usual type used by the Romans, particularly for the larger panes. The method of making it, shown in 1a–d in Figure 106, has changed very little over the years. The process now used is to dip the blowing iron into the molten glass, or 'metal', and to blow the gathering of glass into a pearshaped bulb. By dipping and re-dipping into the pot of 'metal', more and more glass is gathered, until enough has been accumulated to make the desired sheet. The glass is blown and further shaped by a wooden tool, and manipulated and flattened on a 'marver', or smooth flat stone. The thick base is then re-heated and by blowing, swinging, and rotating a large cylindrical shaped bulb is formed. The base of this bulb is removed by cutting, and when the glass has cooled sufficiently, the top is also cut off leaving an open-ended cylinder or 'muff' of glass. This is then cut lengthwise, wedged open slightly, and placed on its side in an oven, where it is gently heated. As the glass softens it tends to flatten out under its own weight, and with the aid of wooden tools and wooden smoothing blocks, a flat sheet is formed. If allowed to cool too quickly, the glass would be very brittle so it is

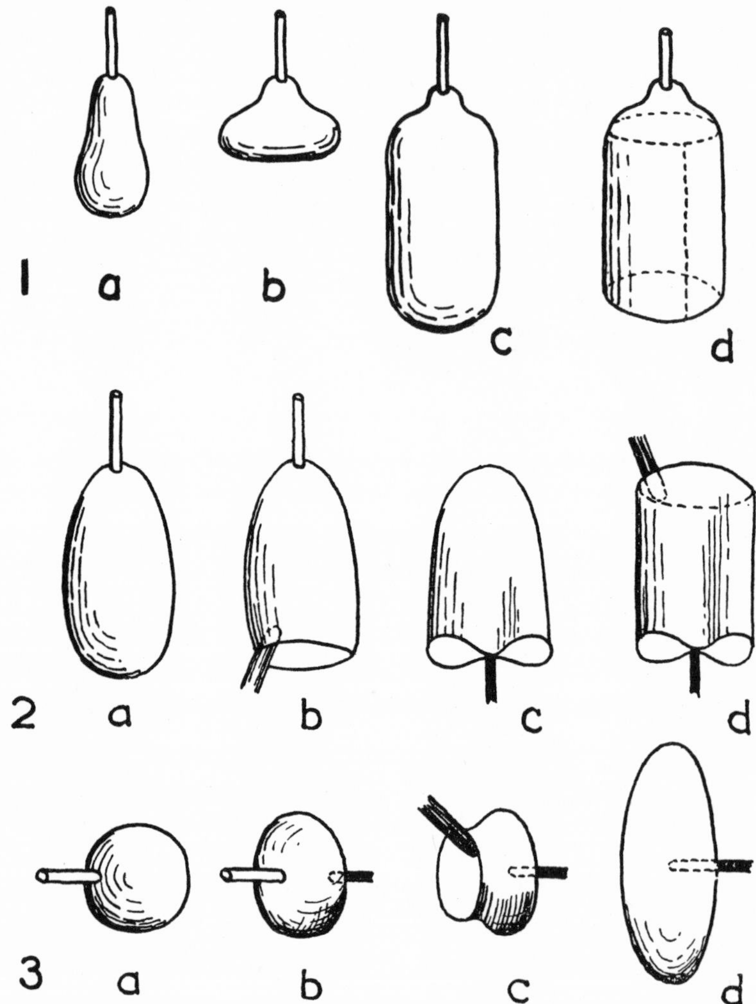

Fig. 106. Old methods of blowing window glass.

placed in an annealing chamber where it is allowed to cool very slowly, and the finished product is thereby toughened.

The earlier way of making the 'cylinder' glass, probably the way the Romans made it, was described by a monk named Theophilus Rogerus[9] in the twelfth century. He described three ovens used in the process: the first, the furnace proper for melting the glass; the second, a dilating and flattening oven—the working oven; and the third, the annealing or cooling oven. The stoking chamber of the melting oven was rectangular and enclosed by thick walls of stone and clay, with an opening at one end through which the stoking was done. At a height of about 4 feet it was covered by a flat floor in which were some vents through which the smoke and flames could pass, and in which the melting pots or clay crucibles could be set. The whole of this oven was then covered over by an arched roof, with windows left in the front wall through which crucibles could be put in or taken out and through which observation could be maintained on the contents of the furnace. The firing was by dried wood and the mixture for making the glass was comprised of two parts of beechwood ashes (to supply the potash) and one part of clean siliceous sand. This mixture was left in the crucibles overnight at a temperature not high enough to cause it to liquefy. The loaded crucibles were then placed in the holes in the furnace floor. Theophilus then describes the method of making the window glass as follows:

> In the morning, however, at the first hour, take the iron tube, and if you wish to make plates of glass, place the end of it in a vase full of glass; when it has adhered to it, turn the tube round in your hand until as much as you may wish has accumulated around it; then withdrawing it, bring it to your mouth and blow slightly, and instantly removing it from your mouth, hold it near your cheek unless in drawing breath you may by chance attract the flame into your mouth. Have also a flat stone before the window [of the furnace] upon which you beat this glowing glass a little, that it may hang equally on every side, immediately and with quickness, repeatedly blowing, so often you remove it from the mouth. When you see it look like a long bladder, bring the end of it towards the flame, and being instantly melted, an opening will appear, and the piece of wood fitted for this work being taken, make the opening as wide as is the glass in the middle. [2a–d in Figure 106]. Then join its mouth together, namely, the upper to the lower part so that on both sides of the junction an opening may appear. Instantly touch this glass near the tube with a moist piece of wood, shake it a little and it will be separated. Presently also heat the tube in the flame of the furnace, until the glass attached to it liquify, and with rapidity, place it upon the two conjoined borders of glass, and it will adhere; directly taking this up, put it into the flame of the furnace until the opening, whence you formerly separated the tube, is liquified, and the round piece of wood being taken, dilate it as the others, and fold together its mouth in the middle, and separating it from the pipe with the moist wood, give it to the boy, who, introducing a piece of wood through the opening, will carry it to the cooling oven which is made moderately warm—This kind of glass is pure and white.

For making coloured glass various metallic substances like those used for colouring glazes were added. Theophilus continued:

> . . . When you have made as much as you have been able to from these colours, and the glass has become cold in the furnace, place out all your work and cause a large fire to be lighted in the furnace, in which it should be dilated and made flat. When glowing take a hot iron, and separating a part of the glass, place it upon the hearth of the glowing furnace, and when it has begun to grow soft, take the iron forceps and smooth piece of wood and opening it in that part in which is your division, you will dilate and smooth it according to your will with the forceps. When it has become quite smooth, immediately taking it out, place it in the cooling oven, moderately warmed; and so that the plate may not be down,

> but stand against the wall, next to which you will place another—also flattened in the same manner, and a third; also all the rest. When these have become cold, use them in composing windows, by separating them into pieces as you wish.

To make *crown glass* a gathering of molten 'metal' is taken on the end of the blowing iron and blown into a bulb, rotating it rapidly during the operation. The bulb is then flattened as shown in 3a–d in Figure 106, into an oblate shape by working it on the 'marver'. A solid iron rod called a 'punty' is then dipped into the molten glass and attached to the opposite centre of the oblate bulb and the blowing iron is detached. By alternately heating and rotating the bulb on the punty, the hole left by the blowing iron is opened out until a flat disc is formed. When the punty is removed a bullion or 'bull's eye' of glass is left at the centre. Discs up to 5 feet in diameter have been made in this way, but when cut up the flat panes of glass are rarely more than 18 inches square. They are usually less in size. The sheet with the bullion in it is also used and is often seen in window panes of old buildings. Crown glass was common in England up to the beginning of the nineteenth century, and gave way to the hand cylinder process from Lorraine.

Since just before the first world war sheet glass has been made by drawing vertically a broad ribbon of viscous glass from a bath of the molten material maintained at a uniform temperature and consistence. The edges of this glass ribbon are passed between cooled rollers to solidify the glass along these edges and to prevent the whole sheet from 'necking'. The solidified ribbon of glass has a brilliant 'fire-finish' but may have slight surface irregularities, and slight variations in thickness resulting from inhomogeneity of the glass mixture. None the less it is quite satisfactory for normal window glazing.

Cast plate glass was introduced into England in the late seventeenth century, and it was made by pouring molten metal on to a heavy iron table and spreading it evenly with a moving roller running on metal bearers to give the desired uniform thickness to the glass. The modern method of making plate glass for large windows is to pass a broad ribbon of the glass at about 1,100° C. through water-cooled rollers, thus rapidly chilling the glass. Any imperfections, or deliberate patterns on the rollers, are impressed upon the surface of the glass. It is then passed slowly through an annealing oven or 'lehr'. Polished plate glass is produced by grinding and polishing both sides of the glass and so producing a sheet of glass free from distortion. The process is costly and the surface obtained is not so brilliant as glass with a 'fire-finish'. Much research has been carried out in recent years to produce plate glass perfectly flat and with a 'fire-finish', and a method has been devised[15] whereby molten glass is poured in a continuous ribbon on the surface of liquid metal, where it becomes quite flat. As the glass sheet is pulled across the surface of the liquid metal, heat is applied both above and below to impart a 'fire-finish'. It then passes to the annealing chamber, where it cools slowly. The product has been called float glass.

REFERENCES

(1) LUCAS, A., 1948, *Ancient Egyptian Materials and Industries*, 3rd revised edition, Arnold.

(2) GADD, C. J., and THOMPSON, R. C., 'A Middle Babylonian Chemical Text', *Iraq*, III, 87–8.

(3) TURNER, W. E. S., 1956, 'Studies in Ancient Glasses and Glass Making Processes', *Journal* of the Society of Glass Technology, XL, No. 192, Part III, 'The Chronology of Glass Making Constituents'.

(4) NEWBERRY, P. E., 1920, *Journal of Egyptian Archaeology*, VI.

(5) BECK, H. C., and SELIGMAN, C. G., 1934, *Nature*, 133, 982. SELIGMAN, C. G., RITCHIE, P. D., and BECK, H. C., 1936, *Nature*, 138, 721.

(6) HARDEN, D. B., 1934, *Greece and Rome*, 3, 140.

(7) MARTIAL, *Epigrams*, translated by W. C. A. Ker, Loeb Classical Library, Heinemann.

(8) BEDE, *Historia Abbatrim in Complete Works*, Latin and English edition by J. A. Giles, 1843, IV, 366, Whitaker, London.

(9) THEOPHILUS ROGERUS, *De Diversis Artibus*, translated by Robert Hendrie, 1847, Murray.

(10) HARDEN, D. B., *Roman and Medieval Window Glass*, Paper read before the Society of Antiquaries of London, 5 February 1959.

(11) MOREY, G. W., 1938, *The Properties of Glass*, Reinhold Publishing Corporation, New York, 19.

(12) DOM TASSIN, 1770, *Histoire Littéraire de la Congregation de Saint-Maur*.

(13) EMERIC-DAVID, M. T. B., 1812, *Discours Historique sur la Peinture Moderne*, J. B. Sajou, Paris, 151.

(14) *Diary of John Evelyn*, Everyman's Library edition, Dent.

(15) PILKINGTON, A., 22 Jan. 1959, 'A New Kind of Glass', *The New Scientist*, V, No. 114.

23

Flues

THE MOST PRIMITIVE method of warming a room was by *direct* heating from an open fire kindled on a hearth, or contained in a brazier. The smoke and fumes must always have been a great source of inconvenience, and when at last man sought to decorate the internal walls of the better class houses with paintings it is not surprising that he should seek some other less objectionable method of heating which would not cover everything with soot and grime. The Romans contrived an *indirect* method by construct-

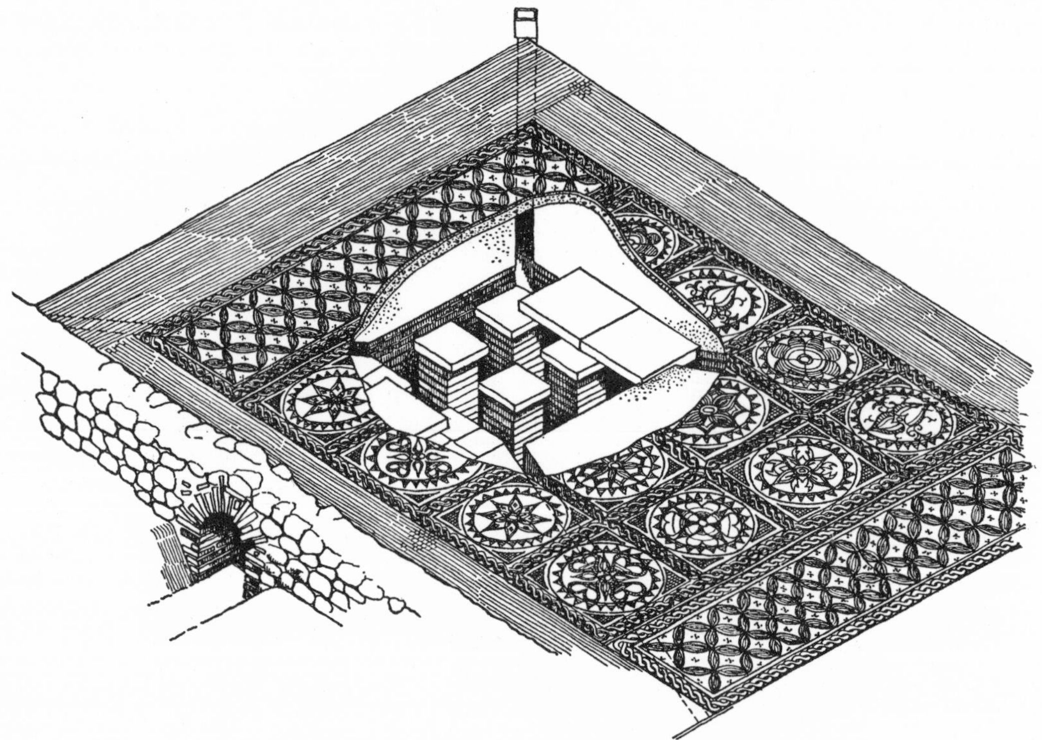

Fig. 107. Arrangement for heating beneath a mosaic floor at Verulamium.

Plate LXI. Mosaic ceiling in the Galla Placidia, Ravenna; fifth century A.D. (see page 185).

Plate LXII. Black and white marble pavement in the church of S. Miniato, Florence; thirteenth century (see page 185).

1.

2.

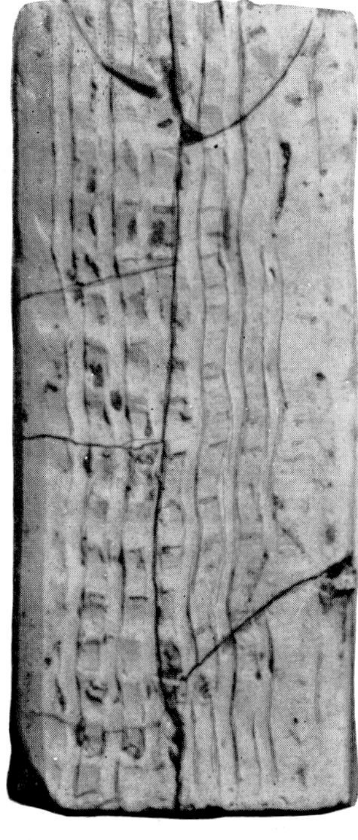

3.

4.

Plate LXIII. Various forms of Roman flue tile (see page 199).

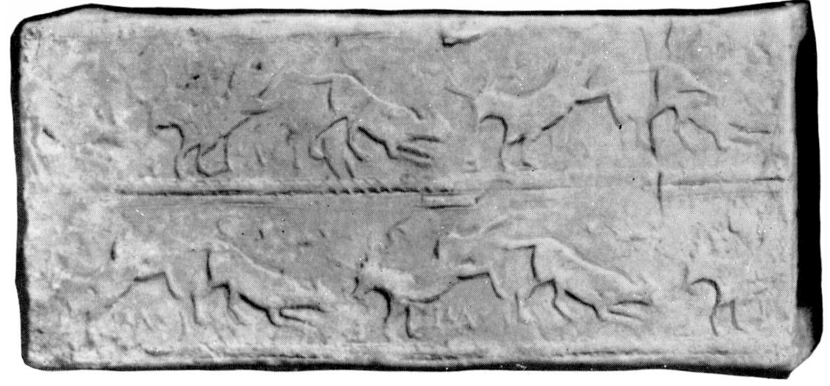

1.

2.

3.

Plate LXIV. Various forms of Roman flue tile (see page 199).

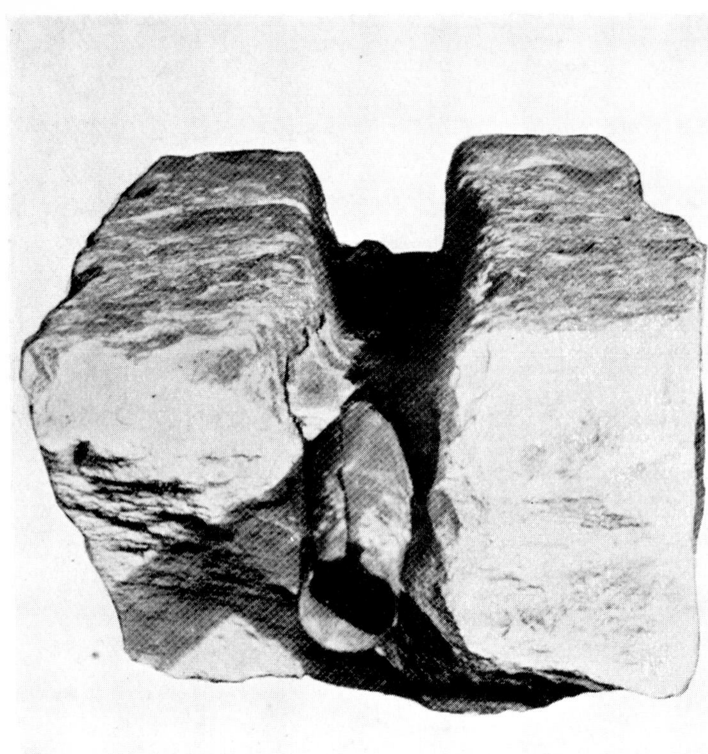

Plate LXV. Copper water-pipe found at Abusir, Egypt; *c.* 2750 B.C. (see page 209).

Plate LXVI. Roman oak water-pipes with iron collars, from the site of the Bank of England (see page 210).

ing heating chambers or hypocausts beneath the ground floor, and conducting the warm gases upwards through flues embedded in the walls. In normal house construction these gases were discharged at eaves level.

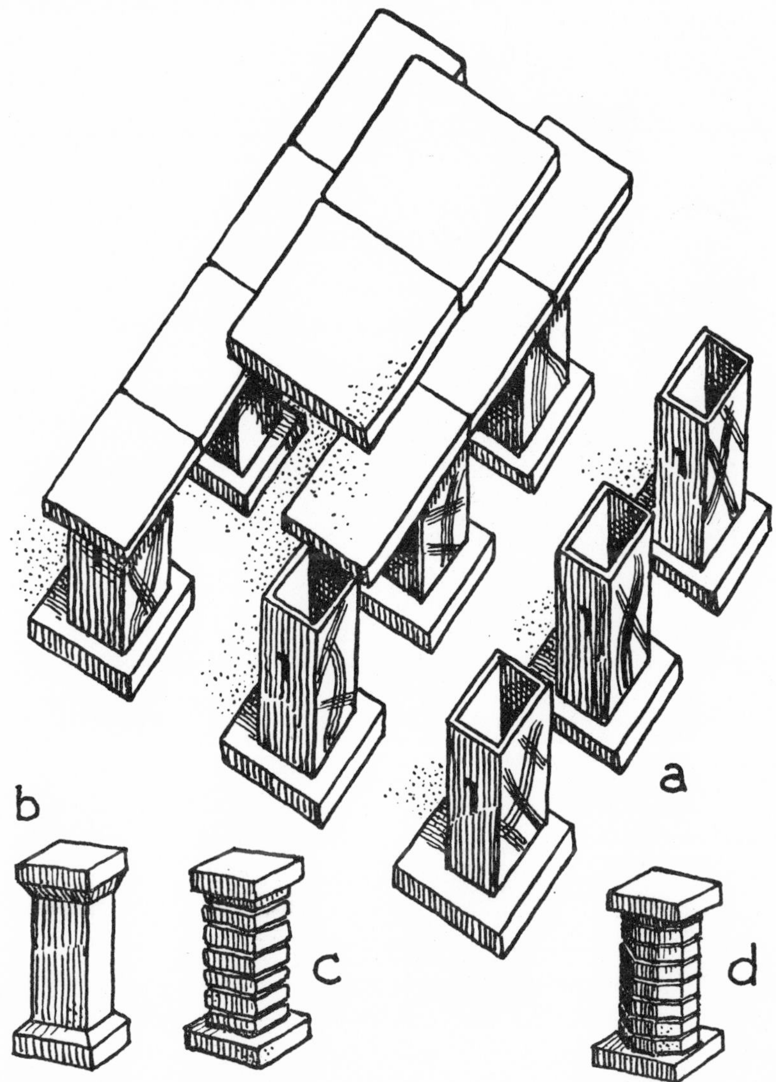

Fig. 108. Alternative methods of supporting the floor in Roman heating systems.

The construction of a typical Roman hypocaust is shown in Figure 107. It can be seen at Verulamium. The hot gases, from the timber or charcoal fire kindled in the stokehole shown on the left-hand side, passed to a chamber beneath the floor, usually placed centrally, but in this instance placed off-centre. The floor and pavement above the chamber are supported on piers and slabs. Although the construction varied in some details

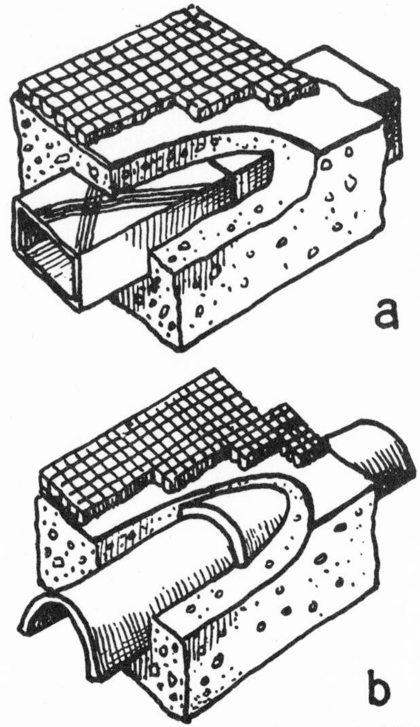

Fig. 109. Roman heating ducts embedded in the concrete floor.

from site to site, the piers were about 2 feet high, and carried slabs 2 feet square upon which the concrete floor was laid. Clay tiles about 8 inches square were commonly used for the piers (or *pilae*) and they were usually bedded in clay, which when subjected to the hot gases became baked and very hard. Flue tiles arranged as shown in Figure 108a were used as an alternative means of support and in stone districts the piers were often cut in one piece from limestone or sandstone (Figure 108b). At the Roman villa at Chedworth in Gloucestershire, the piers were of limestone, as they were also at a nearby villa at Spoonley, but at this latter place the limestone had been rendered with *opus signinum* to protect it from disintegration by chemical attack from the acid fumes. From the central chamber the hot gases were conducted through channels passing beneath or through the floor and thence up the walls. Once the main bulk of the concrete floor had become heated, its high thermal capacity would enable it to remain comfortably warm for a considerable time, and intermittent stoking would only be required in order to compensate for the heat dispersed. The ducts through the floors were often simple tile-lined channels, but other means like those shown in Figure 109 were also adopted. Figure 109a shows flue tiles embedded in the concrete or clay floor, and in Figure 109b roofing tiles (*imbrices*) used for the same purpose.

Roman flue tiles vary in type, but the commonest form is an open-ended box about 16 inches in length, 6 to 6½ inches in breadth, and about 4 inches deep from back to front. Often there is an opening at the centre of each of the narrower sides, measuring about 3½ inches by 1½ inches, but sometimes the opening is circular. The tiles were made by wrapping plastic clay round a wooden former which was moistened and sanded to prevent the clay from adhering to it. The small openings were then cut in the sides, and the clay trimmed to the required length. The broad surfaces of the tiles were then scored, or combed, or pressed with a cylindrical die which was rolled over the surface from end to end of each tile. The purpose of this was to provide a good key for the mortar in which they were bedded, or with which they were to be rendered. When the clay had dried sufficiently the tile was withdrawn from its wooden former, a grip on the clay being obtained by the insertion of two fingers in each of the openings on the sides. The tiles were then fired in up-draught kilns.

Lowther[1] concluded that flue tiles with impressed patterns were made in Britain between about A.D. 80 and 150, although they were sometimes re-used in later buildings up to about A.D. 200. The flue tiles with scored or incised surfaces appear to have been used and re-used throughout the Roman occupation. He found that the manufacture of relief-patterned tiles was confined to non-military sites, and that their distribution implied an industry centred in or near London, although no doubt craftsmen travelled about from site to site manufacturing flue tiles where facilities existed. There is, however, in the Ashmolean Museum, Oxford, a small box tile, described as a hypocaust tile, from the Roman villa at Millhampost, Gloucester, bearing the mark of the 22nd Legion—LEG XXII PP PF, LEG(io) XXII PP(imigenia) P(ia) F(idelis)—impressed upon it.

The patterns are many and varied (Plates LXIII and LXIV): geometrical, including chevron, (Plate LXIII, 4) diamond, lattice, and zigzag; circles (Plate LXIII, 1); vertical and horizontal billets, alternating to form a chessboard pattern; animal, representing a dog and stag (Plate LXIV, 1); and vegetable, including designs based on plant tendrils, buds, rosettes, etc. (Plate LXIII, 2). The incised or scored and combed patterns are not without interest, individual makers appearing to adopt their own particular sign or motif. Plate LXIII, 3, shows a flue tile with the surface grooved by finger impressions, that in Plate LXIV, 2, is incised with an eight-pronged comb, and that in Plate LXIV, 3, from Leicester, is inscribed with the words 'Primvs Fecit', also by means of a comb. These flue-tiles also sometimes have interesting graffiti on their surface. One example (Figure 110) from Silchester, and now in Reading Museum, is inscribed FECIT TVBVL(um) CLEMENTINVS—Clementinus made (this) flue tile. A flue tile found in 1857 at a Roman villa at Plaxtol, in Kent, is illustrated by Lowther, and has rolled upon its surface PARIETAIEVS CABRIABANVS FABRICAVI—I Cabriabanus made this wall tile. This seems more in the nature of a trademark.

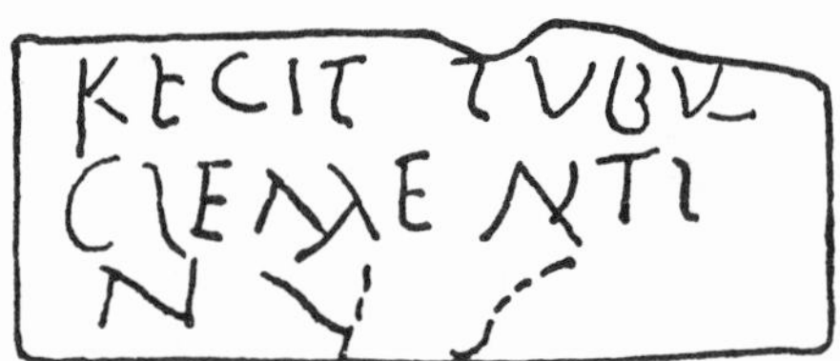

Fig. 110. Inscribed flue tile from Silchester (Reading Museum).

A tile from a Roman bath building at Wiggenholt in Sussex bears an inscription which appears to list different types of tile, and the quantity of each. The final item reading TVB(uli) NDLX is considered to refer to a batch of 560 flue tiles.[2] These Roman tile-makers were not illiterate men. They were skilled and intelligent. An interesting flue tile of the first or second century from Silchester, now in Reading Museum, has scratched upon its surface two words of a quotation thought to come from the Aneid of Virgil, Book II, line 1—CONTICUERE OMNES. The full quotation is 'conticuere omnes intentique ora tenebant'—'all fell silent and regarded him with steadfast gaze'.

The method of fixing the flue tiles is shown in Figure 111. They are bedded to the wall with mortar and given additional fixing with long iron nails driven into the wall behind. A rendering of mortar, and any decorative treatment, were then applied. Another type of flue tile, fixed in the same way and no doubt equally effective, is shown in Figure 112. They are channel-shaped instead of being complete boxes. The examples illustrated have lateral openings which would allow free circulation of the hot gases.

The vaulted ceilings in Roman bath buildings were often heated by hot air which circulated up the walls from the hypocaust beneath the floor. It was important, particularly during the winter months in Britain for example, to avoid condensation on the ceiling of the *tepidarium* and *caldarium*, and the dripping of chilled condensate on to the bathers below. Hollow construction not only improved the thermal insulation of the roof and reduced the heat losses through it, but the additional warming of the vault by

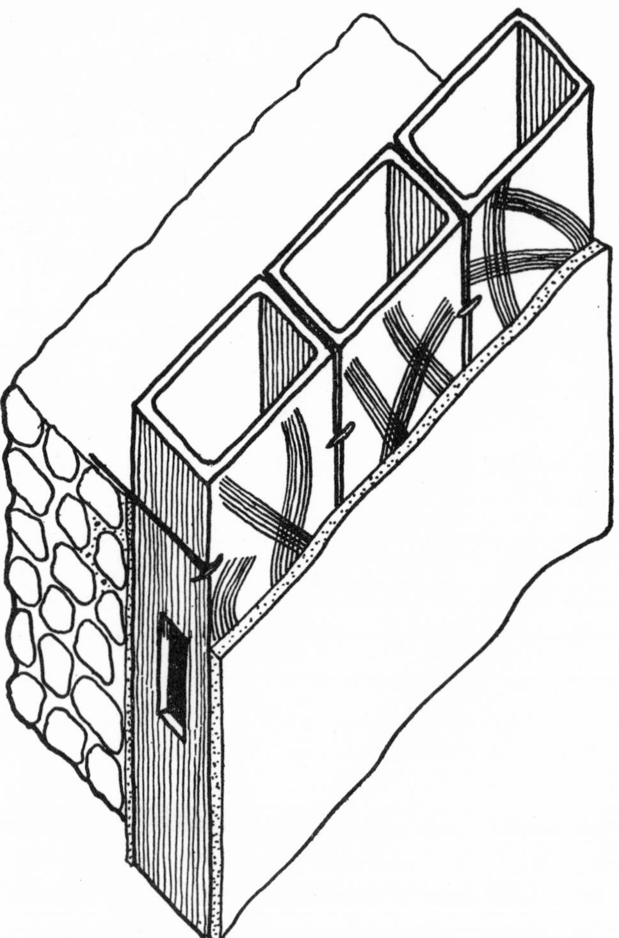

Fig. 111. Method of mounting flue tiles for wall heating.

hot air still further reduced the risk of condensation. There is little doubt that the vaults were given added protection by a normal timber roof, without which, although they were rendered, the vaults would be unable to resist completely the penetration of moisture.

The vaults were constructed in two different ways. The first, as used for example on the vaulting over the great *caldarium* of the public baths of Aquae Sulis (Bath), for the vaulting over the *apodyterium*, or changing room, of the public baths at Uriconium (Wroxeter), and in the baths at Chedworth and Silchester, consisted of specially made hollow voussoir clay blocks (Figure 113c). They were used in the manner shown in Figure 113a to form hollow arch ribs, and were about 4 inches wide and up to 12 or 14 inches in depth. The blocks were specially tapered from top to bottom so that they naturally made up into arch ribs of predetermined span. At Bath, for example, specially made blocks were used to form spans varying from less than 10 feet to over 20 feet.

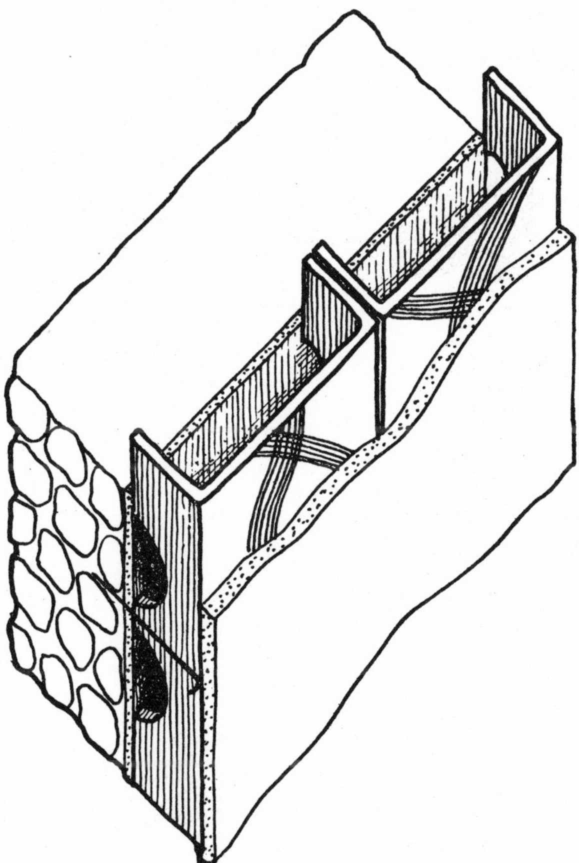

Fig. 112. An alternative method of wall heating.

By using blocks of the type shown in Figure 113b, lateral circulation of hot air from one arch rib to another could be effected, and a more uniform distribution of heat achieved throughout the vault. The second type of construction was also simple but ingenious. Special arch blocks like those in Figure 114 were made of burnt clay, limestone, or tufa. They have been found at Chesters, Leicester, York, Peterborough, and Dover, and were arranged to form arch ribs, suitably spaced so that the intervening gap could be bridged top and bottom by flat clay tiles which rested on shoulders or ledges formed on the individual blocks. Two different shapes of block have been identified. That shown in Figure 114b, being the stronger type, was used in the bath buildings at Chesters.[3]

The blocks were made of calcareous tufa, $5\frac{1}{2}$ inches thick at the top, tapering to $4\frac{1}{2}$ inches thick at the bottom, so that they formed naturally an arch ring of about 10 to 12 feet span. The flat tiles were of two sizes, those at the extrados of the arch having to bridge a larger gap than those at the intrados. Other blocks of the type shown in Figure 114c, carved from oolitic limestone, were found by Mrs Margaret Jones at Stanton Low, but they were only half the thickness of those from Chesters. Only one size of flat tile was needed with this type of block to complete the hollow vault.

In the post-Roman period heating by means of hypocausts ceased in Britain, and

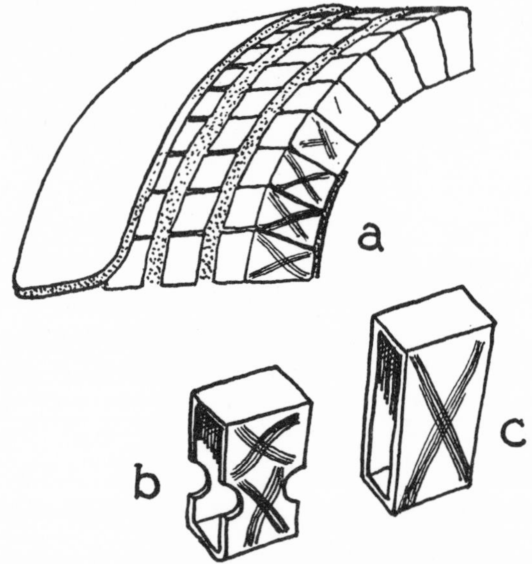

Fig. 113. Arrangement of hollow voussoir tiles for heating the ceiling vaults of Roman bath buildings.

rooms were again warmed by braziers containing wood, charcoal, or peat, and by wood fires on simple open hearths, often in the middle of the floor, the smoke finding its way out through louvres in the roof. The louvres themselves were of most interesting but often weird design, usually made of pottery, and mounted on the roof ridges as terminal features. It was not long before a protective hood was devised above the fire to catch the smoke and conduct it away. In the private chambers or solars of the more wealthy domestic buildings, the hearth was placed against a wall, and the smoke collected in a canopy, and allowed to escape to the open air through a hole made in the masonry. There appears to be no evidence of the use of chimneys in England prior to the twelfth century. Neither in London's first building regulations given by London's first Mayor, Fitz Alwyn, in 1189, nor in the regulations of 1212 was mention made of fireplaces and chimneys, though these regulations were primarily framed to prevent the outbreak of fire. There was considerable danger from fires which bakers and alewives kept stoked with litter during the night, and the decrees, especially that of 1212, made particular reference to them.

Twelfth-century fireplaces may still be seen at Rochester Castle (*c.* 1130), King's House, Southampton (also early twelfth century), and Castle Hedingham, Essex, where the flues went up the wall for a few feet, and then turned out at the back, the smoke issuing from small oblong holes. The fireplaces are complete, that at Rochester having a semicircular back and shafts in each jamb supporting a semicircular arch over the opening, and enriched with zigzag moulding. The fireplace at Southampton also has a semicircular arch

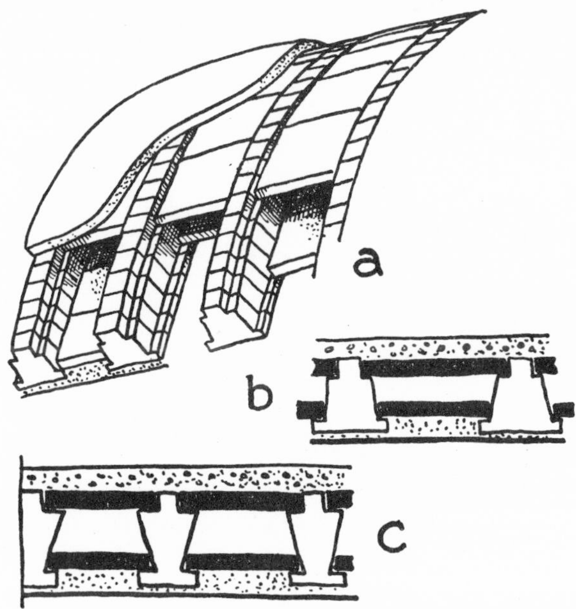

Fig. 114. An alternative method of constructing a heated vault.

with Norman shafts set in the jambs. Fireplaces as elaborate as these only occurred in the larger and more wealthy houses.

Undoubtedly these early fireplaces were far from ideal, the draughts blowing the smoke into the room. The next step, therefore, was to reduce down-draughts, and from this point onwards the progressive development of the chimney stack can be seen. By carrying the flues up through stone chimney shafts built on the outside wall, as at Aydon Castle, Northumberland (*c.* 1280), and by covering the end with a conical hood to prevent rain from entering, a great improvement was made. Better still, some flues were carried up through the whole height of the wall itself, and the tops finished with chimney shafts and hoods of varied form, the apertures often being of trefoil or lancet pattern. Many of these early chimney shafts were of considerable height and were circular, as at Sherborne Abbey, Dorset (*c.* 1300), and they must have greatly increased the up-draught.

In domestic work of the fourteenth century onwards, the chimney pieces inside the rooms assumed considerable architectural importance and soon formed the principal decorative features in many old halls, often occupying the full height of the rooms and being built of stone, marble, and wood. At the same time that these elaborate and often beautiful chimney-pieces were being installed in the large houses, so in the smaller more modest houses the hearths were being set within an ingle, or inglenook.

The great use of brick during the Tudor period resulted in many very beautiful and characteristic chimney stacks; they were often decorated with chevron and other geometric designs, many good examples of such work being seen at Hampton Court Palace; Figure 56 shows others at St Osyth's Priory, Essex. As far as small houses were concerned, the chimney may be looked upon as a Tudor innovation, for it was during this period and particularly towards the end of the sixteenth century that the consumption of coal for domestic purposes increased enormously.

Faulty chimney construction and the close proximity of timber to hearths and flues led to many disastrous fires, and eventually an Act of Parliament in 1709 stipulated that no timber should lie nearer than 5 inches to any chimney flue (which was then called a 'funnel') or fireplace, and that all the flues should be plastered or pargetted on the inside from the bottom to the top.

REFERENCES

(1) LOWTHER, A. W. G., 'A study of the Patterns on Roman Flue Tiles and their Distribution', Surrey Archaeological Society, Research Paper No. 1.

(2) *Sussex Archaeological Collections*, LXXXI, 67, and *Journal of Roman Studies*, 1930, XXX, 188.

(3) BREWIS, PARKER, 'Excavations at Chesters', *Archaeologia Aeliana*, VIII (4th Series).

Plate LXVII. The laminated timber building at the entrance to the Festival of Britain, 1951 (see page 218).

Plate LXVIII. Prestressed concrete roof beams at the B.O.A.C. Hangar, London Airport (see page 219).

Plate LXIX. The reinforced concrete roof of the dance hall at Chianciano Health Centre, Italy (see page 219).

Plate LXX. Reinforced concrete at the Palazzetto dello Sport, Rome (see page 219).

24

Water Supply and Drainage

Two of the major problems that arose as soon as early man settled in small communities were the supply of fresh water, and disposal of sewage and household and industrial wastes. These have continued to exercise his ingenuity ever since. The problem of water supply was simply overcome in the main by carrying water in pottery vessels, as it still is so often done in many parts of the world, from a lake, river, or well. It soon became clear that if the water source lay at a convenient point higher than the habitations, the water could be allowed to flow by gravity in open channels. To prevent loss of water, however, these open channels had often to be lined with stone, or burnt bricks and tiles set in clay or in bitumen where this was available—as in the brick-vaulted sewer at the Akkadian Palace at Eshnunna[1] in Mesopotamia (third millennium B.C.) and other parts of the Middle East. Water flowing in open channels was, however, liable to contamination by livestock, decaying vegetation, and windblown material, and to overcome this trouble they were sometimes covered with stone slabs or arched over with bricks. Nowadays the water is supplied in impervious pipes of cast iron, salt-glazed ware, or concrete.

It was the ingenuity of potters that led to the making of special impervious linings for water supply lines. The fact that baked clay vessels could be made sufficiently impervious to hold water must very quickly have suggested that baked clay tubes, and linings thrown on the potter's wheel or hand moulded, might also be used for conveying water, for supplying it fresh to a building or for draining it away. Some of the early products had profiles curved to shapes already familiar to the potter, but soon it was realized that straight-sided or slightly tapering tubes were more practical for laying.

It is not improbable that sometimes pottery vessels may have had their bases broken off or perforated to allow the necks to be inserted to form a pipeline. A comparatively recent example of this practice, by primitive Hawaiians, came to light in 1958 when a 150-year-old pipeline was unearthed near Honolulu.[2] The pipeline, supplying water, was a mile long and consisted of 6,500 ceramic liquor bottles each 10 inches long and 4 inches in diameter. Jointing had been accomplished by breaking a hole about $1\frac{1}{2}$ inches in diameter in the bottom of each bottle, inserting the neck of the next bottle into the hole and then plastering the joint with dense clay.

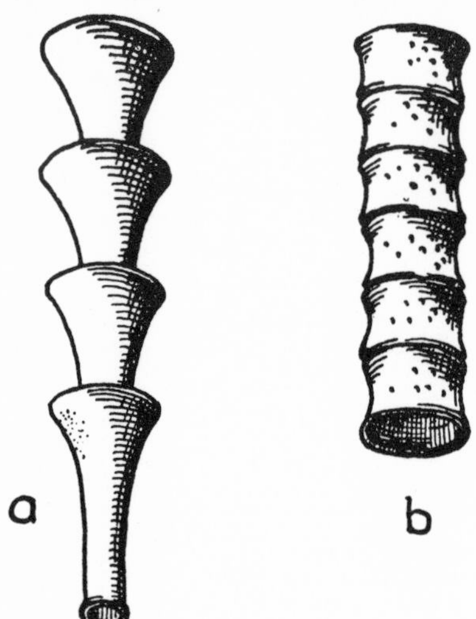

Fig. 115. Drain-pipes from Ur of the Chaldees, found by Woolley in association with graves, from the prehistoric period onwards.

The disposal of domestic and animal waste in large centres of population has also been a major problem. It was early realized that such material was of great value as fertilizer and this resulted generally in the practice of allowing the material to spread freely over the surface of the land, or alternatively of accumulating it in heaps to dry out and be distributed later, or led to shallow soakaway pits.

Possibly the earliest known pottery pipes are the extraordinary ones discovered by Woolley[3] in the tomb mound at Ur of the Chaldees. As shown in Figure 115 they were laid vertically, and Woolley is of the opinion that the intention was not that they should act as soakaways to preserve the tombs from damp, as some had previously supposed, but rather that they should provide a means for conveying libations poured down into the tombs to the god of the underworld. Some of the bell-shaped sections shown in Figure 115a were as much as 5 feet in height, the bell-mouthed opening being about 2 feet 6 inches in diameter. They are thought to date from the prehistoric period. The sections in Figure 115b of 3rd Dynasty date (about 2000 B.C.) are about 1 foot 6 inches in diameter and about a foot in depth.

The pottery pipes shown in Figure 116, possibly the earliest examples of socketed pipes, date from about the third millennium B.C. They were excavated at the palace of Knossos, in Crete, by Evans, and are 2 feet 6 inches long, tapering from 6 inches in diameter at one end to just under 4 inches at the other. About $2\frac{1}{2}$ inches from the smaller end is a

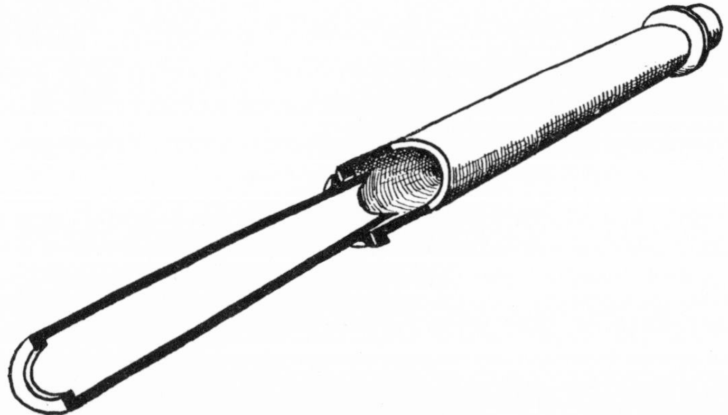

Fig. 116. Water pipes from the Palace of Knossos, Crete, probably of the third millennium B.C.

collar which bore against the end of the next pipe. Some pipes were provided with ring-shaped lugs through which ropes could be threaded so that adjacent pipes could be drawn tightly together.

The pottery pipes from the Canaanite city of Hazor, of the thirteenth century B.C., excavated by the Anglo-Israel Exploration Society, are about 3 feet long. They are almost ellipsoidal in shape and show an early and interesting attempt to connect two lines of piping. Some had a hole cut in the side, as shown in Figure 117, so that a branch pipe

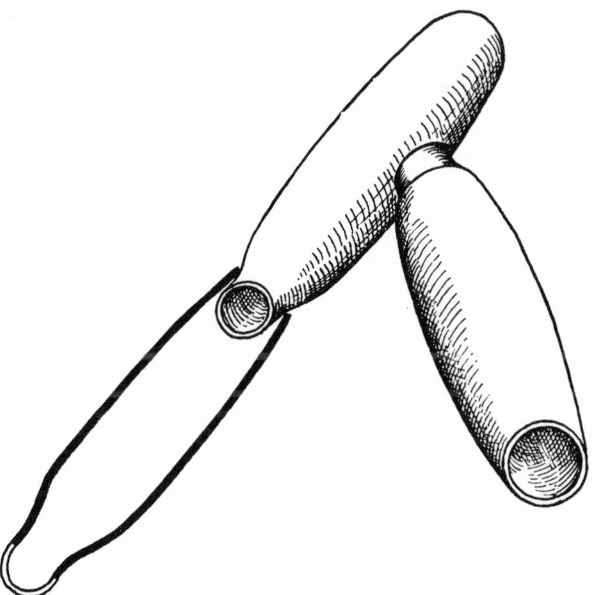

Fig. 117. Water-pipes from the Canaanite city of Hazor; thirteenth century B.C.

could be fitted obliquely into it. Pipes used in ancient Greece varied greatly in shape and dimensions, and some had well-formed sockets. A series from Olympia is shown in Figure 118, based on examples described by Finch.[4] Sometimes, as at Pergamon, the pipeline was supported on stone blocks set up at intervals and perforated with round holes through which the pipe sections passed. By the Roman period, pipes had become almost entirely parallel sided, with well-formed sockets.

Examples are shown in Figure 119, from Verulamium (a), from the Baths of Caracalla (b), and from the aqueduct at Lincoln (c). Pipes like these were sometimes bedded in concrete, not only to hold them rigidly in position, but to seal the joints. Vitruvius[5] records that the jointing was done with a mixture of quicklime and oil. The laying of the pipes in the aqueduct at Lincoln was very carefully carried out and has been described by Thompson.[6] A trench was first dug to a width of approximately 4 feet and to the required depth. Along the bottom were placed limestone slabs, with an average thickness of 3 inches and approximate width of 2 feet. These provided a firm foundation, and on this was erected shuttering, probably of wood, with an internal width of 15 inches, into which the first layer of concrete was poured. The pipes were then laid and the joints carefully sealed with mortar, after which more concrete was poured in to a total height of rather more than 1 foot, enough to embed the pipes completely. The upper surface

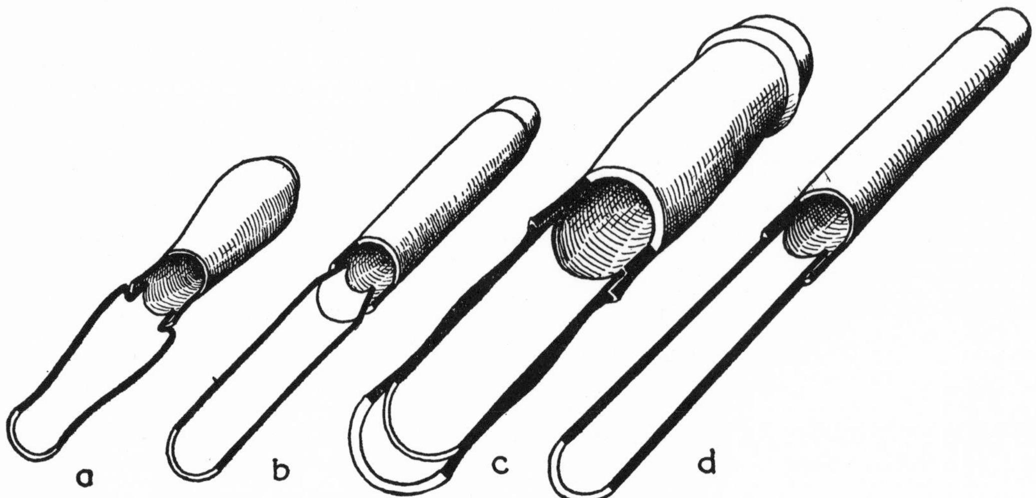

Fig. 118. Water-pipes from Ancient Greece.

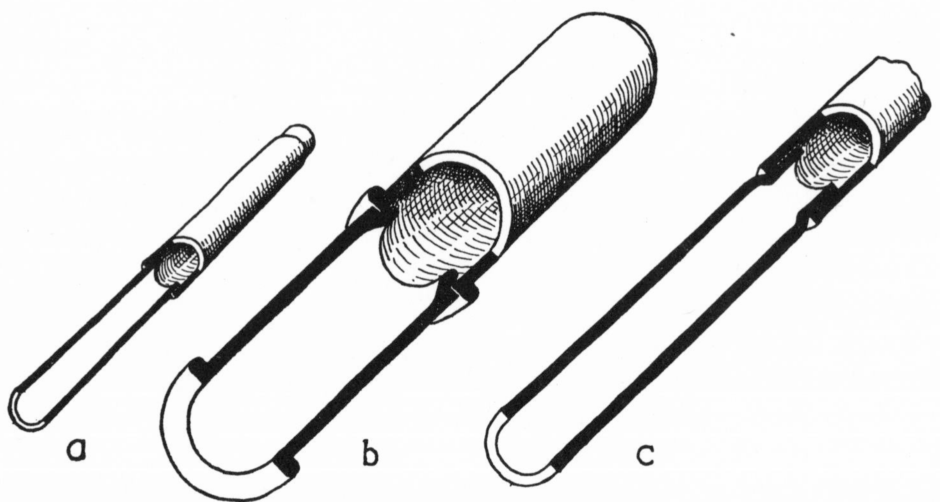

Fig. 119 Roman water-pipes.

of the concrete was then given a smooth finish. The shuttering was apparently withdrawn as the laying proceeded and the sides of the concrete encasement packed at intervals with limestone blocks, presumably to prevent lateral displacement of the concrete before it had thoroughly hardened. Finally the trench was filled to ground level with soil. An analysis of the concrete showed that it contained the equivalent of about 1 volume of lime, assumed to have been used in the form of a 'putty', and $1\frac{1}{4}$ volumes of crushed tile. This type of mixture was used by the Romans for hydraulic works, particularly where it was important to resist the penetration of moisture. The compounds of silica and alumina present in the crushed tile combined with the hydrated lime to form stable insoluble compounds. The ceramic pipes used today are of salt-glazed ware.

Metals have also been used since very early times for water-pipes. Possibly the earliest example is a copper pipe now in the National Museum in Berlin (Plate LXV), found in the temple of King Sahura (variously spelt Sa-hu-Re, Sahoure) at Abusir in Egypt. It dates from the 5th Egyptian dynasty, in the latter half of the third millennium B.C. The piece of pipe now preserved is 3 feet 6 inches long and about 3 inches in diameter. The total length of pipeline was about 1,200 feet, made up of sections about 2 feet 6 inches long. These were formed from beaten copper sheets about $\frac{1}{16}$ inch thick simply bent to form a circular tube, the seam being closed merely by folding one edge over the other and hammering them together, without soldering or riveting. The pipe was set into a groove cut in the stone bedding, with a mortar composed of approximately equal parts of gypsum and calcium carbonate. This completely surrounded the pipe and prevented any serious leakage.

Lead was used in great quantities by the Romans for piping. They made pipes in lengths usually of about 10 feet and of many different sizes up to 9 inches or more in diameter, by folding sheet strips of rolled or beaten lead over a mandril. The sketch in Figure 120 of a section of a large pipe in the National Museum in Rome shows how one edge of the sheet metal was formed to overlap the other edge, and then the longitudinal seam soldered with lead. The pipes usually assumed a pear shape like that illustrated; and the lengths were joined together by enlarging the diameter at one end of one length by beating, to enable one end of another length to be inserted, and soldered.

It was many years later that seamless lead pipes, like those of today, were to be formed by extrusion, a process originating in France by which the lead in a semi-molten condition was forced through special dies by hydraulic pressure.

Lead has had many other uses in building, for forming gutters, troughs, spouts, cames for window panes, flashings, and roof coverings. Salzman[7] records a reference by Bede to the removal by Eadberht in the second half of the seventh century A.D. of thatch from a wooden church which had been built by Finian at Lindisfarne, and of its replacement by sheet lead.

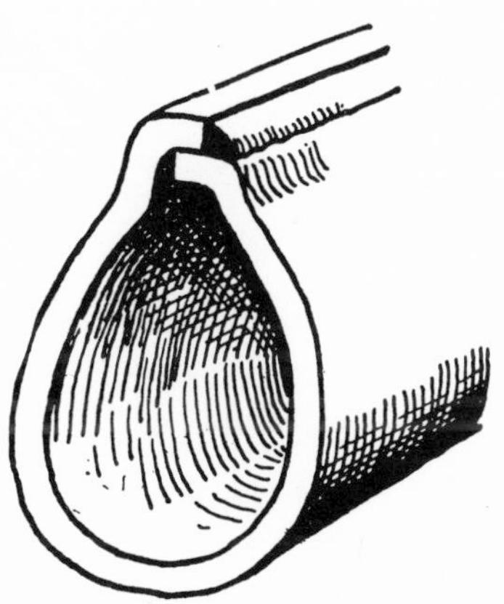

Fig. 120. Section of a Roman lead pipe in the National Museum Rome.

The Romans also used other materials for water-pipes. Rectangular blocks of stone were sometimes bored throughout their length to provide a conduit, and occasionally spigots and sockets were formed at the ends.[8] Stone blocks were also carved out to form open channels and gulleys. Wooden conduits like the examples now in the London Museum were more commonly used (Plate LXVI). They formed part of a drain or conduit found on the site of the Bank of England in London, and consisted of lengths of squared oak, $7\frac{3}{4}$ inches by $4\frac{1}{2}$ inches, with a central circular hole about $1\frac{3}{4}$ inches in diameter. Watertight junctions between the timber pipes, often about 5 feet in length, were made by means of iron collars, about $3\frac{1}{2}$ inches in diameter, which were driven to a depth of $\frac{1}{2}$ to $\frac{3}{4}$ inch into the adjacent timbers in such a way as to enclose the central channel.

Pliny[9] recorded that:

> Pines, pitch pines and alders are hollowed to form pipes for conveying water, and when buried underground will last a number of years; but they age quickly if not covered over, the resistance they offer being remarkably increased if their outside surface is covered with moisture.

The use of oak for Roman water-pipes is in contrast to the timbers suggested by Pliny, and to the medieval and later practice of using elm. During the Great Fire of London in 1666, roads were torn up, and the long trunks of hollowed elm which carried the main water supply from the New River were cut so that fire buckets could be filled. The supply of water ran to waste and in sections of the City the pipes and cisterns were empty when most needed.[10]

Very few wooden pipes were laid in London after the end of the eighteenth century. The Metropolis Paving Act of 1817 prohibited their use and this date marks the approximate beginning of the extended use of cast-iron water-pipes. A few had already been used in the previous two or three decades.

Concrete pipes were not introduced into England until 1906, and this material, often reinforced with steel, is now commonly used for large-diameter pipes. Asbestos cement pipes made of Portland cement reinforced with asbestos fibres were first made in Italy, and later in England, in 1928. Another material now used for domestic water-pipes is polythene plastic, and is an invention dating from the second world war.

REFERENCES

(1) Frankfort, H., Jacobsen, T., and Preusser, C., 1934, *Iraq Excavations of the Oriental Institute*, Third Preliminary Report, Chicago University Oriental Institute Communication No. 17.

(2) *Journal* of the American Water Works Association, Nov. 1958, L, 11.

(3) Woolley, C. L., Oct. 1926, 'The Excavations at Ur 1925–6', *Antiquaries' Journal*, VI (4).

(4) Finch, J. K., 1958, 'The Greek Architekton', Part 2, *Civil Engineering*, United States.

(5) Vitruvius, *De Architectura*, Book VIII, VI.

(6) Thompson, F. H., July 1955, 'The Roman Aqueduct at Lincoln', *Archaeological Journal*, CXI.

(7) Salzman, L. F., 1952, *Building in England*, Oxford University Press, 262.

(8) Herschel, Clemens, 1899, *Frontinius and the Water Supply of the City of Rome*, Boston.

(9) Pliny, *Natural History*, Book XVI, LXXI, translated by H. Rackham, Loeb Classical Library, Heinemann.

(10) Bell, W. G., 1951, *The Great Fire of London*, Bodley Head (revised edition), 60.

25

Metals

BOTH NON-FERROUS and ferrous metals have had many uses in building from very early times, for plumbing and protective coverings, for decorative finishes, for structural components, and for fittings and tools. The most important metals of the non-ferrous group are copper, lead, tin, zinc, aluminium, and alloys of these, and of the ferrous metals wrought iron, cast iron, mild steel, and alloys of steel.

Copper, possibly the earliest metal used by man, is obtained by smelting copper pyrites, a compound of copper, iron, and sulphur, and was produced in Egypt as far back as the fifth millennium B.C. In Britain it was not until the end of the third millennium or the beginning of the second that copper was smelted to any appreciable extent. The sulphur in the ore was partially removed by burning, and the calcined ore then placed in a furnace in layers alternating with charcoal. When the melting temperature of the copper was reached, the slag which accumulated on the surface was removed and the copper ladled into a cavity formed in the ground. The circular cake-shaped ingots so produced varied in size, one of Roman date in the British Museum from the Parys mines at Amlwch in Anglesey being 11½ inches in diameter and about 1½ inches in thickness and weighing about 26¾ lb., and another from Carnedd Llewellyn, Carnarvonshire, being 15 inches in diameter. The copper ingots also very often bore an official mark. In the pure state copper is soft and, like lead, easily beaten into sheets and strips. With the addition of tin a harder product was obtained, known as bronze, and by the middle of the fourth millennium B.C. its use had become well established for making cutting tools such as axes, chisels, and saws. Other alloys of copper were produced later on: copper and antimony, when tin was scarce; copper and lead for a softer alloy, easily melted and used for example for statuary bronzes in ancient Greece and in China during the Han dynasty; and copper and zinc, often with a small addition of lead, to form an alloy known as brass. All these alloys were in use two thousand years ago. There are several outstanding examples of the use of bronze. The dome of the Pantheon in Rome was once roofed with bronze tiles which were later stripped off and taken to Constantinople. Bronze plates from the interior of the building were melted down in the seventeenth century to supply the metal required by Bernini for making the baldacchino in St Peter's, Rome. Bronze rosettes and mouldings that once decorated the coffers on the interior surface of the

Pantheon dome have also disappeared. Another notable example of bronze work is the very beautiful east door of the Baptistery of S. Giovanni in Florence, with gilded bas-reliefs showing Biblical scenes, and called by Michelangelo the Porta del Paradiso (Gate of Paradise). It is one of two doors made by Lorenzo Ghiberti in the first half of the fifteenth century. The doors of the Henry VII chapel at Westminster Abbey, the work of another Italian artist, Torrigiano, a hundred years later, are also worthy of note.

A modern alloy of copper and aluminium called 'aluminium-bronze' is not a true bronze. It has, however, a high strength, and being ductile and resistant to corrosion is used for piping, grilles, statues, and components exposed to the weather.

At the present time there are many kinds of brass, formed by adding to the essential copper and zinc, other metals such as tin, iron, nickel, manganese, and aluminium. Those with under 40 per cent of zinc in them are ductile but have a relatively high strength which makes them suitable for rolling into sheets, and drawing into tubes, rods, and wire; while those with over 40 per cent and up to about 46 per cent of zinc are suitable for casting and for hot working, to form by rolling and extrusion mouldings of many shapes, like window frame sections which are very tough and resistant to corrosion. The small addition of lead improves the workability of brasses, while aluminium produces a pale yellow brass, and manganese a brownish alloy having the appearance of bronze. The addition of nickel to the brass produces an alloy called 'nickel-silver' or German silver, and these nickel brasses with up to 20 per cent of nickel are extrudable and used for handrails and balustrades. This material, German silver, is recorded as having been used for the coins of Euthydemos of Bactria (235 B.C.).[1]

Lead, early examples of which were found at Hissarlik (*c.* 3000 to 2500 B.C.), is obtained by smelting galena (lead sulphide). By the time of the Roman occupation of Britain mining was well established.[2] By Roman law minerals belonged to the State, but it seems that sometimes rights to mine for minerals were granted to private individuals, for in the British Museum are pigs of lead not only stamped with the Emperor's name, but also several bearing names which appear to be of Greek origin—Abascantus, Protus, and Trophimus. As in other parts of the Roman Empire, the metal trade was largely in the hands of Greek freedmen.

The chief mining areas for lead in Britain were in Yorkshire, Derbyshire, North Denbighshire, Flintshire, Shropshire, and the Mendip Hills in Somerset. The molten metal was formed into pigs by ladling it into moulds which had an inscription on the bottom. Some pigs bore the letters EX ARG. or EX ARGENT indicating that silver (*argentum*) had been extracted. Some of the 'pigs' in the British Museum weigh up to 185 lb.

Tin mined by the Romans in south-west Britain was also formed into ingots; one from Carnanton, now in the Truro Museum, weighs as much as 39½ lb., and a second in the Penzance Museum, from Trereife, weighs 29½ lb.

Zinc, a later discovery in about the sixth century B.C., is obtained by smelting zinc blende (zinc sulphide) or calamine (zinc carbonate). Both lead and zinc have been used in sheet form for roof covering and flashings. Zinc is also used for galvanizing mild steel to improve its resistance to corrosion.

Aluminium, historically the most recent metal to be used in building, does not occur in nature as a pure metal but is produced principally from bauxite (one of the hydroxides of alumina) or from cryolite (one of the fluorides of alumina). Earliest examples date from the middle of the nineteenth century. Manganese and magnesium added to aluminium improve its strength; silicon increases its strength and fluidity and thereby improves its casting qualities; copper increases its strength; while zinc forms a very strong alloy. Some of the aluminium alloys, particularly those for structural purposes, may contain several of these elements, the principal ones containing magnesium, or silicon and manganese.

Iron of meteoric origin was the only iron available to man up to about the fourth millennium B.C. in a form he could use, and then in very small quantities. This is the only form in which pure iron occurs in nature. It seems that some time in the third or fourth millennium B.C. man discovered the art of smelting iron ore on charcoal fires, and produced a material comparable with wrought iron. Early examples of its use are for an iron tool, with hammer marks upon it, from the Great Pyramid of Khufu at Gizeh in Egypt, now in the British Museum; a dagger blade found in the Diyala valley at Tell Asmar which is the oldest evidence of ironworking in Mesopotamia; and pieces of non-meteoric iron found by Mallowan in a Ninevite grave at Chaga Bazar, of early third millennium date. There seems little doubt that by the second millennium B.C. the practice had become well established.

The iron ore was reduced by heat to a spongy mass, soft and malleable because it contained little or no alloyed carbon. By hammering out or forging the metal, reheating it in a charcoal fire, and quenching it in water, it was found that the metal could be hardened sufficiently to produce good cutting tools, as efficient at least as the bronze ones. The iron ores suitable for refining are magnetite (Fe_3O_4), haematite (Fe_2O_3), ochres (Fe_2O_3 hydrated), and siderite ($FeCO_3$). In Roman Britain and for many years after the occupation, iron ore was mined chiefly in the Forest of Dean and in the Weald of Kent and Sussex. It was softened in a furnace and the pasty mass withdrawn from the furnace and hammered into 'blooms' for transport to local forges where it was resoftened and used as required. Three 'blooms' can be seen at the Roman villa at Chedworth. They vary in weight from about $3\frac{1}{2}$ cwt. to over 5 cwt., and another found at Corstopitum, near Corbridge, weighed just over 3 cwt. The subsequent development and improvement of the smelting process at least in Britain owes much to the monks, who as early as the twelfth century mined iron ore, smelted and forged it. The Cistercian monks for example established ironworks in that century at Kirkstall Abbey and at Ardsley near Leeds.

By the fifteenth century taller furnaces with stronger air blast enabled the temperature to be raised sufficiently high to liquefy the iron. The slag which accumulated on top of the molten metal was tapped off and the liquid iron run into moulds to produce bars of iron called 'pigs'. During the process of melting, the iron absorbed up to about 4 per cent of carbon from the charcoal fuel, with the result that the product was very hard and brittle.

Cast iron, or foundry iron as it came to be known, was made in various districts where iron ore, charcoal, and water power were available. In England, the Forest of Dean and the Weald of Kent and Sussex continued to be important areas of production; as they had previously been during the Roman occupation. The ore was smelted in stack furnaces lined with brick and stone and the air blast was provided by bellows driven by water power. It was a great step forward when in 1709 Abraham Darby of Coalbrookdale in Shropshire, followed by his son of the same name, succeeded in smelting iron, using coke as fuel instead of charcoal. As coke was harder than charcoal and was better able to support the layers of the heavy iron ore the furnace stacks could be made higher, and consequently more efficient. By the second half of the eighteenth century the iron-smelting industry had been transferred from the forest areas to the coal-mining districts. Coke furnaces were erected and the water-driven air bellows were superseded by blowers operated by steam power.

The cheapening of cast iron by the Darbys led to a great increase in the use of that metal for building purposes from 1750 onward, and by the end of the century, under the influence of designers and architects such as James Adam (1730–94), Robert Adam (1728–92), William and Henry Haworth, Lewis Cottingham (1787–1847), and John Nash (1752–1835) it was used in great quantities for decorative features such as balustrades, balconies, and verandas, and grate furniture. The first structural cast iron beams by Charles Bage (1754–1822) were used in a five-storey flax mill built at Shrewsbury in 1796 and 1797.[3]

In the early nineteenth century an improvement in smelting was obtained by preheating the air blast. This effected a saving in coal of about 30 per cent and cast iron became much cheaper, and during the rest of the century it was used for many building components such as hollow columns, beams, water-pipes, rainwater and drainage fittings, railings, and staircases.

Two main types of cast iron 'pigs' are now produced, one termed 'Basic' iron with a high phosphorus and low silicon content, and the other 'Haematite' iron which is low in phosphorus and high in silicon.

Wrought iron, which is comparatively soft and malleable, is almost pure iron, with less than 0·25 per cent of carbon, and is very like the early iron produced by man three thousand years ago. Up to the middle of the eighteenth century wrought iron had been occasionally used structurally, for reinforcing bands round masonry structure, like the circumferential bands used by Wren in the construction of the dome at St Paul's Cathedral, London; or for brackets, straps, cleats, hinges, railings, nails, and fastenings of many types. These were often the work of blacksmiths who hammered out the metal to the required shape. Wrought iron is now obtained by remelting cast-iron 'pigs' in a puddling furnace, where the amount of carbon in the iron 'pigs' is reduced by oxidation, by admixing an oxidizing agent such as haematite ore, and by passing air across the hearth of the furnace. As the amount of carbon in the iron decreases its melting temperature is raised, and it gradually solidifies sufficiently for it to be gathered into convenient lumps for hammering or rolling into rough shaped bars. This puddled 'bar iron' is then reheated and reformed as required to produce the finished product. In the latter half of the nineteenth century a great deal of wrought iron was used for structural members, for fabricating bridge beams, and roof trusses, but by the end of the century mild steel had almost superseded wrought iron for this purpose.

Steel is now made from 'pig' iron by either of two methods, the Bessemer converter process or the Siemens-Martin open hearth process. In the Bessemer process the furnace is bricklined, with inlets at the bottom through which air is blown. The furnace is charged with molten 'pig' iron, and as the air is blown through the mass, some of the carbon and other impurities are fused out, leaving behind purified metal with from 0·15 to 1·5 per cent of chemically combined carbon. The metal is poured into ladles, and spiegel, an alloy of manganese and iron, is added to degasify the melt, after which it is poured into ingot moulds.

In the Siemens-Martin process the furnace of the open hearth type is a shallow basin with a flat roof, provided with openings at one end through which gas and hot air is blown. The flames sweep through the furnace and out through openings at the other end, and into chambers filled with bricks laid in chequer fashion. These absorb the waste heat, and at intervals the flow of gases through the furnace is reversed and the recovered heat is returned from the chambers to the furnace hearth. The furnace is charged with 'pig iron', and iron scrap and limestone are also added. In the chemical reactions that take place between the iron oxide formed and the impurities in the metal, the impurities either disappear as gases or accumulate as slag. When the reactions are complete, sometimes in a matter of eight to ten hours, the molten metal is tapped off from the furnace into ladles from which the slag overflows and the finished steel is cast into ingots. These ingots of steel can then be hot rolled into various shapes—angles, joists, rods, flat and corrugated sheet—and for some purposes may be cold-formed to produce structural members.

There are many *steel alloys* in use today, each with special properties imparted to it by the addition of two or more metallic additives. These additives, or more correctly alloying elements, are added to the molten steel either while the latter is in the furnace, or in a ladle after refining. *Boron* is alloyed with steel to improve its hardening properties; *chromium* in small amounts produces an alloy of finer texture of great hardness and tenacity, and in larger amounts, and usually in conjunction with *nickel*, renders the steel more resistant to corrosion; *cobalt* is used for making magnet steels and alloys, and for high speed cutting steels where in addition to abrasion resistance, hardness at high temperature is needed. *Columbium*, also known as *niobium*, is used in some stainless steels that may have to be welded, or used at high temperature. *Copper* improves the corrosion resistance; *manganese* acts as a scavenger, deoxidizing and desulphuring the melt, and making the alloy very tough; *molybdenum* refines the grain of the steel, thus increasing its strength, particularly at high temperatures, its wear resistance, and resistance to fatigue; *nickel*, like copper, imparts very high strength and toughness, and increases its resistance to heat and acids, while with chromium it is one of the principal alloying elements for stainless steels; *silicon* lowers the melting point and produces an alloy of very high strength; *titanium* is used for high temperature steels; *tungsten* increases the hardness of steel without making it brittle, and is much used for high speed tools such as drills, reamers, and saws; *vanadium* refines the grain and produces alloys suitable for high speed cutting tools; *zirconium* acts as a scavenger to rid the steel of impurities like sulphur, nitrogen, and oxygen.

Some of the alloys are complex, containing in addition to carbon such combinations of other elements as nickel and chromium (for machine tools), vanadium and chromium (for high speed cutting tools), molybdenum and chromium and tungsten and chromium (for very hard tool steels), nickel and molybdenum, silicon and manganese, and silicon and chromium.

The only reason for mentioning them here is that many of these and other alloys are used in making tools used in modern building operations.

REFERENCES

(1) ROBINSON, A. E., 1938, 'Ancient Metallurgy', *Transactions* of the St Albans and Hertfordshire Architectural and Archaeological Society.

(2) WHITTICK, G. CLEMENT, 1931–2, 'Roman Mining in Britain', *Transactions* of the Newcomen Society, XII.

(3) SKEMPTON, A. W., Sept. 1956, 'The Origin of Iron Beams', *Actes du VIIIe Congres International d'Histoire des Sciences*, Florence.

26

Modern Trends

MANY NEW MATERIALS and techniques have been developed in recent years to meet the functional requirements of modern buildings, with all their complexities of design. Building today is carried out on such a vast scale that the economical use of building materials has also become a factor of first importance. Ways and means of improving their quality and uniformity, and of making them more durable, have been closely studied.

In many great urban areas, where available land for building is becoming scarce, and increasingly costly, the tendency is to build higher and higher, and blocks of dwellings and offices up to twenty storeys or more in height have become a familiar sight. There has been an increasing demand for materials and structural components of lighter weight in order to lighten the superstructure and so reduce the load on the foundations.

The greater use of prefabricated components has speeded up the whole process of building. Apart from considerations of planning and the proper provision of heating, lighting, ventilation, and sanitation, other problems of comfort have arisen such as thermal insulation and sound insulation, and these factors often determine the choice of the building materials best suited to the work.

It would be a serious omission to conclude this history of building materials and techniques without at least a brief reference to a few of the more recent developments.

Timber

The present trend is towards a greater use of laminated timber, in sheet form like plywood, and in built-up structural members. For several hundreds of years up to the beginning of the twentieth century there had been little change in the principles of timber construction. Since then, however, there has been a marked change due principally to the use of new adhesives for bonding and jointing timber. These glues, mainly casein and synthetic ones of the urea-formaldehyde, pheno-formaldehyde, and resorcinal types, have enabled thin layers of wood, placed with the direction of the grain alternating at right angles in successive layers, to be bonded together so that the properties of the timber in the built-up member are the same in two directions. This overcomes the natural weakness of timber in the direction perpendicular to the grain, and eliminates much of the shrinkage that normally occurs in this direction.

Large numbers of comparatively short pieces of timber can now be efficiently glued together to form large structural members, for example, the 100-foot span laminated parabolic arches shown in Plate LXVII which were erected at the entrance to the Festival of Britain in 1951. Large timber shells can also now be made like those used in 1957 to roof a new weaving shed at the Wilton Royal Carpet Company. Even wood-waste like sawdust, chips, and shavings can now be converted into wall boards, straw into straw-boards, and other cellulose wastes into fibreboards for use as linings to interior walls and ceilings, and provide good thermal insulation.

Bricks

Before the introduction of machinery, clay bricks were hand moulded, the plastic clay being thrown into wooden moulds, the base-board of which often carried a shallow block which formed a recessed panel, or 'frog', on the moulded brick. Nowadays bricks are mostly machine moulded, by either the so-called 'full-plastic' or the 'soft mud' process. Sometimes a slightly stiffer clay is extruded through a rectangular aperture on to a smooth table to form a long block which can then be cut up into bricks by means of a series of equally spaced wires which are drawn through the clay. Such bricks do not have 'frogs' and are referred to as wire-cut bricks, but occasionally they are re-pressed to form a denser product, in which case they may be impressed with a 'frog'.

Modern brick-kilns are often constructed so that the air entering the kiln is led downwards inside the wall of the kiln, thus preheating it and resulting in more economical working. Such kilns are known as 'down-draught' kilns.

Although it is only in the twentieth century that sandlime bricks have been produced on a large scale, the process of making them had been patented in England as far back as 1866, by Van Derburgh, and by Michaelis in Germany in 1880. The bricks, made from siliceous sand and hydrated lime, are moulded under pressure and hardened by exposure to high-pressure steam in chambers known as autoclaves. Under these conditions, the lime reacts with the silica of the sand grains to form hydrated calcium silicate on the surface, a strong and durable cementing agent which binds the sand grains together. The bricks can be produced in various shades of colour.

Hollow Clay blocks

In face of increasing competition from other materials such as precast concrete, the clay brick industry, in addition to improving the quality of the common brick, is concerned with the production of facing bricks and hollow bricks or blocks, often glazed. Most of the modern hollow clay blocks are made by extrusion of the clay and cutting by wires. In 1849 Roberts patented a hollow block which was used in the construction of cottages shown at the 1851 Crystal Palace Exhibition, but it was not until later in the nineteenth century that hollow blocks became commonplace for floor construction, and today many floors consist essentially of reinforced concrete ribs with the hollow clay blocks between, the latter in fact acting during construction as permanent shuttering for forming the ribs, and for supporting the concrete floor topping.

Reinforced Concrete

The reinforcing of concrete with steel rods has given engineers great scope in developing new forms of structure. The early development of this valuable structural material owes much to two Frenchmen, Joseph Monier (1823–1906) and François Hennebique (1843–1924). The ability to mould the material to the desired form has led to the creation of a great variety of buildings and structures and the two examples chosen to illustrate this versatility are both works designed by Pier Luigi Nervi in Italy. The first in Plate LXIX is the roof of the dance hall of the Chianciano Health Baths, slightly oval in plan, spanning 66 feet in one direction and 69 feet in the other; and the second in Plate LXX is the Palazzetto dello Sport in Rome, erected for the 1960 Olympic Games, with a shell dome 200 feet in diameter. This latter building was designed by Nervi in collaboration with Annibale Vitelozzi.

Prestressed Concrete

It was Eugène Freyssinet who in France in 1904 conceived the idea of improving the tensile strength of reinforced concrete structural members and of avoiding cracking by replacing the ordinary mild steel reinforcement by high tensile steel wires or rods pretensioned, or stretched, so that they put the concrete into initial compression sufficiently to prevent cracking of the member when load was subsequently applied.

It was not until 1930 that the Freyssinet technique became widely applied, but its great value was realized at the end of the second world war when there was an acute shortage of steel. One of the most impressive uses of prestressed concrete in Great Britain was for the roof of the B.O.A.C. hangar at London Airport. The roof beams spanned 150 feet and had the appearance, as seen in Plate LXVIII, of being almost as slender as steel plate girders. Coupled with the use of high grade concrete, the saving in steel and cement was considerable.

Lightweight Concrete

Mention has already been made of the importance of reducing the weight in modern multi-storey buildings, and in recent years the use of lightweight concrete, in place of dense concrete, has been encouraged. It has been produced either by the use of lightweight aggregates prepared mainly from waste products of industry, like blast-furnace slag, colliery shale, boiler clinker, pulverized fuel ash, and slate waste, or by aerating the concrete. The methods of producing lightweight aggregates are briefly described. *Foamed*

Blast-furnace Slag is made by treating molten slag, which is the waste residue of blast-furnace pig-iron manufacture, with a small amount of water or other volatile liquid or gas. The slag is expanded to form a spongy mass and as it is chilled it hardens and retains this porous and lightweight character, and looks very like natural pumice. *Sintered Clay or Shale* is made from brick-earth or colliery shale. After grinding in the dry state, the material is wetted and formed into pellets, which are fed on to a sintering hearth which moves continuously under an ignition hood heated by oil or gas. The fuel remaining in the pellets is ignited at a high temperature and the pellets reach a state of incipient fusion when the gas evolved in them causes swelling or bloating of the clay particles. The material emerges in the form of a continuous cake, greyish brown in colour and of open pored texture, and it is finally crushed and graded to the sizes required for making concrete. *Pulverized Fuel Ash*, a very fine dust, is the residue of the granulated coal burnt in thermal power stations. It is produced in vast quantities and its disposal as a waste material is extremely difficult and costly. However, it is possible to produce an excellent lightweight aggregate in a manner very similar to that already described for dealing with sintered clay. After wetting, the ash is formed into pellets of suitable size which, when heated, are converted into hard, honey-combed nodules. *Expanded Slate* is another good lightweight aggregate produced by sintering waste slate.

Aerated concrete is usually made from cement or lime with sand or other siliceous material, to which a small amount of aluminium powder is added. This reacts with the lime and the gas produced forms voids in the mass.

Steelwork

In the latter half of the nineteenth century mild steel became a serious competitor for wrought iron and gradually replaced it. The Forth Bridge in Scotland, completed in 1890, is an early example of the use of the material. The first steel-framed building in England was Robinson's Emporium at West Hartlepool in 1896, and the first of importance in London was the Ritz Hotel, erected in 1904. Since that time steel-framed buildings have become commonplace. The hot-rolled steel sections normally used are unfortunately often of a minimum thickness which cannot be readily reduced in the normal rolling process. This often leads to extravagance in some parts of the structure, as for example in floor and wall panels. In order to utilize steel more efficiently a new type of steel member has been developed. It is fabricated from sheet or strip steel, cold formed in such a way as to produce much more economical members. So far the material has mostly been used for flooring units and wall panels, but new shapes for larger stanchions and girders have also been developed.

Aluminium and its alloys

It is only since the end of the first world war that aluminium and its alloys have been gradually used for building construction. The greatest use for the material has been in

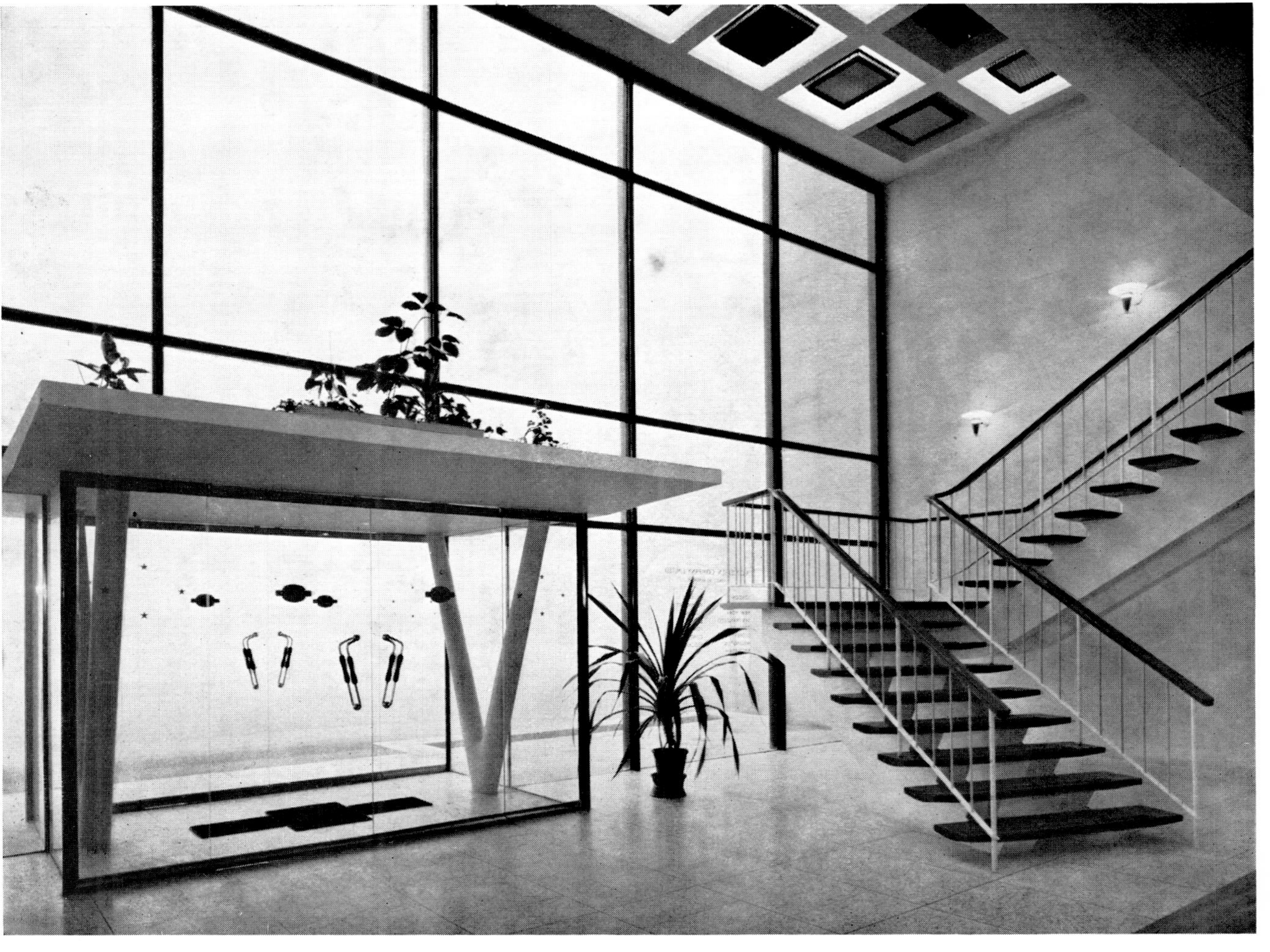

Plate LXXI. 'Armourplate' glass doors at the entrance to Neilsen House, Oxford, with plate glass façade (see page 221).

Plate LXXII. Coloured glass panel infilling on the sixteen-storey block of flats and adjacent maisonettes, Golden Lane Estate, London (see page 221).

the aircraft industry where lightness in weight combined with strength are such important factors. The impetus to its use in buildings came at the end of the second world war when the great wartime stocks of aluminium had to be put to other purposes, and the aluminium bungalow, so familiar to many people, was designed for emergency housing. Since then an increasing number of aluminium alloy structures have been built and today alloys of many grades and with diverse properties are available for structural use in various extruded sections, plates, and sheets. A most striking use of the material was for the Dome of Discovery built in 1951 for the Festival of Britain.

Glass

In addition to its use in windows, glass has become a material for the external cladding of buildings. The strength of plate glass has been greatly improved, and the so-called toughened ('armourplate') glass first produced in 1941 is very resistant to shock and to high temperature. In addition to being strong, it has the great merit that if it should be broken it will not splinter, but will fall in comparatively harmless pieces roughly cubic in shape. An unfortunate drawback is that it cannot be cut to size or worked in any way after manufacture. The toughened glass is often used for swing doors of the type shown in Plate LXXI, at the offices of A. C. Nielsen, Marketing Research, Oxford. The façade surrounding the entrance is of polished plate glass.

In Plate LXXII glass is seen in use for the infilling on the exterior of the sixteen-storey block of flats, and on the adjacent maisonettes erected on the Golden Lane Estate, London. The colours of the glass sheets are yellow, red, and blue. Translucent walls and panels are also built either with glass bricks, or with compound glass sheets consisting of a thin layer of glass fibre sandwiched between two sheets of ordinary glass. This latter type gives a diffused light and is often used in art galleries and museums.

In fibre form, glass is an excellent heat insulator, and in recent years there have been many developments. Foamed glass, first produced in 1940, is made, as its name implies, by foaming or aerating molten glass, and is used in block form for walls, floors, and ceilings. Being extremely light it gives high heat insulation. Glass fibres are now made by centrifuging molten glass so that it is forced out through fine holes to form fibres, which are subjected to further heating while in flight to increase their fineness. These glass fibres are then laid to form blankets for lining roofs and ceilings for insulation purposes.

Plastics

The development in recent years of synthetic resins has led to entirely new building materials and techniques. Rather loosely called 'plastics', they cover many organically different materials capable of being moulded when heated and pressed. There are two main groups of 'plastics', those called 'thermo-plastic' which can be softened and re-softened indefinitely by the application of heat and pressure, and the 'thermo-setting plastics' which undergo chemical change when subjected to heat and pressure and are converted into insoluble and infusible masses incapable of being re-formed by further heat and pressure. There are a number of natural materials that have been used from earliest times that fall into the thermo-setting groups, substances like resin, pitch, and bituminous materials.

It was not until 1865, however, that man-made thermo-plastics were developed. In that year Joseph Parkes of Birmingham discovered that cellulose nitrate could be plasticized with camphor to form a mouldable material that hardened on cooling, a material which was subsequently called celluloid. The next major development occurred early in the twentieth century when Baekeland and others found that by heating phenol with formaldehyde a useful resinous product was formed. This led to the production in 1916 of the first thermo-setting moulding powder called 'Bakelite'. Since then many other types of plastics have been produced, and have found their uses in the building industry.[1,2] The following are a few typical examples.

Of the *thermo-plastics*, acrylic resin (polymethylmethacrylate) is used in transparent or translucent form for domed roof lights, panels for ceiling lights, corrugated roof sheets, lighting fittings, and generally as a substitute for glass; bitumen-based plastics are used for various moulded fitments such as flushing cisterns; cellulose acetate for lighting fittings, finger-plates on doors, and covering to handrails; coumarone indene resins for 'thermo-plastic' tiles; isocyanate (polyurethane) as a cellular thermal insulator; polythene for cold-water service pipes, as films to provide a moisture barrier, and for various moulded products; styrene (polystyrene) for thin decorative wall tiles, or when foamed for thermal insulating materials; vinyl (polyvinylchloride, p.v.c., polyvinylacetate, p.v.a.) for wall and floor tiles and coverings, and for emulsion paints.

Of the *thermo-setting plastics*, amino plastics (melamineformaldehyde, urea-formaldehyde) for decorative veneers on walls, for ceiling linings, and coverings to counter and table tops, water resisting adhesives for plywood and for wood chip-boards, various moulded products like seats; phenolic resins (phenol-formaldehyde, cresol-formaldehyde, resorcinol-formaldehyde) for wall linings and plywood, corrugated roofing sheets, various moulded products like electrical fittings, door furniture; polyesters, which are usually reinforced with glass for translucent corrugated roof lights, baths, and sink units; and water-soluble cellulose derivative (sodium carboxy methyl cellulose) as a binder for distempers and crack filling compositions and for wall-papering adhesives.

It is much too early in the history of 'plastics' to say how they will endure.

REFERENCES

(1) Building Research Station Digest No. 103, October 1957, *Plastics for Building*, H.M.S.O., London.

(2) Yarsley, V. E., and Couzens, E. G., 1941, *Plastics*, Penguin Books.

Appendix

BUILDING TOOLS

TOOLS USED IN building processes are almost numberless, and it is clearly not possible to give here an exhaustive selection. Instead a few tools, some of early date, that have become traditional to particular building crafts, have been selected; some may be considered almost as prototypes. The outline sketches of the tools in the accompanying illustrations are intended to show little more than their general form.

Mason's tools (Figure 121)

(*a*) Vertical plumb bob (Egyptian, *c.* 1000 B.C.) consisting of a straight edge which is applied to the vertical surface being tested. The truth of the surface is indicated by a line and plumb bob which hangs over a projecting short bracket. When the surface is truly vertical the line just touches a lower projecting bracket of the same length as the upper one. Such implements were in use in Egypt at a very early date (an original is in the Museum of Antiquities, Cairo, and many copies have been made, one being on view at the Science Museum, London).

(*b*) Mason's level and square (Egyptian, 19th Dynasty) consisting of a wooden set-square combined with a plumb bob and line. When the extremities of the set square are applied to a horizontal surface the line reads against a mark on the crosspiece. When the line is coincident with the mark the surface being tested is horizontal (a model of one of these levels was found in the tomb of an Egyptian architect named Sennehem and is now in the Museum of Antiquities, Cairo, and a copy is in the Science Museum, London).

(*c*) One of a pair of wooden straining pegs (Egyptian, *c.* 3000 B.C.) used for pegging a stretched line into the joints of a masonry wall to check the setting of the blocks. They are very similar in purpose to the steel pegs used by bricklayers and masons today (Science Museum, London).

(*d*) Boning rods (Egyptian, *c.* 1580 B.C.) similar to those shown in the drawing on the wall of Rekhmara's tomb at Thebes (Figure 122), and used for checking the evenness of surface of a masonry block as it is being worked (copy in Science Museum, London).

(*e*) Mason's bow saw (Roman Period in Egypt). An example from the Fayum is in the Egyptian Collection at University College, London. Originally the band saw with raked teeth was pinned at each end into the wood frame, but as the latter shrank and contracted in use, the surplus length of the blade was taken up by bending one end of the blade round the end of the frame.

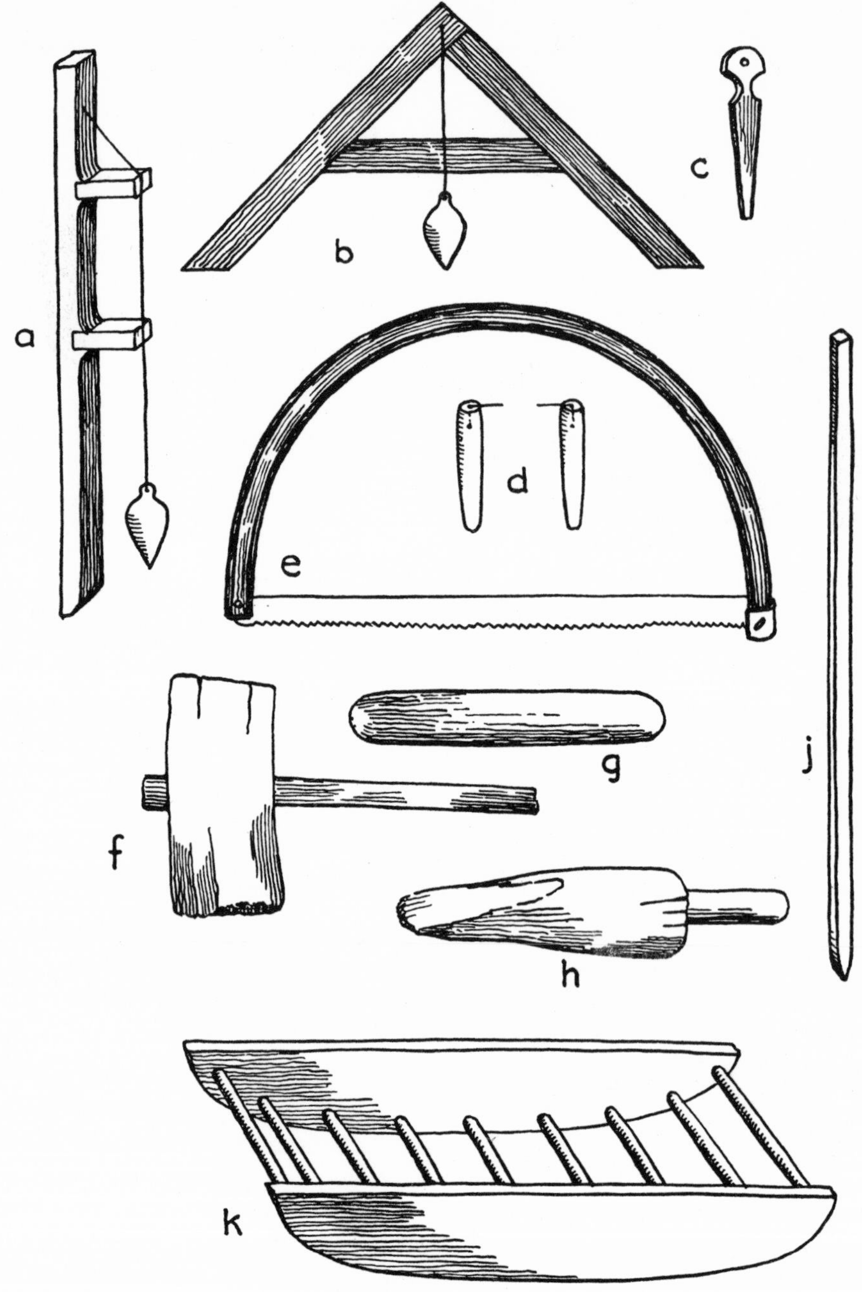

Fig. 121. Egyptian mason's tools.

(*f*) Socketed wooden mallet (Egyptian, 26th Dynasty) in the Petrie Collection at University College, London.

(*g*) Wood roller for manœuvring stone blocks (Egyptian 12th Dynasty) in the Petrie Collection at University College, London.

(*h*) Wood wedge (Egyptian 12th Dynasty) used for manœuvring stone blocks (Science Museum, London).

(*j*) Bronze chisel (Egyptian, *c.* 1400 B.C.) from a copy in the Science Museum, London.

(*k*) Cradle for moving stone blocks (Egyptian, 18th Dynasty) from a copy in the Petrie Collection at University College, London.

The late Sir Flinders Petrie[1] prepared an excellent inventory, liberally illustrated, of the many tools in the Egyptian Collection at University College, London, and this should be consulted by readers who wish to study the subject in more detail. Many of the tools are shown in use in the drawing on the wall of the Tomb of Rekhmara (Figure 122).

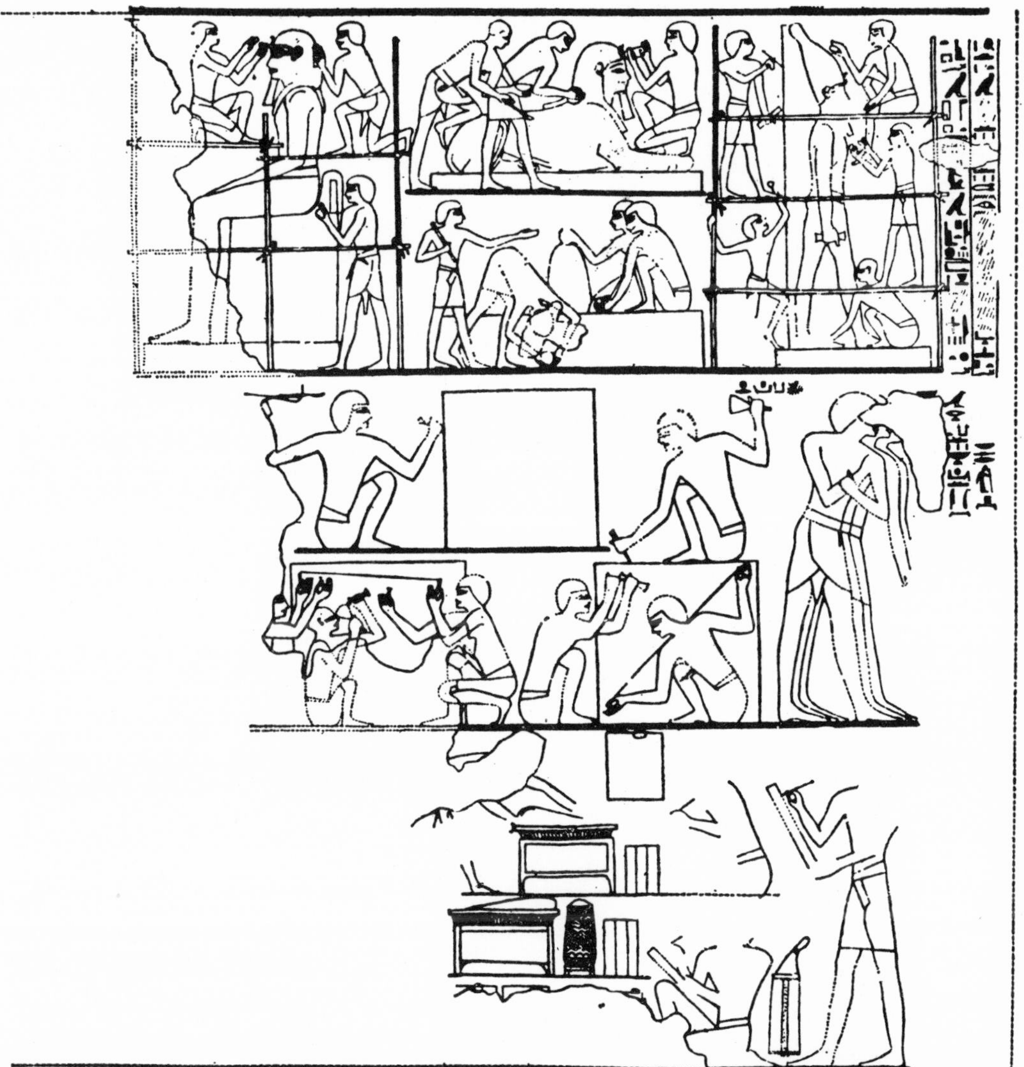

Fig. 122. Stonemasons depicted in the drawing on the wall of the tomb of Rekhmara at Thebes.

Quarryman's tools (Figure 123)

(*a*) Jad, a pickaxe for tapping or 'jumping' a hole in a block of stone to allow the insertion of a steel wedge, or scale.
(*b*) Hammer-headed or pole pick.
(*c*) Mason's pick, chisel ended, examples of which occur in the Roman period (Guildhall Museum, London).
(*d*) Mattock, or grubber, for clearing away unwanted material in order to expose the stone which is to be quarried.
(*e*) Crowbar for levering heavy blocks of stone. A small Roman example of the first century A.D. from the Walbrook, London, can be seen in the British Museum.
(*f*) Jumper, held by a leather grip while it is driven into the stone to make a hole in which to place a blasting charge.
(*g*) Stone mallet for use with mason's chisels.
(*h*) Lifting 'dogs' or scissors for gripping and raising heavy blocks of stone.
(*j*) 'Lewis', for lifting.
(*k*) Sledge, or sledge-hammer, for driving wedges and jumpers into the stone.
(*l*) Lifting 'dogs' or scissors similar to Roman example from Mainz in Germany.
(*m*) 'Lewising' chisel of Roman date with slightly curved end to enable an undercut slot to be formed in a stone block so that a 'lewis' can be inserted for lifting. An example is in the Guildhall Museum, London, and a chisel of this form from the Roman site at Chesterholm was carefully examined and revealed that local heat treatment had been applied with the evident object of hardening the cutting edge.[2] With regard to the hardening of tools it would appear from statements by Pliny (*Natural History*, XXXIV) that the Romans were well acquainted with the method of hardening steel by quenching and that they even practised such refinements as the use of oil, in place of water. Hanemann[3] has obtained metallographic evidence of this by occurrence of martensite in tools of the first century A.D. from Römhild, Thüringen. Carpenter and Robertson[4] state that the Egyptians from 1200 B.C.

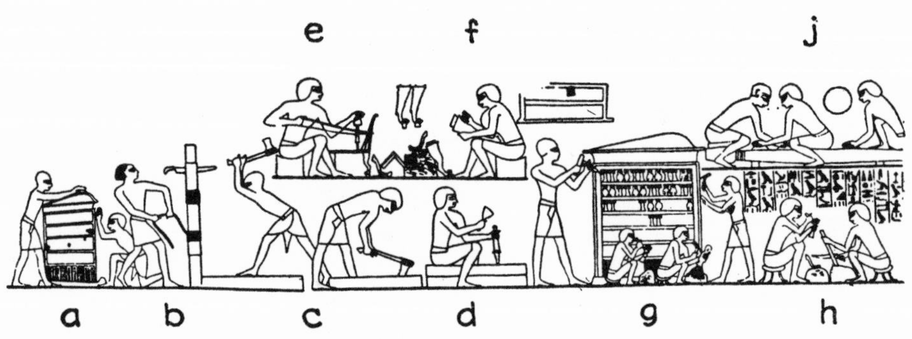

onwards were acquainted with the process of carburizing and quenching, as methods for hardening steel tools.

(*n*) Mason's point. Roman examples can be seen in various museums, e.g. the Guildhall Museum, London.

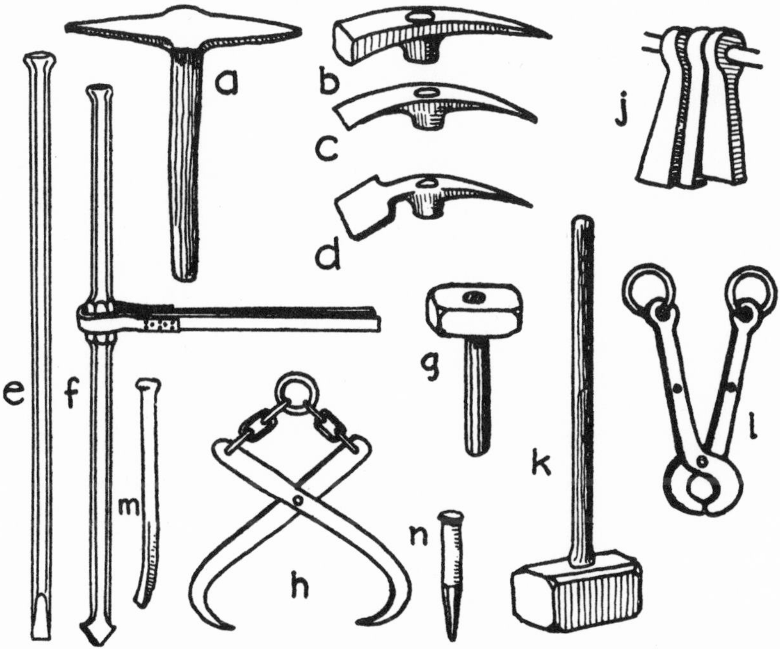

Fig. 123. Quarryman's tools.

Woodworking Tools

Although there are other and earlier illustrations of woodworking in Egypt, that dating from the 18th Dynasty shown in Figure 124 reproduced from the careful drawings

Fig. 124. Carpenters and their tools depicted in the drawing on the wall of the tomb of Rekhmara at Thebes.

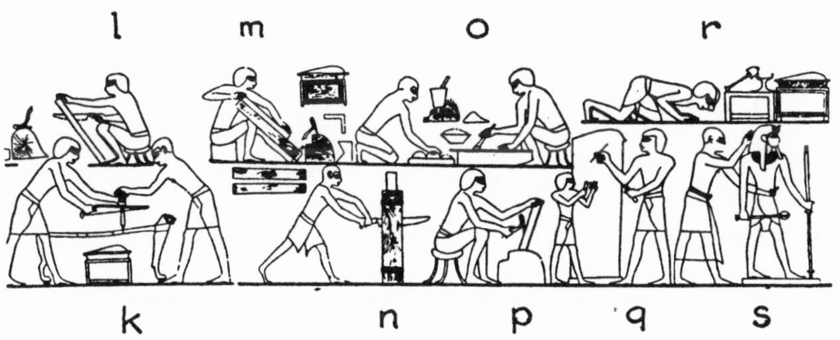

made by Newberry[5] of the scenes depicted on the walls of the tomb of Rekhmara at Thebes is the most detailed. It shows carpenters at work and an almost complete range of tools. Starting from the left-hand side at (*a*) two men are seen polishing a completed cabinet. At (*b*) a man is tying a piece of rough wood to a stake set vertically in the ground in order to saw it into planks. Egyptian saws like that shown had straight teeth and were not set crisscross as in modern saws, and in consequence they tended to jam. Sawing commenced at the top and after proceeding for some way, the sawn parts were held apart by inserting a rope between them to prevent the saw from jamming; sawing then continued as shown at (*n*). Two men at (*c*) are shaping rough wood with copper axes, and a joiner is at work at (*d*) apparently cutting a mortise with a chisel and mallet. The bow-drill is seen in operation at (*e*) and again at (*k*), and the man at (*f*) has been shaping wooden legs for a couch. The adzes used and the wooden block on which the work was done are shown. A set square is shown, and another at (*m*). At (*g*) four men are working on an elaborate shrine, inlaid with ivory and precious stones. The man standing on the left is using a chisel and a mallet which is a roller-shaped piece of wood. The two men seated are shaping the inlays, and the fourth man standing on the right is using an adze on the side of the shrine. Two more men seated at (*h*) are also working on various detailed parts of the shrine; the inscription just above them has been interpreted by Newberry as . . . 'making shrines in ivory, ebony, sesenezem wood, meru wood, in new cedar wood of the hills . . .'. At (*j*) three men are working on a wooden column with a lotus-bud capital, and the two at (*k*) are drilling a hole in a couch with the aid of a bow-drill. The man at (*l*) like one of the men at (*h*) is sawing a piece of wood and the man behind him at (*m*) is testing a piece he has worked, for straightness and accuracy of surface. A veneer of ornamental wood is being cut at (*n*) and another piece is being glued at (*o*), the glue being heated in a pot over a charcoal fire. An artist at (*q*) is engaged in painting a finished cabinet and on the extreme right at (*s*) a completed statue of Thothmes III is ready for presentation to Rekhmara, as also are various pieces of furniture at (*r*), by the two attendants who humbly kiss the ground.

In Figures 125 and 126 are shown various woodworking tools. Those in Figure 125 are of Egyptian origin.

(*a*) A saw of the 6th Dynasty, in the Petrie Collection.
(*b*) A saw of the 12th Dynasty, in the Petrie Collection.
(*c*) A bow drill, in the Berlin Museum.
(*d*) A copper axe from Thebes, in the Petrie Collection.
(*e*) An iron axe head of the eighth-ninth centuries B.C. (Egypt) from a copy in the Science Museum, London.
(*f*) A wooden mallet, examples of which are in the Science Museum (*c.* 1370 B.C., from Tell el Amarna), Berlin Museum, and in the Petrie Collection.
(*g*) A chisel, in the Berlin Museum.
(*h*) An adze, in the Petrie Collection.
(*j*) Bronze chisel of the 3rd Dynasty.
(*k*) Bronze chisel of the 6th Dynasty, in the Petrie Collection.

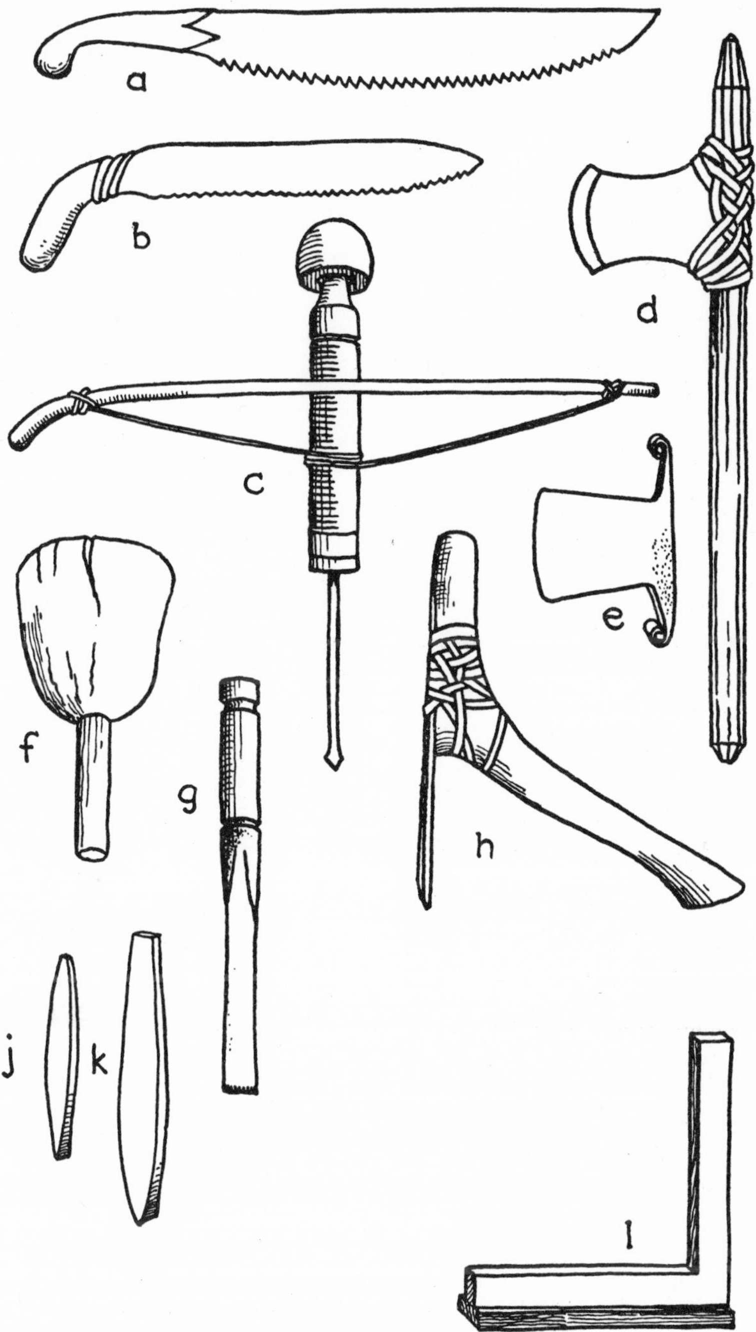

Fig. 125. Egyptian woodworker's tools.

The woodworking tools in Figure 126 are of Roman date except (*a*) and (*b*), which are Bronze Age.

(*a*) Hollow gouge from Heathery Burn (Bronze Age).
(*b*) Bronze chisel from Heathery Burn (Bronze Age).

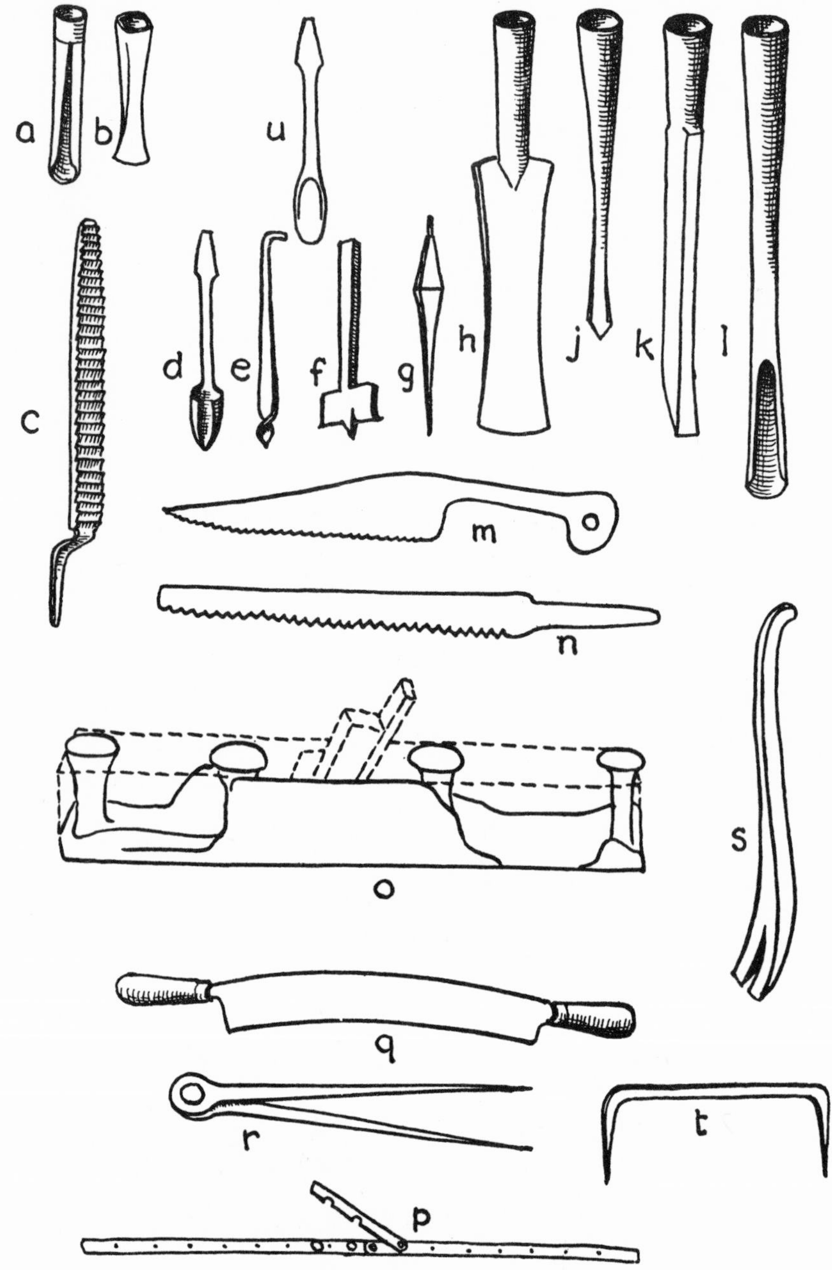

Fig. 126. Bronze Age and Roman woodworker's tools.

(*c*) Iron rasp from Silchester, in Reading Museum.
(*d*) Spoon bit, in Zurich Museum.
(*e*) Twist drill, in Zurich Museum.
(*f*) Centre bit, in Zurich Museum.
(*g*) Iron awl or bit, examples of which are in London Museum and Guildhall Museum, London.
(*h*) Socketed chisel, in London Museum.
(*j*) Pointed chisel, in London Museum.
(*k*) Mortising, or lewising, chisel from Silchester, in Reading Museum, and another example in Guildhall Museum, London.
(*l*) Socketed gouge from Silchester, in Reading Museum, and another example in Guildhall Museum, London.
(*m*) (*n*) Iron saw blades, in London Museum.
(*o*) Plane from Silchester, in Reading Museum, similar to other examples from Verulamium, Saalburg, and other places.
(*p*) Folding rule. Several have been found; examples are in the London Museum and the Guildhall Museum, London.
(*q*) Draw knife from Saalburg. Another example is in the Guildhall Museum, London.
(*r*) Dividers. Many have been recovered, and there are examples in the London Museum and the Guildhall Museum, London.
(*s*) Claw from Saalburg; another example in Guildhall Museum, London.
(*t*) Joiner's dog.
(*u*) A gouge bit from Bucklebury, Berks, in the British Museum.

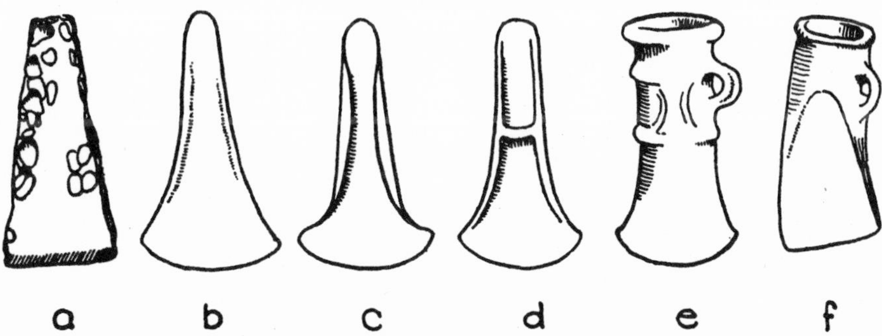

Fig. 127. Transition from stone axe to Iron Age socketed celt.

In Figure 127 is shown the development of the axe from the stone axe (*a*) to the socketed iron celt (*f*). After the change from stone to bronze, the first major improvement came when a stop was introduced as shown in (*d*) which prevented the forcing of the axehead into the haft and splitting it. In the next stage the axehead was made with a socket (*e*) to house the haft completely. A loop on the axe enabled it to be tied to the haft. The transition to an iron axe is shown in (*f*).

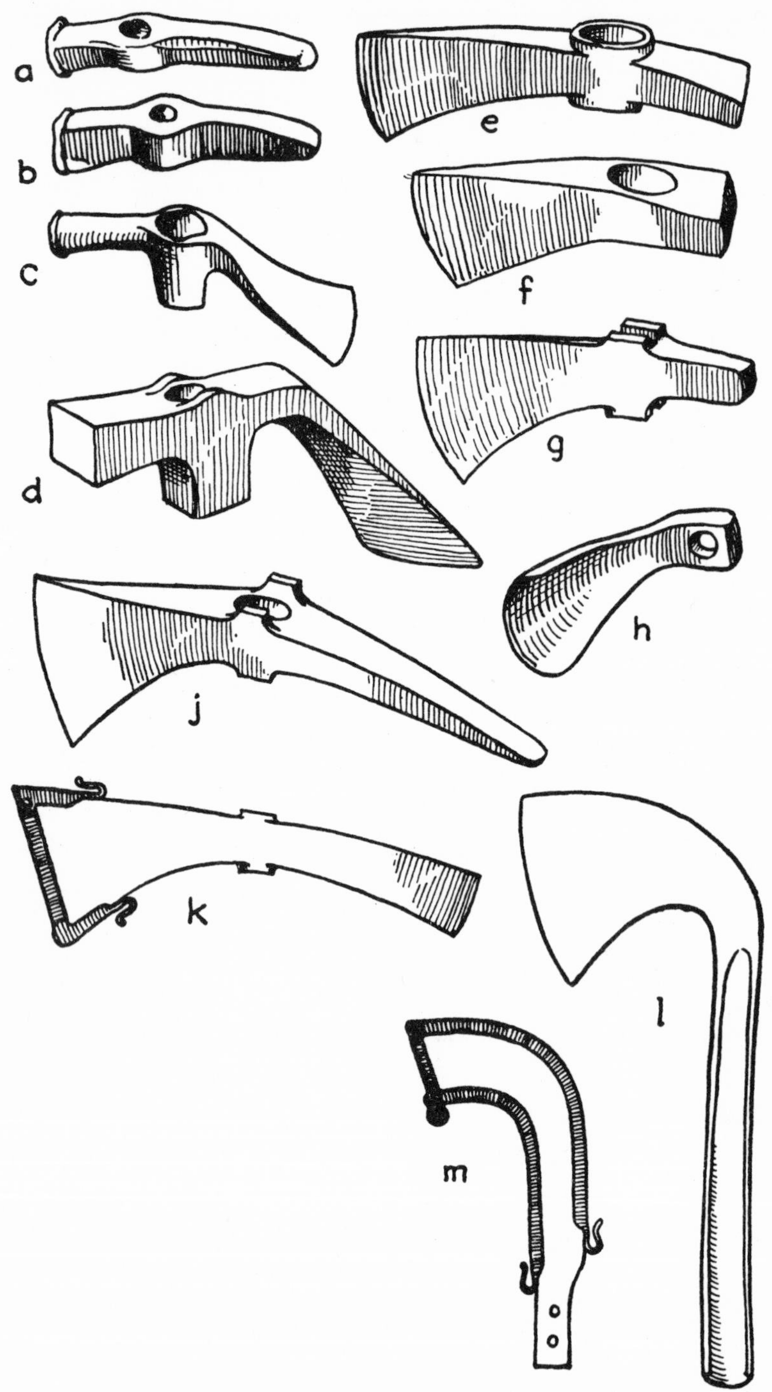

Fig. 128. Roman hammers and axes.

In Figure 128 are shown various kinds of Roman hammers and axes.

(*a*), (*b*), (*c*) Iron hammers from Silchester, in Reading Museum.

(*d*) Adze hammer of the first century A.D., in British Museum.

(*e*), (*f*), (*g*) Hammer ended axes; (*e*) and (*f*) from Silchester, in Reading Museum, and (*g*) in London Museum.

(*h*) Hollow adze from Silchester, in Reading Museum.

(*j*) Axe with pick end from Hod Hill, in British Museum.

(*k*) Double ended axe with bronze guard from the River Rhine near Mainz, in Mainz Museum.

(*l*) Pole axe from Walthamstow, in London Museum.

(*m*) Hatchet with bronze guard, in Mainz Museum.

Woodman's Tools

Some typical woodman's tools are shown in Figure 129.

(*a*) Adze.

(*b*) Lathing hatchet.

(*c*) Single hatchet.

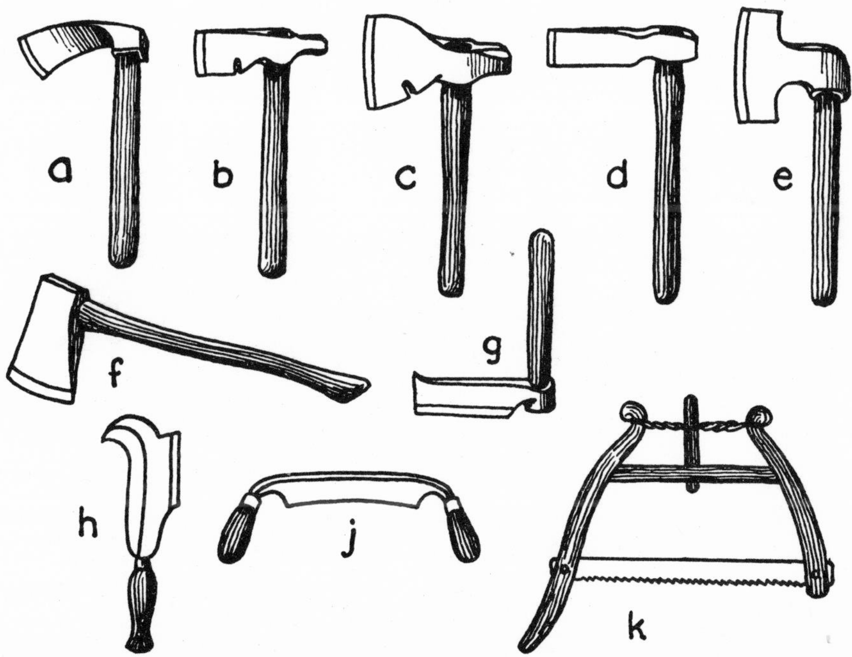

Fig. 129. Woodman's tools.

(*d*) Mortising axe.

(*e*) Side axe, an ancient tool for splitting timber into palings. An example dating from the ninth to eleventh centuries A.D. from Sunbury and another dating from early eleventh century to mid-fourteenth century A.D. from Hedsor Weir can be seen in Reading Museum, the blade of the latter being pointed at the top rather than flat ended like that illustrated.

(*f*) Felling axe.

(*g*) The fromard, froe, or frow is a side knife for cleaving wood to make laths and shingles. The handle is held vertically, the blade being placed on the wood which is to be split, and the back of the blade is struck with a wooden froe club or mallet.

(*h*) Bille or bill hook.

(*j*) Draw knife.

(*k*) Woodman's bow saw and frame.

Plasterer's Tools

Plasterer's tools of Egyptian and Roman date are shown in Figure 130.

(*a*) Iron mortar rake (Egyptian, *c.* 300 B.C.), in Petrie Collection.

(*b*) Bronze mortar rake (Egyptian, *c.* 300 B.C.), in Petrie Collection.

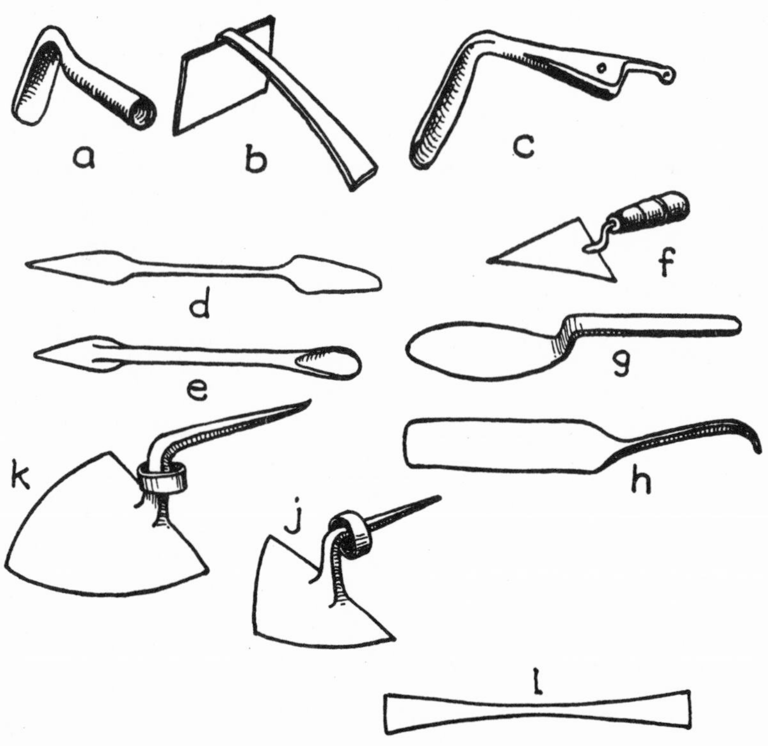

Fig. 130. Early plasterer's tools.

(*c*) Iron rake from Park Street, near Verulamium (Roman).
(*d*) Double ended spatula (Egyptian), in Petrie Collection.
(*e*) Double ended spatula (Roman) from Newstead, in Petrie Collection.
(*f*), (*g*), (*h*) Roman trowels from Pompeii, in Petrie Collection.
(*j*), (*k*) Roman trowels, in Guildhall Museum, London.
(*l*) Double ended spatula (Roman), in Guildhall Museum, London.

Corder[6] has described the several types of Roman iron spades. They all consist essentially of an iron sheath or shoe fixed in various ways to a wooden blade. Examples can be seen in the British Museum, Verulamium Museum, Letchworth Museum, and in many other museums.

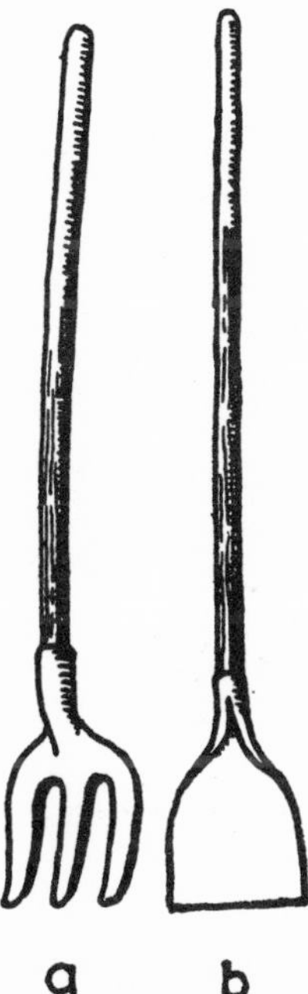

Fig. 131. Tools for cob-walling: (a) Cob pick. (b) Paring iron.

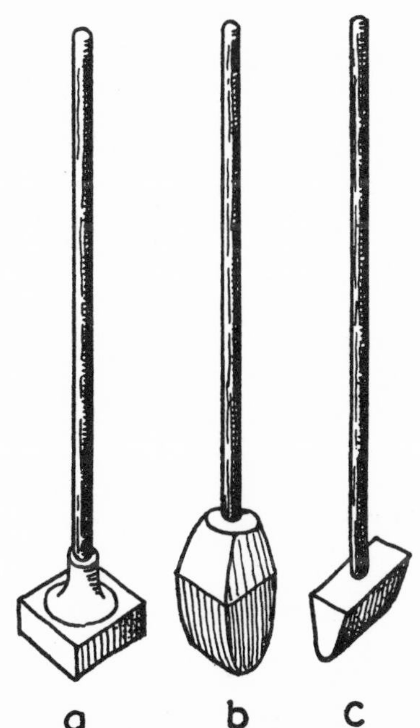

Fig. 132. Tools for pisé work: (a) Flat iron rammer. (b) Wooden rammer. (c) 'Heart-shape' iron.

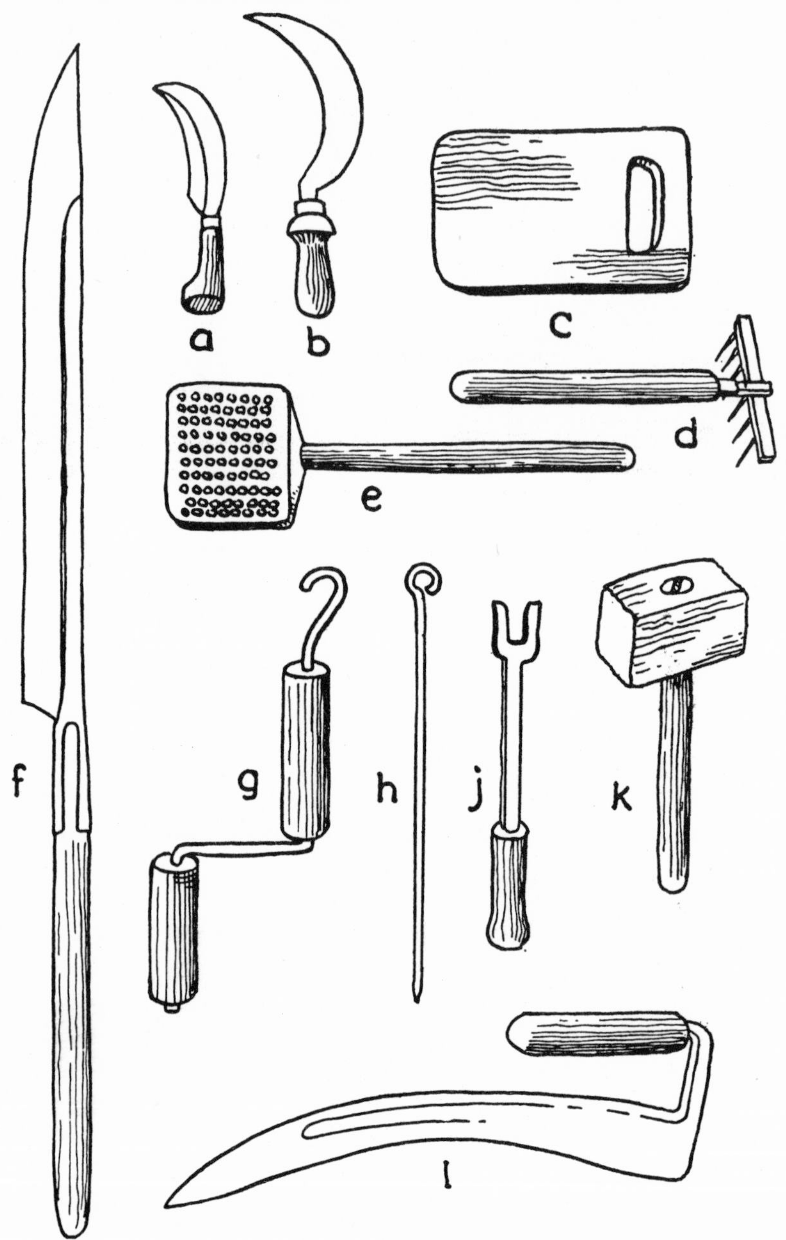

Fig. 133. Thatching tools: (a, b) Brotch hook or spar hook. (c) Thatching spud. (d) Combing rake. (e) Legget, or biddle. (f) Long knife. (g) Throwcock, twister, or turner. (h) Needle. (j) Stringing board, or stringer. (k) Mallet. (l) Thatcher's knife.

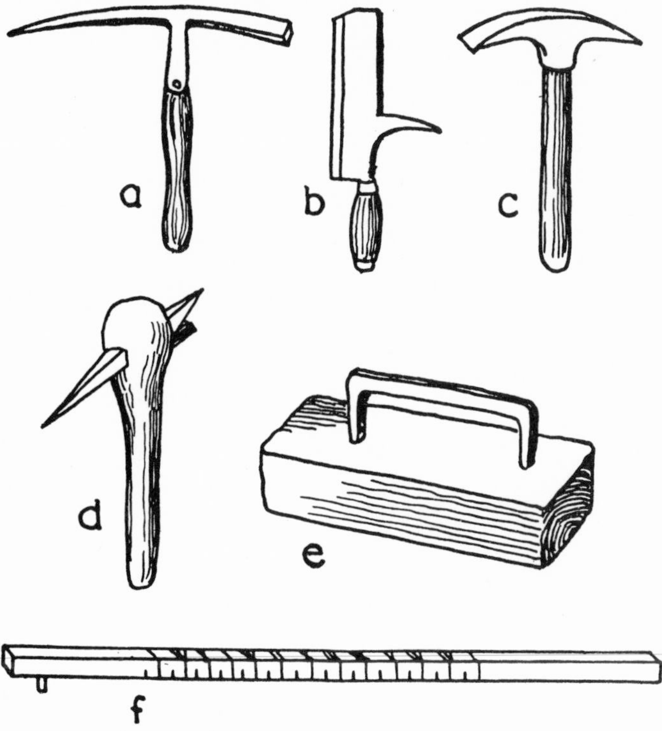

Fig. 134. Slater's tools: (a) Slater's pick. (b) Saxe, or zax. (c) Slatting hammer. (d) Slat pick, or pittaway. (e) Dressing iron. (f) Slater's rule.

REFERENCES

(1) Petrie, W. M. Flinders, 1916, *Tools and Weapons in the Egyptian Collection in University College*, British School of Archaeology in Egypt, University College, London.

(2) Pearson, C. E., and Smythe, J. A., 1934, *Proceedings* of the University of Durham Philosophical Society, IX (3), 141.

(3) Hanemann, H., 1913, *International Journal of Metallurgy*, IV, 248.

(4) Carpenter, H. C. H., and Robertson, J. M., 1930, *Journal of the Iron and Steel Institute*, 121–417.

(5) Newberry, P. E., 1900, *The Life of Rekhmara*, Constable.

(6) Corder, P., 1945, 'Roman spade irons from Verulamium, with some notes on examples elsewhere', *Archaeological Journal*, C, 224–31.

Index